THE INFLUENCE OF TEMPERATURE
ON THE MECHANICAL PROPERTIES
OF METALS AND ALLOYS

The Influence of Temperature on the Mechanical Properties of Metals and Alloys

E. M. SAVITSKY SAVITSKII

Director of the Laboratory of Alloys of Rare Metals
Institute of Metallurgy
Academy of Sciences, U.S.S.R.

Edited by
OLEG D. SHERBY

Stanford University

Translated by
D. SHERBY

Stanford, California 1961
STANFORD UNIVERSITY PRESS

First Published in Russian, 1957
Publishing House of the Academy of Sciences, U.S.S.R. Moscow

Stanford University Press
Stanford, California

London: Oxford University Press

© 1961 by the Board of Trustees of the
Leland Stanford Junior University

Library of Congress Catalog Card Number: 61-7797

Printed in the United States of America

Editor's Foreword

It is indeed a pleasure to have had the opportunity to act as technical editor for the translation of Professor E. M. Savitsky's book on the mechanical properties of metals and alloys at high temperatures.

The current methods of translating individual articles that appear in foreign technical journals are very costly, and the articles themselves often contain little information of lasting interest to the scientist. Moreover, the distribution of such translations is often very limited. A translation of a foreign book, on the other hand, usually becomes widely known, yielding useful information about the nature and extent of research activities in its field in the country of the author. This is certainly true of Professor Savitsky's present work, in which a large body of information is reviewed and admirably discussed and evaluated. Over three quarters of the 500 references quoted by Savitsky cite work by Soviet scientists—evidence, indeed, that activity in this area of research is at a high level in Russia. Much of the material presented by the author has never before appeared in English.

The material covered in the book, much of it based on first-hand experimental data of the author and his associates, is summarized rather carefully in the final chapter, Conclusions, and hence no discussion of the contents is given in this foreword. The continuing productivity of this group of scientists is attested to by the recent appearance of the author's short monograph "Rare Metals and Alloys" (in Russian, Technical House, Moscow, 1959).

We gratefully acknowledge the kind cooperation and consideration of Professor Savitsky, who has contributed much time and effort to accelerating the translation of this book. The translation was made possible by a grant from the U.S. National Science Foundation, and we wish to thank that agency for its assistance. In addition, the editor wishes to acknowledge the conscientious and able assistance given him by the staff of the Stanford University Press.

OLEG D. SHERBY

Stanford University
Stanford, California

Preface to American Edition

This monograph, unlike other works describing investigations on the strength and ductility of metallic materials, is designed to view the subject from a physicochemical aspect. Guided by N. S. Kurnakov's doctrine of physicochemical analysis and using various metallic systems as examples, I have striven to show that a systematic investigation of mechanical and other physical properties, as a function of temperature and composition, permits of a deeper understanding of the physicochemical nature of metals and especially of their alloys.

Judging by reviews on this work which have appeared in our scientific and technical literature, the effort was timely and successful.

In the three years since the work was published in Russian, the science of physical metallurgy has shown vigorous progress, especially in relation to high-melting alloys of tungsten, molybdenum, rhenium, tantalum, niobium, chromium, titanium, rare-earth metals, and others. The theory of dislocation has been more highly developed. It seems to me, however, that the new experimental material confirms the basic concepts presented in the book. Later on, time permitting, I shall publish a second edition which will include all new available data. It will benefit science if similar monographs are written by other authors; as truly stated by an American scientist, Kurnakov's ideas work on both sides of the ocean. Russian scientists value highly the achievements of their foreign colleagues; contacts among Soviet, American, and West European scientists have greatly increased in recent years. We are learning to know and respect each other, by visiting institutions of education and research and scientific conventions, and by exchanging information. This interchange of ideas and experimental data leads to a rapprochement of scientists regardless of their nationality and enhances mutual understanding and friendship.

Unfortunately, the language barrier often hinders closer communication and timely sharing of information on studies and ideas among scientists. Translations of the more important works help to narrow this gap. In this country we endeavor to publish translations of all outstanding works by foreign scientists.

I express my grateful thanks to the National Science Foundation, to the Stanford University Press, and to Professor Sherby for the initiative and work done on the English translation of my book. This I consider to be a friendly gesture to scientists of our country.

I dare hope that this translation, being published on the centennial of Kurnakov's birth, will provide an opportunity for a large group of American and other scientists to acquaint themselves with some of the results achieved by followers of Kurnakov, and that this acquaintance will contribute to a further growth of mutual understanding and encourage mutually useful contacts among scientists of our countries.

E. M. SAVITSKY

Moscow,
December, 1960

Preface

The present treatise was prepared during the postwar period at the Laboratory for Mechanical Testing of the N. S. Kurnakov Institute of General and Inorganic Chemistry. It was given final form at the A. A. Baikov Institute of Metallurgy, U.S.S.R. Separate parts of this treatise represent material gathered from experiments conducted in research laboratories at various periods, directed to solve the more scientifically and practically important problems. However, the experimental data obtained may be covered by this general title because, in every experiment, attention was mainly directed to the temperature dependence of the mechanical properties of metals and their alloys, i.e., of various metallic bodies. Part of the experimental data mentioned here was presented at various conferences of the Science Committee and of the Analysis Section of the Institute of General and Inorganic Chemistry as well as at some of the other scientific institutes. Data on mechanical properties of intermetallic compounds and alloys were presented at the session of the Academy of Sciences, U.S.S.R., and at the second and third conferences on physicochemical analysis.

On some of the problems the author consulted with G. G. Urazov, member of the Academy; N. V. Ageyev, associate member; Doctors of Chemistry S. A. Pogodin, V. I. Anosov, I. I. Kornilov, and G. B. Boky; Doctor of Technical Sciences D. A. Petrov; Doctor of Physico-Mathematical Sciences V. K. Semenchenko; and other members of the Institute.

In the experimental section the material presented, as attested by published articles and reports on completed studies, the following laboratory co-workers should be mentioned: V. V. Baron, V. F. Terekhova, M. A. Tylkina, V. P. Lebedev and V. P. Vinokurov. V. F. Terekhova greatly assisted the author in the preparation of this book.

The author wishes to express his grateful thanks to all those who have contributed to the success of this research and would gratefully welcome any and all criticisms from readers of this monograph.

Contents

THE INFLUENCE OF TEMPERATURE
ON THE MECHANICAL PROPERTIES
OF METALS AND ALLOYS

Introduction

For whatever purpose a given metal or alloy may be used, the product must of necessity possess certain mechanical properties such as strength and ductility. Without them, regardless of all other properties, the use of the material is limited. It may be said without exaggeration that, in the overwhelming majority of cases, the mechanical properties determine the use of one or another alloy in the nation's economy. Because of their great practical importance, strength and ductility present one of the basic problems of contemporary metallurgy.

Ductility is a very important property of metals for engineering purposes because it permits products to assume the required shape and prevents them from fracturing after prolonged use. Furthermore, when plastic deformation takes place, a change takes place not only in the shape but also in the properties of the material. One of the basic aims of processing metals by working and heat treating is the achievement of specific mechanical properties.

Strength and ductility depend on the composition and structure of materials and also on the conditions under which the materials are either processed or tested. For this reason the study of mechanical properties has great practical and scientific value and is being applied with increasing intensity in research on solids, mainly metals and alloys.

Science in the U.S.S.R., including metallurgy, has a glorious history. The Soviet Union received a great scientific heritage from outstanding scientists and inventors of pre-revolutionary Russia. An important part of this legacy was the relatively advanced knowledge of the chemistry of metallic alloys. In the history of industrial metallurgy in ancient Russia, we see that in the twelfth to fifteenth centuries Russian metal artisans already had a concept of the properties of alloys and their composition and were able to find experimentally the right composition for alloys possessing the properties essential for the product. Studies on the mechanical properties of materials in Russia began in the time of Peter the Great, when "test huts" for fracture testing of cast iron were built at the various metallurgical plants. Since its establishment in 1724 the Petersburg Academy of Sciences has conducted studies on the mechanical properties of materials (Academicians Kupfer and Bulfinger) [1]. A new era of studies on the relation of properties of solids to their composition started with Lomonosov, who was the first in the history of chemistry to adopt a whole

3

series of physical, chemical, and mechanical methods for the study of matter and of its transformations. In 1741, this great creator of atomic theory on the structure of matter, in his "Elements of Mathematical Chemistry," said that whosoever wished to understand chemistry's deep truths should study mechanics. Thus, not by chance, equipment for testing strength was used in the first Russian chemical scientific laboratory organized by Lomonosov more than 200 years ago. Lomonosov studied the properties of copper alloys and their strength variation in relation to their composition, and the properties of solid mercury. He studied the hardness of solids "by pressing and by breaking" and was the first to discover the relationship between the strength of a material and its molecular bonding.

Anosov, a remarkable Russian research metallurgist (1797–1851), was the first to demonstrate that the mechanical qualities of steel could be radically changed and improved by the addition of components such as chromium, manganese, nickel, and so forth, and thus established a metallurgical basis for quality steel. In 1831 Anosov was the first to use a microscope for steel studies and analysis, well ahead of metallurgists of all other countries; he also was the first to determine that the properties of steel depend not only on composition but also on structure [2], [3].

Chernov (1839–1921), founder of scientific metallography, who discovered the laws of crystallization and the phenomenon of iron polymorphism, studied intensively the conditions under which stronger products, such as gun barrels and armor plates, could be manufactured [4]. In 1870 he discovered slip traces on the surface of a deformed specimen.

Extensive use of metals as a basic material for machinery and construction in industry was begun in the middle of the last century. At that time laboratories equipped with special devices for testing properties of metals were started in Russia.

The first testing equipment was a "chain testing" machine used in the eighteen-thirties. Professor Sobko of Petersburg organized the first laboratory for testing building materials at the Institute of Ways and Means of Communications in 1853. In 1866 the growth of this organization led to the creation of the first separate laboratory for mechanical testing. The founder of mechanical testing of metals and building materials in industry was the eminent Russian scientist, Professor Beleliubski, who in 1873 was named director of the Institute; in 1912 he was elected president of the International Society for Testing Materials.

Toward the end of the nineteenth and in the beginning of the twentieth century, valuable contributions to the science of mechanical properties of materials were made by Zhuravsky (cleavage stress), Kalakutsky (measurement of residual stress), Yasinsky (theory of longitudinal deflections), Rzheshatarsky (influence of temperature on the brittleness of steel), Kirpichev (the law of similarity), Baboshin (mechanical properties of rails), Dragomirov (impact testing), Minkevich (correlation of hardness to strength in steel), and Kurdiumov (mechanical properties of brasses).

Toward the end of the last century, laboratories for testing were started at various engineering colleges and in the large industrial plants of Russia [5]. A parallel development of metallographic laboratories was likewise taking place. In 1895 Rzheshatarsky founded the first industrial metallographic laboratory at the Obukhovsky Mills (now Bolshevik Mills) in Leningrad. At the same time Professor Bochvar, founder of the Moscow school of metallographers, founded the metallographic laboratory at the Moscow Technical College. A metallography and metallurgy laboratory was created at the Petersburg Polytechnic Institute at the beginning of this century by the Academician Baikov.

For the establishment of metallography as a science at the end of the nineteenth and beginning of the twentieth century, much credit should be given to the English scientists Roberts-Austen, Heycock, and Neville; to the French Osmond and Le Chatellier; to the Japanese Honda; and to the German Tamman. Each of these scientists established institutes or laboratories devoted essentially to studies of metallic alloys.

In the realm of mechanical testing in the same period, Russia was first to develop a whole range of important equipment and methods. A unique testing machine, Gagarin's press, built in 1895 by Gagarin, achieved widespread popularity.

In 1900, considerably prior to the Austrian scientist Ludwig, Kubasov, a Russian engineer, suggested a method for measuring hardness by indentation with a steel cone; he used the method for gaging the quality of rails [5].

The creator of the periodic system of elements, Mendeleyev, a leader of world science, was also interested in the mechanical properties of metals. On the basis of a large number of experiments, Mendeleyev discovered the law correlating the period of oscillation of a pendulum with the hardness of the pivot on which the pendulum knife rests. This law was first applied by Mendeleyev in 1898 to determine material hardness; to this end he built several versions of sclerometric pendulums (Fig. 1) [6]. These devices are in the Mendeleyev Museum. Twenty-five years later an English scientist, Herbert, obtained a patent for a different version of the pendulum device [7].

Academician Kurnakov, originator of physicochemical analysis, was the first to

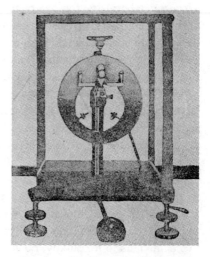

FIG. 1. Sclerometric pendulum (after Mendeleyev).

introduce a series of systematic studies on the correlation of mechanical properties such as hardness and flow stress in metals and salts with the composition of the system. Mechanical properties that can be gaged by physicochemical analysis were classified by him as basic, because they enable one to determine the properties of materials with respect to molecular cohesion [8]. Kurnakov wrote [9, p. 324]:

"Recent studies indicate that it is the mechanical properties which are called to serve as sensitive indicators of characteristics pertaining to the smallest changes in solids during physicochemical transformations."

In his work schedule, set up in the period 1908 to 1910 for studies on the nature of metallic alloys, Kurnakov stressed the necessity of studying the mechanical properties of alloys—hardness, rupture strength, brittleness, ductility— and the effects of machining, tempering, and annealing. He also emphasized the need to clarify any effect of impurities on the mechanical properties of commercial metals and alloys. At Kurnakov's urgent request, a universal machine for mechanical testing to record the findings of Gagarin's press was installed at the Laboratory of General Chemistry of the Petersburg Polytechnical Institute. Kurnakov was the first to apply the knowledge of mechanical properties to solving problems of general chemistry. In his letter to Stepanov dated August 14, 1912, Kurnakov wrote [10], [11]:

"Electrical conductivity of metallic alloys, hardness and the other closely related properties is our scientific victory which should be retained by us. To this end planned, systematic endeavors of a whole group of conscientious and independent workers are needed."

In 1934, Gubkin and his associates, under the direction of Kurnakov, organized a special laboratory for mechanical testing at the Institute of General and Inorganic Chemistry of the Academy of Sciences of the U.S.S.R.

The closest associates and students of Kurnakov—Gubkin, Urazov, Zhemchuzhny, Ageyev, Pogodin, Nemilov, Grigoriev, Efremov, Kornilov, Mikheyeva, Shamrai, and others—always paid close attention to research on mechanical properties in their work on physicochemical analysis of metallic properties. In their scientific treatises, these scientists showed that a systematic study of the mechanical properties of metals, as well as of their other properties, leads to a deep understanding of the chemical nature of phases in experimental materials and permits one to choose the alloys best suited for industry [12].

After the great October Socialist Revolution, research on physicomechanical properties of metallic alloys was further developed. Soviet science and technique continued to be developed by powerful scientific associations.

Beside the work done by Kurnakov's group, contributions were made by: Academicians Joffe, Baikov, Bochvar, Gudtsov, Kurdiumov, and Rebinder; member of the Academy of Sciences of the Ukrainian Soviet Republic Davidenkov; member of the Academy of Sciences of the White Russian Soviet Republic Gubkin; associate members of the Academy of Sciences of the U.S.S.R.

Pavlov, Oding, Kuznetsov, and their associates. Treatises were also prepared by large scientific associations in a number of professional institutes, higher technical schools, and industrial laboratories. Among the foreign scientists successfully developing the physical theory of metals, one must mention F. Seitz of the U.S.A., Mott and Hume-Rothery of England, and Ke of China.

A distinctive characteristic of work done in the ·U.S.S.R. is its truly scientific approach. As a rule, properties of alloys are studied systematically in relation to the composition of the alloy, its structure, and its processing, whereas in capitalist countries the prevalent approach to the determination of properties of specific alloys is sporadic, inasmuch as research is sponsored by private enterprise.

Another no less important characteristic of research on the mechanical properties of materials as conducted in the U.S.S.R. is its purposeful effort to select alloys of the best quality for the needs of the nations's technology and, primarily, for its newest industries; also to select the most effective and economical conditions of processing these materials and of their utilization in manufacturers' products. In this respect our scientists have attained great success and, in a number of instances, have surpassed the achievements of foreign science, not only in selecting alloys of the most favorable composition, but also in creating theories giving a scientific basis for selecting alloys with the required properties and defining the conditions required for their mechanical and thermal processing (theories of physicochemical analysis, strength, heat stability, creep, plasticity, recrystallization, deformation, and so forth).

The predominating tendency of our national science is toward a deep generalization of experimental results, whereas in certain American treatises one notes the absence of any generalization as well as a disregard in principle of such complex phenomena as strength and plasticity (work of McAdams and others). On the other hand it should be noted that in the field of strength of materials a series of significant experiments on problems of material mechanics and mechanical tests of metals conducted in foreign lands is most fully illuminated in monographs by such foreign scientists as Sachs, Siebal, Nadai, and Bridgeman.

Development of nuclear and rocket technology, chemistry, radio engineering, and other specialized branches of industry requires a high rate of production of heat-resistant and other special alloys. In its letter of instruction to industry, the 20th Congress of the Soviet Communist Party covering the sixth five-year plan required a sixfold increase in the production capacity of heat-resistant alloys. The 20th Congress likewise directed industry [13, p. 11]:

"···to intensify scientific and industrial research on investigation of less expensive methods of producing nonferrous metals and on further perfection and mastery of production technology of rare metals as well as a thorough study of their properties and of their utilization."

In conjunction with extensive metal-production development during the sixth five-year plan, research on the dependence of physical and mechanical properties of metals on their composition and on temperature should be greatly accelerated.

Research on the effects of temperature on the mechanical properties of metallic materials is now considered of great scientific and practical importance. A great number of parts in such equipment as aviation and automobile motors, reaction engines, turbines, boilers, and metallurgical furnaces operate at elevated temperatures. On the other hand, parts of refrigerating machinery, airplanes, railroad equipment, and other apparatus frequently function at temperatures below 0°C. Many pressure processes (forging, rolling, extruding) are carried out at elevated temperatures, whereas the thermal treatment of certain special alloys has been recently conducted at extremely low temperatures.

Maximum utilization of all intrinsic properties of a given alloy may be realized only as a result of thorough experimental research based on the latest theoretical achievements.

New technological needs demand new materials with special properties, primarily materials that are wear-resistant at high temperatures and under stress. These requirements have brought about new testing methods of research at high temperatures.

Russia has no peer in the area of research on determining the effect of temperature on the properties of metallic alloys. It is appropriate here to mention:

1. Work done by Shishokin, Pogodin, and Gubkin (1929–1937) on the effect of temperature on the deformation characteristics (hardness, yield stress, ultimate tensile strength) of metals and alloys [12], [14].

2. Work done by Shishokin and his associates (1930–1938) on hardness, yield stress, and temperature coefficients in eutectic-type systems formed by low-melting-point components [14].

3. Research started in 1946 by Academician Bochvar and his associates (Zakharov, Korolkov, and others) on hardness and heat resistance of certain solid solutions and mixtures of nonferrous and light alloys [15].

4. Work done by Gubkin and his associates on the deformation of nonferrous and light metals and alloys at various temperatures [16].

5. Research done by Kornilov and his associates at the Laboratory of Metallic Alloys of the Institute for General and Inorganic Chemistry and the Metallurgy Institute, on the heat resistance of iron, nickel, and other metals [17]; also research on the heat resistance and creep of steels and other industrial alloys conducted by VIAM, TSNIICHM, TSNIITMASH, TSKTI, and other scientific research organizations.*

6. Research in the laboratories for mechanical testing at Kurnakov's Institute of General and Inorganic Chemistry dealing with the influence of temperature on the mechanical properties of metals and alloys in metallic systems.

Kurnakov's classic laws on the relation of physical and mechanical properties

---

* The above acronyms have been transliterated from the Russian text without attempting to ascertain the actual names of the organizations to which they refer.

to changes in the composition of thermodynamically stable systems have served as the scientific base for all of these studies [8, 9, 12, 18].

As mentioned previously, Kurnakov was the first to apply mechanical testing in research on physicochemical processes and phenomena to gain a deeper understanding of the properties of matter. However, his research on the mechanical properties of systems was done at ordinary temperatures. Temperature, one of the factors of thermodynamic equilibrium, changes materially and very often radically the physical properties of matter and, naturally, its mechanical properties such as ductility and strength. Heat and cold are among the most powerful means of achieving a desired result in matter. Kurnakov's death prevented his investigating experimentally the effect of temperature on the mechanical, physical, and chemical properties of metallic systems.* This problem must be solved by his students and colleagues. In the light of requirements presented by today's technology and especially by its newest branches, systematic and experimental research on the ductility and strength of metals and various metallic alloys at high and low temperatures should be given the highest priority.

The development of new alloys and of new ways to process and utilize these alloys will be furthered by intensive and extensive studies on the influence of various equilibrium factors, crystal structure, and chemical composition on the properties of metallic materials. A systematic compilation of experimental data in such studies will bring us considerably closer to the creation of materials with predetermined properties.

In the current literature we have found no books that analyze systematically the effect of temperature on the mechanical properties of metallic systems; this book has for its goal the filling of this gap.

In this presentation, an attempt is made to examine experimentally and systematically the influence of temperature on the mechanical properties of typical metallic systems in relation to the type of crystalline structure and the character of chemical interaction of the components. This book also examines the present-day status of the problem and presents experimental data on the mechanical properties of various metals and typical metallic alloys at various temperatures. A basis is given for a rational choice of the most favorable temperature conditions for hot working these metals and alloys.

Research on the influence of temperature on the mechanical properties of metals and alloys is difficult; full understanding can be achieved only through the collective efforts of a number of outstanding institutes. For this reason the author felt compelled to limit the scope of his research; this book examines only the mechanical properties observed in experiments of short duration. We do not investigate the influence of the duration of the experiment, changes in properties (such as creep and tensile strength) observed during prolonged testing, or, as a rule, the changes in the mechanical properties of alloys which result

---

* In conformity with the generally accepted terminology, the term "metallic systems" designates materials consisting of one, two, or more metallic components.

from various methods of thermal processing (hardening, homogenizing, aging). Because insufficient experimental data on the influence of temperature on the mechanical properties of ternary metallic systems have been accumulated to date, this book examines basically the temperature dependence of metallic properties in single-component and stable binary alloys.

1

Present State of the Art

Internal Structure and Mechanical Properties of Solids

In the present stage of development of physical and chemical analysis it is necessary to correlate the results obtained with our existing knowledge of the structure of materials.

As noted by Kurnakov, the solid state presents many variations in its behavior as compared with the other main states (liquid and gaseous). Kurnakov also states that the behavior of plastics subjected to stress is intermediate between that of liquids and that of solids. Under slow deformation,* plastic bodies behave like liquids with great internal friction, whereas under rapid deformation they behave like brittle elastic bodies. Brittleness and ductility characterize the opposite extremes of the solid state, as defined by Kurnakov [9].

The properties of materials, including mechanical behavior, depend on their structure. All known metals are crystalline—that is, when they are solid, the atoms are arranged in a space lattice—while amorphous materials (glass, tar, Plexiglas, vitreous quartz, rosin, camphor, and others) are characterized by the random arrangement of their molecules. This difference in structure leads to a difference in one particular characteristic—plastic deformation—which sharply distinguishes metals (especially face-centered-cubic ones) from amorphous materials. Metals exhibit plastic deformation even at temperatures approaching absolute zero, while amorphous bodies are incapable of plastic deformation without fracture at high rates of deformation and, even at low rates or elevated temperatures, the plastic deformation they exhibit is more nearly related to the viscous flow of a liquid than to deformation in crystalline bodies. Deformation is in the direction of applied stress in amorphous bodies, and viscous flow may take place at very low stress levels. Amorphous materials are extremely brittle at low temperatures.

---

* The term "deformation" is used to designate any change in the arrangement of the parts of a solid body as a result of the application of an external force; as a rule, this process is accompanied by changes in form and volume [19].

Plastic deformation is a characteristic of crystalline bodies, since only in a crystal lattice is there a gradual, coordinated transition of a large group of atoms from one state of equilibrium to another. Also, plastic deformation is anisotropic and takes place in certain crystallographic planes and directions.

Crystals undergo plastic deformation without changing their crystal structure, whereas in amorphous bodies the resulting arrangement of atoms is not equivalent to the original arrangement [20].

The symmetry of a crystal, the character of the interatomic forces, and the relative orientation of the crystals with respect to the applied force determine the resistance to deformation and, consequently, the mechanical properties of crystalline bodies. Hence, the properties of crystalline bodies are inseparable from their crystal structure, which in turn is determined by the type of chemical bonding of the atoms. It is known that all forms of chemical bonding occur in crystalline bodies, and that the type of bond is dependent on the interaction of valence electrons of the atoms involved. Molecular bonding in organic crystals and in rare gases in the solid state is dependent on the material polarization of the concomitant molecules (van der Waals forces); because of the interactions involved, substances formed of these crystals exhibit low strength. Ionic crystals, such as natural salts and some minerals, exhibit electrostatic bonding and consequently are brittle under ordinary conditions. These crystals, to be plastically deformed, must be either heated or subjected to an irregular hydrostatic pressure [21]–[23].

A metal, because of the natural cohesive forces in both the solid and liquid states, differs sharply from a nonmetallic material. The present-day concept of a typical metal is that of an array of positive ions immersed in a "cloud" of electrons which are not restricted to any particular ion [24]. The character of the electron cloud thus formed is dependent on the individual properties of the atoms of the given metal. The cohesive forces holding the metallic atoms together in a solid are determined by the attraction of the positively charged ions to the negatively charged electrons. The hypothesis of free electrons in metals enables one to explain a number of properties of metals—the relatively free movement of electrons in a metal accounts for the high thermal and electrical conductivity in both the solid and liquid states. In the vapor state (as gases), however, metals are insulators.

One of the outstanding characteristics of metals, their high plasticity, is closely related to the special features of metallic cohesion. Further, in the majority of cases, plasticity may be used as a criterion to establish whether or not a specific body is metallic. Lomonosov has written: "Metals are bright bodies, which may be forged" [25]. Single crystals of some metals, such as zinc magnesium, and aluminum, can be extended from 100 to 1000 percent of their original length.

In studies on the mechanical properties of various nonmetals, we often observe the great importance of strength (hardness) in some (such as diamonds, carbides nitrides, and borides) and of ductility in others (for example, a number of tars, and even glass at sufficiently elevated temperatures). However, the combination of strength and ductility is inherent in metals alone.

Almost all metals are capable of interacting with other metals to form liquid and solid solutions and compounds. Those compounds which retain the characteristic properties of metals are known as metal alloys [26]. Some of these alloys play an enormous role in the nation's economy. The strong tendency of metals to form alloys is of great importance, comparable to the relation of their oxides to water.

Differences in the chemical bonding determine the behavior of a material relative to its mechanical deformation. Thus, metallic and ionic crystals behave oppositely, although both are crystalline bodies.

A property common to both metallic and ionic crystals, however, as well as to amorphous solids, is the increase of ductility at higher temperatures.

It has been observed that chemical bonding in crystals is rarely of a single type; usually two or more forms are present. Graphite is a specific example (Fig. 2). Interatomic bonding of carbon in the same plane of the graphite lattice is covalent, whereas the bonding of carbon atoms on different planes is metallic. The latter type of bond is considerably weaker. It is possible that the lubricating qualities of graphite are associated with the ease with which atomic planes slide over one another under low stresses [27], [28].

The presence of both types of bond is typical of a number of metallic phases —such as the γ phase in the Al-Mg system [29]. Metallic α manganese apparently should also be classified as having mixed bonds (Fig. 3). The distribution of electrons in α manganese points to the complex character of chemical bonding for many other pure metals (magnesium, copper, nickel). In every case, complicated chemical bonding in a crystal should not be viewed as a simple summation of elementary types of chemical bonding [30], [31].

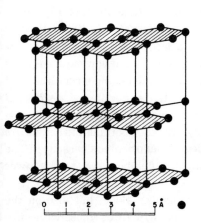

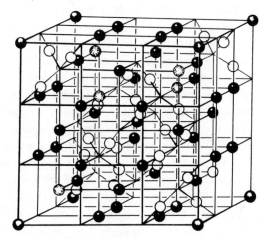

FIG. 2.   Crystal structure of graphite.   FIG. 3.   Crystal structure of α manganese.

No experimental data as yet exist on the influence of mechanical deformation on the character of binding forces. A hypothesis advanced by Akimov says that strengthening of a metal is explained by the conversion of metallic bonds to atomic ones, and the concomitant formation of a "hard" electronic shell encircling the ions; recovery and recrystallization are explained by the restoration of metallic bonds by heating the deformed metal [32]. In any event, the relationship of ductility to the distribution of electrons presents an interesting problem. Forces of attraction as well as of repulsion exist between particles of solids; by means of these forces the equilibrium of the whole system of parts is achieved. The resultant curve of interaction of forces is shown in Fig. 4.

At close distances, repulsive forces predominate; at long distances, forces of attraction. When the material is stretched (i.e., when the distance between particles is increased), forces of attraction predominate; when it is hydrostatically compressed, resistance is caused by forces of repulsion. At point r_0 the resultant force of interaction between particles is zero, and this distance corresponds to a condition of equilibrium at absolute zero and to a minimum value of energy. At a distance equal to r_m the composite force reaches a maximum. The difference $r_m - r_0$ results in the maximum increase of the distance between particles for which it is still possible to reinstate the stable condition of equilibrium, provided the force acting on the particles is removed. The value of this force F_m characterizes the ultimate tensile strength [33].

Atoms of solids tend to arrange themselves so that their interaction energy is at a minimum. Hence, proper alignment of particles takes place within the space determined by the form of the crystal lattice. Usually the atoms of metallic crystals are densely packed. Figure 5 shows three types of packing of atoms in metallic crystals.

The properties of metals are determined by the cohesive properties of their atoms; of material significance here is the number of atoms subject to mutual contact. The most tightly packed face-centered and hexagonal lattices have the greatest possible coordination number, 12—i.e., in a lattice of this type each atom is surrounded by 12 equidistant neighbors. This value is tied in with a characteristic of metallic bonding which insures a large degree of freedom for the arrangement of the atoms in space, thereby creating favorable conditions for the tightest packing in metallic crystals. Close-packed-cubic structures with the coordination number 12 are the most likely to be ductile. The crystal structure of gold, copper, lead, platinum, nickel, and other metals is of this type. Nonmetallic crystals have considerably lower coordination numbers because the interatomic bond has, to a certain degree, an oriented character. The reason that a number of metals, with a coordination number of 8, have a lower packing density is still not clear [34].

Ductility does not depend on the coordination number alone, but also on the type of crystal structure. The more tightly packed structures (those with face-centered-cubic and hexagonal lattices) differ radically in ductility at ordinary

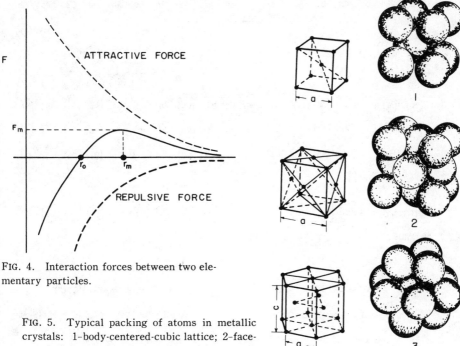

FIG. 4.   Interaction forces between two elementary particles.

FIG. 5.   Typical packing of atoms in metallic crystals: 1–body-centered-cubic lattice; 2–face-centered-cubic lattice; 3–hexagonal-close-packed lattice.

temperatures, the variation reflecting differences in the number of slip systems inherent to the various lattices.   Thus Dehlinger's assertion that plastic deformation of metals increases invariably with an increase in coordination number [35] appears to be incorrect.

The crystal structure of an element is a function of the structure of its atoms.

It is difficult to define the boundary line separating metals from nonmetals. Such metals, for instance, as arsenic, antimony, and bismuth possess metallic properties of comparatively low degree, whereas such nonmetals as carbon, silicon, selenium, and tellurium display certain metallic properties.

Elements having a first ionization potential below 10 ev [36] are usually metals; of the 98 chemical elements which have been long identified, 72 may be classified as metals.

At the Geneva International Scientific Technical Conference on peaceful uses of atomic energy, discovery of elements 99, 100, and 101* of Mendeleyev's table was announced; these elements have been named for outstanding scientists—einsteinium, fermium, and mendeleyevium.

Figure 6 shows the crystal structure of chemical elements as compiled by Boky [38].   As shown in this figure, Mendeleyev's periodic law manifests itself also in the crystal structure of elements; elements found in the same subgroup

* According to Kapustinsky, the periodic system should number 118 elements [37].

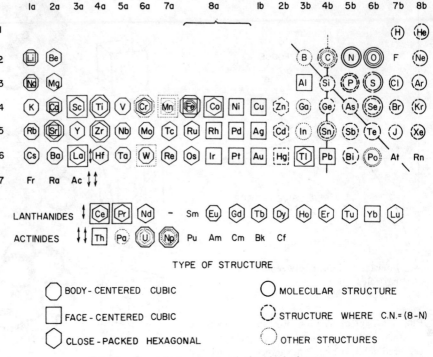

FIG. 6. Crystal structures of chemical elements.

have, as a rule, the same crystal structure. The metallic character of bonding increases in each group of the periodic system with an increase in atomic number.

A conditional dividing boundary may be set between subgroups IVa and IVb with regard to specific structural features. Elements to the left of this boundary, because of uniform metallic cohesion, have simple, compact structures; those to the right, because of their oriented character and low covalent bonding, have considerably more variable and complex crystal structures [18], [38]. As we know, the physicochemical properties of elements are determined by their position in Mendeleyev's periodic system.

The structure of electronic shells is periodically recurrent in the structure of atoms; thus we have a periodic repetition of the basic physicochemical properties of elements and of the mechanical properties as well. Figure 7 shows changes in certain mechanical properties of elements in relation to the atomic number in Mendeleyev's periodic system of elements [39]–[42]. Strength characteristics are most significant in the middle of the periods, i.e., in those elements which have the least symmetrical structure of electronic shells. The maximum strength is present in elements of higher valence (4 and 6): carbon (diamond), silicon, ruthenium, tungsten.

As pointed out by Academician Fersman, the melting temperature and hardness of elements in the periodic system follow parallel patterns as a function of the atomic number [43].

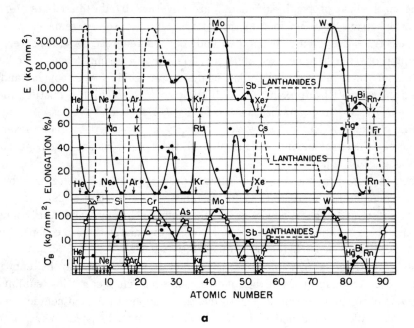

a

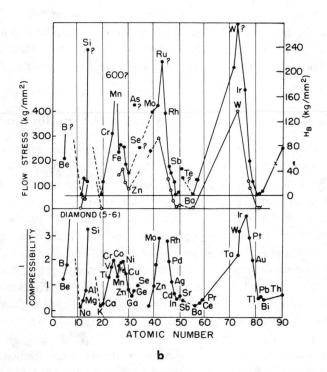

b

FIG. 7. Dependence of mechanical properties of elements on their position in the periodic table.

The mechanical properties of metals are governed by the distribution of conduction electrons between ions in the lattice. It is in the extreme case, when
these electrons are evenly distributed and may be regarded as almost free, that
metallic properties become most apparent. The highly symmetrical cubic-lattice
crystals of such metals as the alkalis, aluminum, gold, silver, copper, and the
metals of group VIII are examples. All these metals are highly ductile. Metals
of group II, which crystallize in the hexagonal system, have less pronounced
metallic characteristics. Their lower plasticity is explained by their hexagonal
symmetry. As experimentally demonstrated, their electrons are inhomogeneously
distributed [30], [44].

When at least a portion of the electrons are bound to the lattice ions, brittleness is considerably increased, as for instance in α manganese [29].

It is unfortunate that knowledge of the relationship between the character
of cohesive force and the properties of solids, especially their mechanical properties, is still far from being on a quantitative basis.

The strength of interatomic cohesion in metals and alloys may be tentatively
estimated by the magnitude of the following physical characteristics: sublimation
energy, melting temperature, recrystallization temperature, heat content, energy
of activation of diffusion and self-diffusion, mean thermal displacement of atoms
from their equilibrium positions, elasticity moduli, coefficient of thermal expansion, and characteristic temperature. Bonding is considered to be stronger
when each of the enumerated characteristics is greater (except for the expansion
coefficient and mean thermal displacement of atoms from their equilibrium
positions). However, none of these properties fully characterize the cohesive
forces.

Mechanism of Plastic Deformation of Crystalline Solids

Mankind from time immemorial has used ductile materials when it has seemed
useful or necessary to alter the form and size of solids without fracture. However, the science of plasticity was born only at the close of the last century.
In spite of their apparent simplicity, the plastic changes in matter are complex
chemical and physical phenomena. Therefore, in studies of plasticity, not only
mechanical methods but also appropriate physical and chemical methods are
applied. The solutions of numerous theoretical and practical problems linked
to plasticity depend primarily on physical and physicochemical studies. At
present, thanks to efforts by the soviet scientists Joffe, Kuznetsov, Gubkin,
Bochvar, Davidenkov, and many others, the nature and the mechanism of plasticity have been clarified to a great extent; however, a whole range of problems
still remains unsolved.

In contrast to amorphous bodies, crystalline materials are deformed by a special
mechanism of plastic deformation. Depending on the nature of the crystals and
their response to stress, plastic deformation takes place either by slip or by

mechanical twinning, or by both simultaneously. In both monocrystalline and polycrystalline metals, the mechanism is mainly slip. In monocrystalline minerals and rocks, twinning and, to a lesser extent, slip are the deforming mechanisms; in polycrystalline minerals and rocks, the basic mechanism is intercrystalline slip [45].

Figure 8 illustrates slip. Plastic deformation in a body is caused by stresses present in the slip plane, i.e., shear stresses; stresses normal to the slip plane may either contribute to plastic deformation or hinder it. Slip begins only when a certain value of shear stress is reached in the slip plane. Critical shear stresses are small—of the order of tenths of a kilogram per square millimeter for the majority of technically pure metals. Once started, slip is soon inhibited in the initial plane but spreads to other slip planes; strengthening results and, in order to produce further deformation, the value of the shear stress must be greater than the initial one.

Slip in crystals develops only in certain crystallographic planes and directions. As a rule, slip takes place along planes and in directions of densest packing of atoms (such planes are faces with lowest indices). At ordinary temperatures, there are four such octahedral planes in the face-centered-cubic lattice, but only one basal plane in the hexagonal lattice. Therefore, metals crystallizing in a hexagonal lattice are less ductile than those crystallizing in cubic lattices. Slip planes of metals crystallizing in the body-centered-cubic lattice have yet to be determined; such metals have several planes which are equivalent for slip [21]. The packing of atoms in a body-centered lattice is less dense than in a face-centered one (28 as against 74 percent). Plastic flow will take place more easily in the most densely packed layers of atoms. Less densely packed layers of atoms are less conducive to plastic deformation because the atoms of one layer sink deeper into the spaces between atoms of the adjoining layer and

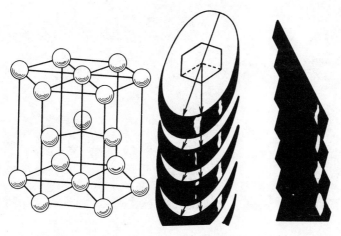

FIG. 8. Model of a crystalline lattice and schematic diagram illustrating slip in a single crystal of magnesium (Mark, Polanyi, Schmid).

thus will contribute to the mechanical resistance. Therefore, other conditions being equal, a metal with a body-centered-cubic structure will be less ductile than one with a face-centered-cubic structure [38].

Slip does not occur on only one crystallographic slip plane but in a group of slip planes of a certain type; thus slip lines or bands appear on the surface of the specimen—Chernov-Luders lines (Fig. 9).

The electron microscope reveals the fine structure of slip traces in deformed aluminum crystals. Slip traces at deformations of up to 20 percent have an approximate width 0.25 μ and are often found in groups of four or five traces separated by distances of the same order of magnitude. At deformations of 20 percent and over, in certain cases, the number of slip traces becomes so great that the entire specimen is covered by them. It has been found that a slip trace ordinarily shows up as a set of thin, equidistant "lines" or submicroscopic slip traces of about 200 to 250A width, with the same distance between the "lines." This finding leads to the assumption that slip on atomic planes occurs on a scale commensurate with the lattice parameter [46] (Fig. 10).

In the absence of softening phenomena (recovery or recrystallization) the critical shear stress depends only slightly on temperature.

As the temperature increases, other atomic planes which are the next most densely packed may enter into the slip process. Experiments with single crystals have shown that in single crystals of aluminum, copper, gold, silver, and lead at 450°C slip takes place along octahedral planes (111), whereas above 450°C slip also takes place along cubic planes (100). In monocrystals of magnesium,

FIG. 9. Slip lines in crystalline grains of a solid solution of silicon in nickel, ×600 (Lashko).

zinc, and cadmium slip takes place along the basal planes (0001), but at 225°C and over, slip also occurs along the planes (10Ī1) or (10Ī2).

The more homogeneous a metal is, the more plastic it will be. Addition of a small quantity of another metal to a given metal increases the magnitude of the critical shear stress tenfold (Fig. 11) [22]. In a soluble mixture the critical shear stress increases in proportion to the difference in the properties of the elements comprising the mixture. The strengthening action of solid solutions is explained as follows. Plastic deformation of crystals consists mainly of slip of layers along certain planes and directions. If foreign atoms get into these planes, they distort the crystalline lattice and act like thorns, increasing the shear stress [47]. When precipitation from a solid solution occurs in the form of isolated inclusions, the foreign atoms no longer block the slip planes and, at times inversely, facilitate the deformation of the polycrystalline aggregate.

Slip is a complicated physical process; its mechanism is still not clear. Because slip may be caused in metallic monocrystals by even very low values of the shear stress, it is apparent that at any given moment only a small section of a crystal is involved. Achievement of simultaneous slip in the whole crystal would require stresses hundreds or even thousands of times greater. In essence, plastic deformation by slip does not have the meaning conveyed by the general interpretation of the word, but describes a displacement of one part of a crystal relative to another, via a specific process of gradual transition of atoms in the most densely packed layers. One of the latest physical hypotheses explaining the slip mechanism is the dislocation hypothesis. The term dislocation is understood to designate a specific distortion of the normal arrangement of atoms as a consequence of their thermal motion, lattice defects, and so on. When a

FIG. 10. Group of slip traces in an aluminum crystal deformed 20 percent. Electron micrograph, ×21,000 (Yakutovich, Yakovleva, Lerinman, and Buynov).

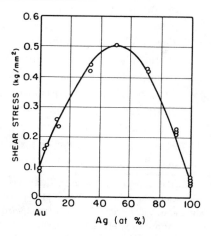

FIG. 11. Influence of composition on the magnitude of the shear stress in Au-Ag alloys.

stress of the proper magnitude is applied, dislocations move in specific directions in a crystal; thus the irreversible change of its shape is explained. However, this hypothesis is not applicable for quantitative calculations, because methods have not been established to determine dislocation density in metallic samples. A thorough criticism of dislocation theories on ductility and strength is presented in articles by Stepanov [48], Klassen-Nekliudova, Kontorova [49], and others.*

Plastic deformation is feasible not only by slip but also by twinning (Fig. 12). Deformation by twinning occurs by the rearrangement of atoms in a crystal into a new arrangement that is the mirror image of the crystal on the other side of the twin plane. In face-centered-cubic metals, slip and bending in the lattice of the crystal are, apparently, basic types of deformation. In metals of other systems, twinning of crystals takes place as well as slip. In cubic metals twins appear; however, these are not caused by deformation but by annealing of metals with a face-centered-cubic lattice (Fig. 13). Twins from annealing usually show up as stripes limited by parallel facets intersecting the grains; the parallel boundaries coincide with the (111) twinning planes. Deformation twins are formed in some metals with a body-centered-cubic lattice, but only at low temperatures.

When twinning of crystals takes place, especially in metals of the hexagonal system, it is often accompanied by a characteristic crackling sound indicating an abrupt deformation (as first observed by Joffe and Klassen-Nekliudova) [52].

In polycrystalline metals a so-called viscous flow, consisting of displacement of grains in relation to each other, takes place [53].

Plastic deformation is accompanied by the following basic phenomena:

1. Ultimate strength and resistance to further deformation are increased. In single crystals, this resistance may be increased by tens of times.

2. Simultaneously, the phenomenon of recovery may occur. Recovery takes place at the expense of recrystallization and so reduces the metal's strength. The higher the temperature, the higher the rate of recovery. The magnitude of strengthening depends on the relationship of the rate of strengthening to that of softening.

3. An overwhelming portion of energy expended on plastic deformation is dissipated as heat; some of the energy (from 10 to 20 percent), however, is retained internally and acts to distort the crystal and to produce internal stresses. The higher the rate of deformation, the more energy is consumed and the less retained.

---

* *Editor's Note*: Although Russian scientists have shown a general lack of interest in dislocation theory, they have placed considerable emphasis on the field in recent years. Oding *et al.*, for example, have published a book on the theory of creep [50], in which they devote approximately 100 pages to dislocation theory. A seminar on the theory of dislocations was held from November 11 to December 4, 1959, at the Physical Technical Institute in Leningrad. Physicists and metallurgists attending the seminar proposed that the theory of dislocations be included in courses given at universities and higher technical schools. A glossary of terms used in describing dislocations was also adopted at the seminar [51].

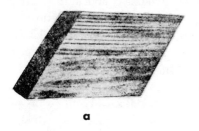
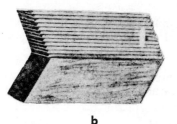

a   b

FIG. 12. Schematic illustration showing
twinning (after Mugge).
     a. before slip; b. after slip.

FIG. 13. Annealing twins in brass, ×155
(Zholobov).

4. In the process of plastic deformation, not only the form and size but also
the physicochemical properties of solids are changed as a result of the
activating stresses and temperatures. When the amount of deformation
is great, these changes are quite significant. It might be well also to
mention changes in the structure of the material (fragmented grains,
texture), increase in strength and brittleness, and so on.

Research on plastic deformation, which should also cover all these phenomena,
has only begun. As a rule, attention is directed to studies of only one phase
of this complex process.

Seeking an elucidation of all the complex phenomena of plastic deformation,
Bochvar suggests four different mechanisms of flow: (1) slip or dislocation,
(2) amorphous diffusional deformation, (3) phase transitions via dissolution or
precipitation, and (4) grain-boundary shearing and recrystallization [15].

According to Bochvar, the slip or dislocation mechanism has practical value
only at very low temperatures. At temperatures of the order of one third to
one half of the absolute melting temperature (T_m), diffusion of atoms becomes
possible and the amorphous diffusional-flow mechanism takes over. Because the
process of recrystallization begins at about these same temperature levels, the

possibility of intergranular flow without fracture is simultaneously assured. The diffusional mechanism of flow is inherent in two-phase and in the more complex alloys only. Its minimum temperature—i.e., the lowest temperature at which there is a noticeable development of diffusion—is not less than $0.3 T_m$. This mechanism achieves maximum development in the temperature range in which the mutual solubility of alloy phases is substantially altered. At constant temperature the relative role of diffusion mechanisms of flow increases as the rate of deformation decreases. Thus, according to Bochvar, all forms of plastic flow could, in theory, be classified as diffusional phenomena, which develop either within the crystal along its atomic planes (dislocation under the influence of stress), or along the surface of one-phase crystals, or, finally, along the surface separating two phases.

However, as Gubkin has pointed out, the application of a stress field results in a mechanism of diffusional slip substantially different from that of ordinary diffusion, regardless of the fact that in both cases atomic displacement takes place [54]. In the first case, atoms are expelled from their environment as a result of the stress; in the second case, as a result of heat fluctuations.

Diffusion mechanisms in prolonged experiments are discussed in a series of studies by Oding [55]. To differentiate our approach to the mechanism of plasticity from the mechanical, mathematical, and purely physical approaches, we call it the physicochemical approach. In this connection it is pertinent to note the trend of research on the mechanism of plastic deformation of metals and minerals subjected to the action of surface-active substances (Rebinder effect) advanced by the school of the Academician Rebinder [56].

Plastic deformation of monocrystals has been rather completely studied, especially the tensile deformation of monocrystals of metals with hexagonal symmetry [21], [22]. The phenomena which occur in plastic deformation of monocrystals are also present in the deformation of polycrystalline samples, but the mechanism of plastic flow in monocrystals, especially in the initial stage, differs distinctly from that in polycrystals. As deformation progresses, monocrystals gradually become polycrystals.

Some of the factors which distinguish the plastic flow of polycrystals from that of monocrystals are their smaller grain size, the influence of certain grains on the deformation process of neighboring grains which impede the slip of crystals and create an internal stress, and the specific role of grain boundaries.

An irreversible change in the form of a polycrystal can be caused by any of the following: slip, crystal twinning, diffusion, and the motion of one grain with respect to another [57]. All these mechanisms can sometimes occur simultaneously. Deformation with recrystallization (growth of new, undeformed grains) caused by the motion of some crystals in relation to others is less damaging to the strength of polycrystals than deformation without recrystallization. Grain boundaries of alloys have a distinct structure (influenced by composition and surface effects) and are more amenable to the physicochemical factors applied in processing alloys, especially at high temperatures.

Attempts to determine the theoretical strength of solids refer to perfect solids only [21], [24], [27], [33]. Because of the presence of impurities and lattice defects, and the influence of grain boundaries, real solids differ radically from perfect solids. Further, as attested by recent X-ray and electron-microscope studies, real crystals, especially metallic crystals, have a "mosaic" structure. It was found that metallic crys-

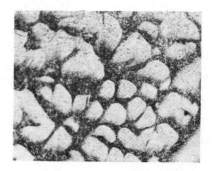

FIG. 14. Annealed copper crystal, ×20,000 (Bunin).

tals are composed of blocks (in sizes between 10^{-4} and 10^{-5} cm) which have more or less perfect atomic arrangement but are somewhat mutually disoriented (to an angle of a few minutes of arc). Mosaic structure is shown in Fig. 14, an electron micrograph of an annealed copper grain pickled with ferric chloride [34].

It has been shown that, when a steel sample is stretched at the usual rate of deformation, its crystalline blocks are fragmented. Fragmentation ceases at about 12 percent deformation [58]. A pronounced fragmentation of blocks and an increase in angle between them is noticeable in cold-worked, quenched, and annealed alloys. Thus, in tempered steel with 1 percent carbon, blocks measure 2×10^{-6} cm [59]. The smaller the mosaic blocks, the smaller the possibility of crystallographic slip (which creates conditions for change in shape by deformation). When heated to certain temperatures (350–550°C for steel) blocks start growing rapidly. All real crystals should be considered mosaic to a greater or lesser degree. Grain boundaries represent areas of great atomic distortion.

Metals, like all crystalline solids, are anisotropic. The physicomechanical properties of noncubic-system metals are subject to radical changes with orientation. In metals such as zinc and tin, elongation in one direction is negligible, whereas in other metals it reaches several hundred percent. The anisotropy of metals increases in various directions with decreasing temperature.

A mass of experimental data on the plasticity of solids and, particularly, metals has now been accumulated, but a complete theory of plasticity has not yet been formulated.

The phenomena of plasticity and fracture are still unexplained from the viewpoint of the contemporary theory of crystallography. Meanwhile, despite many hypotheses, theoretical research on the mechanical properties of solids is lagging badly behind other phases of theoretical physics [60]–[62].

The term "theoretical strength of crystals" is understood to mean the magnitude of the critical stress determined by computation of interacting electrical forces within the crystal lattice. Modern methods of computation prove that the theoretical strength is hundreds, even thousands, of times greater than the experimental strength [63]. (Table 1 gives pertinent data.) For monocrystals

TABLE 1

THEORETICAL AND EXPERIMENTAL RUPTURE STRENGTH OF ANNEALED
PURE POLYCRYSTALLINE MATERIALS

Material	Critical Rupture Strength (kg/mm²)		Ratio of Computed to Observed Strength
	Computed	Observed	
Aluminum	372	9.2	40.1
Gold	782	12	65
Copper	885	22.6	39
Lead	261	1.1	237
Platinum	125	12	10.4
Tin	357	1.4	255
Zinc	580	13	44.5
Sodium chloride	84	10	8.4
Quartz	1000	11.6	86

Sources: Schmidt and Boas [22]; Seitz [27]; Schreiner [33].

this divergence is still greater. The theoretical strength of ductile bodies (lead and tin) is hundreds of times their experimental strength, whereas the theoretical strength of brittle bodies (quartz, sodium chloride) is only tens of times their experimental strength. This discrepancy between ductile and brittle bodies may be explained by the fact that in brittle materials, not subject to plastic deformation, resistance to rupture more nearly coincides with theoretical strength. For ductile bodies, which fracture by shearing, comparison of theoretical with ultimate strength is open to question, since the ultimate strength does not determine the resistance to fracture but the resistance to plastic deformation. For brittle bodies, fracture strength and surface energy of the crystal are related by the equation

$$\alpha = \frac{\sigma_{fr}^2}{2E} \cdot b \, ,$$

where E is Young's modulus and b is the interatomic or interionic distance.

Several hypotheses on the causes of the lower strength in real crystals have been advanced, but they all converge to a comparison of perfect with real crystals, because the lower strength of the latter is related to some structural defect such as surface or volume flaws, weakened binding, mosaic structure, or dislocation mechanism of plasticity ([64]–[78]). The problem would be more definite if it were possible to obtain a truly perfect crystal and to establish that its fracture stress is of the right order of magnitude. Let us hope that, with the growth of our knowledge of the internal structure of solids and the aid of the factors already known (energy of the crystal lattice, surface energy, distribution of electrons, and so on), new factors will be found that will lead us to a more realistic computation of the theoretical strength. However, the assumption that the experimentally observed strength is not a property of the crystal lattice but is related only to its imperfections is incorrect [48] because it ignores the individual nature of matter. Furthermore, flaws and cavities reduce the strength of brittle materials but may increase the static strength of plastic substances.

Data on the moduli of elasticity are in better agreement. Computations based on the interatomic bonding for certain metals reveal values which are close to those obtained experimentally [22]. A real cause of divergence between theoretical and real strength arises from the following procedure. When theoretical strength is calculated, a determination is made of the force required to shear simultaneously all the atoms present in a given section of a metal, from the closest parallel atomic layer, whereas in real plastic deformation or fracture of a metal, at any given moment, only a small part of the atoms present in the deformed section participate in plastic deformation, and they are deformed consecutively, not simultaneously. As deformation progresses, a gradual break of interatomic bonding takes place; this break results in the formation of local flaws and ultimately ends in fracture.

When the divergence existing between the theoretical and the real strengths is examined, a very important factor should be borne in mind, namely the scaling factor. Experiments have shown that small specimens have greater unit strength than large specimens of identical material. In some cases the experimental strength of small specimens reaches and even surpasses the theoretical strength. Thus, for instance, the rupture strength of a filament of fused-quartz glass approximately 1μ thick approaches $1000 \, \text{kg/mm}^2$, which is equal to the theoretical strength of crystal quartz and is close to 100 times the strength of comparatively thick quartz samples [33]. The same situation prevails roughly in metals also. A noticeable increase in tension and compression strengths usually begins to appear in samples of less than 1-mm diameter. This increase is caused mainly by the growing importance of surface energy coincident with a decrease of sample diameter and a change in character of stress distribution. The presence of defects and impurities contributes to the inception of the rupture process in large samples. The dependence of strength on the linear dimensions of samples is well described by the following equation,

$$p = \frac{\alpha}{l} + P_0 \, ,$$

where p is strength, l is linear dimensions of the sample, P_0 is strength of a large-cross-dimensional specimen, and α is the proportionality coefficient.

It is also difficult to explain the work hardening of metallic materials during the process of plastic deformation. Several hypotheses have been advanced to explain the nature of strengthening—the thorn-and-slip interference hypothesis [67], numerous versions of the "hooking" and lattice-distortion hypotheses [68]–[71], old hypotheses on the appearance of a brittle amorphous layer on grain boundaries and on slip planes [72], [73], the hypothesis of changes of the very same atoms when deformed [74], the dislocation hypothesis ([75]–[77]), the carbide hypothesis of steel hardening [79], and the previously mentioned hypothesis on the change in type of chemical bonding in the deformation process [32]. The abundance of hypotheses testifies to the fact that the physical nature of hardening has not been established as yet.

The majority of hypotheses are speculative and are more reflections of the researchers' points of view than statements of fact. The carbide hypothesis of steel hardening is critically viewed at present [80], [81].

Block fragmentation, which occurs in plastic deformation, is now considered by a number of scientists to be the basic cause of strengthening.

Akimov's theory, which explains metal strengthening by a conversion of metallic cohesion into atomic cohesion [32], appears to be quite plausible. However, this theory needs as yet unavailable experimental confirmation of the influence of deformation on the type of change in chemical cohesion. Plastic deformation is a physicochemical process accompanied by a continuous change in the properties of the material subjected to the process of deformation, during which, as a result of the effect of stress, various forms of chemical transformations are possible. The final theory of strength will probably incorporate many aspects of this complex physicochemical phenomenon.

The most effective scientific way to obtain materials with the required properties, and also to find a rational technique for their processing, is physicochemical analysis. For metals and their alloys the method is metallography—a division of physicochemical analysis—which examines the physicochemical nature of metallic alloys on the basis of their composition, formation, structure, and properties. Phase diagrams present a general and reliable picture of the chemical interaction of components which ultimately governs the structure and properties of alloys and determines directly their phase composition and structure as a function of temperature under equilibrium conditions.

Phase diagrams and diagrams of composition versus property are of great importance to the development of the theory of metallic alloys and their practical use in engineering. The establishment of the relationship of mechanical and other physical properties of alloys from their nature and structure and from changes in basic equilibrium factors, in order to develop alloys with predetermined properties, is the main problem of modern metallography. To these equilibrium factors (concentration, temperature, and pressure) should be added such factors as stress, electric, acoustic, magnetic, and other fields. Although the chemistry of metal alloys is relatively new, increasing use of this area of science in research and industrial laboratories has already led to the introduction of new alloys and to the development of effective production techniques.

Current Methods of Determining Mechanical Properties

Mechanical properties are the physical properties of solids which describe the behavior of the solids during deformation. As a rule, the mechanical properties of a material become apparent only in the process of deformation caused by external forces. Existing methods to determine certain mechanical characteristics of metals with respect to changes of physical properties have as yet only minor value. Mechanical properties of polycrystalline materials, as now measured, are only average statistical values and are not strictly physical properties of the crystal lattice; they do not, as a rule, yield to a precise physical explanation. Although metal working was known in ancient times and has now reached enormous proportions, and although the processing of manufactured products is governed by means of mechanical tests, the theoretical principles of mechanical testing are still in the most elementary stages [5], [82]. Practice in this respect is ahead of theory. Most mechanical characteristics have only qualified significance inasmuch as their magnitude depends on the conditions of the experiment in which the data were collected, and the forms and sizes of specimens. An experiment requires samples of material to be subjected to stress by means of appropriate machinery and instruments and constant physical conditions under which the experiments are conducted. It follows, therefore, that in mechanical testing the following test conditions should be standardized: geometrical (form and size of specimen), mechanical (load condition), and physical (external physical conditions, temperature, power process, and so on) [5]. Determination of mechanical properties is related to transient conditions which are difficult to analyze, such as ductility, strength, brittleness, and fracturability. As stated by Davidenkov, mechanical properties of materials may be classified as basic and secondary. The first—which comprise the limits of elasticity and plastic flow, ultimate strength (temporary resistance to fracture), shear and tear resistance, elongation and contraction, work-hardening coefficient, and fatigue limit—are mutually independent. The second—which may include toughness, strength of a notched sample, hardness of all forms, and so on—are essentially functions of the basic properties. The precise relationship between the first and second groups of properties has not been fully established [83].

Mechanical testing—determination of fatigue, creep, hardness, and strength—may be of short or long duration. Long-duration testing will not be discussed here; short-time testing is used most often to determine hardness and tensile strength.

In the plastic deformation of metals, three overlapping processes are encountered: elastic deformation, plastic deformation, and fracture [34], [84]-[86]. The behavior of metals subjected to mechanical action is most frequently described by diagrams which correlate stress with deformation (Fig. 15).

Curve section OA shows the metal's behavior in elastic deformation, section BC shows the plastic deformation, and point C shows the stress and amount of

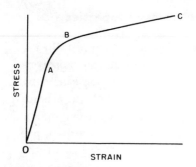

FIG. 15. Relationship between stress and strain.

deformation at which fracture occurs. The deformation is elastic when it does not produce any permanent change in form—if application and removal of stress produce reversible changes of metallic properties. In actual tests even at low stresses, a deviation from elastic behavior in metals is noticeable. The so-called brittle materials such as glass, quartz, amorphous bodies in general, and ionic crystals (at ordinary temperatures and in the absence of lateral pressure) do not exhibit plastic flow; rather, they fracture when the applied force exceeds their elastic limits. There are also metals in which the process of plastic deformation is not necessarily followed by fracturing (Pb, Cu, Al, Au, Ag, and other face-centered-cubic metals). The notion that plastic deformation occurs first and fracture takes place afterward applies only to macroscopic samples. Experience shows that, long before fracture, cracks occur in separate sections of the material [87].

As Hooke's Law states, the magnitude of elastic deformation is proportional to the magnitude of the applied stress. The basic mechanical characteristics of materials in the elastic region are the modulus of elasticity in tension, the coefficient of contraction, and the shear modulus. Depending on the orientation of the crystal in the lattice, the elastic modulus in monocrystals may change from 2 to 4 times, but the change in the shear modulus is only by a factor of 2 to $2\frac{1}{2}$ [5]. Studies on the tendency of metals to absorb vibration have been made recently [88].

Studies on elasticity characteristics of materials are as yet rare, probably because of the difficulties encountered with the methods of physicochemical analysis; however, this is an urgent problem because elastic constants, to a certain degree, are yardsticks of the strength of molecular chemical cohesion of solids.

Elastic properties of materials are not very sensitive to changes of various factors, particularly to thermal and mechanical processing. The magnitude of the elasticity modulus increases with an increase of lattice density. As a result of heating, an increase in interatomic spacing occurs, together with a simultaneous diminution of the normal elastic modulus. Thus, for iron and steel in the temperature range of -195 to $+20°C$, the elastic modulus changes about 5 percent; for aluminum, when heated from 20 to 200°C, the elastic modulus drops from 6000 to 5500 kg/mm^2 [86].

The elastic limit and yield point characterize the properties of materials in the transition from elastic to elastic–plastic deformation and are more nearly related to the plastic range.

The transition from the elastic range to the plastic is a gradual process.

Hence, as the precision of determining the first sign of deformation increases, the lower the value of the elastic limit becomes. The elastic limit and yield point do not differ in principle—the elastic limit of $\sigma_{0.001}$ may be measured by precise instruments only, whereas the yield point of $\sigma_{0.2}$ can be adequately determined on a diagram by graphic means [85].

Data on elasticity and small plastic deformation contribute to the mechanical-mathematical theory of plasticity, by means of which structural strength may be computed. This theory views all solids as an idealized "continuous medium" irrespective of the atomic and molecular structure of real solids. In this respect, as stated by Shchapov, the terms "stress" and "deformation" are conditional and, to be precise, their application is really appropriate only for a continuous medium [87].

Elastic deformation is a prerequisite for plastic deformation; it brings the metal to a state of stress. Because of the thermal vibrations of atoms, the condition of stress may be lessened with time and a relaxation of stress may occur.

The plasticity and viscosity of metals and alloys are interesting from two viewpoints—technological (adaptability to pressure processing) and structural (suitability for construction purposes and machines, where these properties contribute to stress redistribution under overload conditions). Plastic deformation, in contrast to elastic deformation, is of much greater magnitude. Thus, for instance, elastic deformation constitutes only a fraction of a percent of the original dimensions of the tested materials, whereas, depending on the test conditions, plastic deformation may increase the original dimensions from ten to several hundred percent.

There is a difference between ductility and viscosity of materials. Ductility permits a solid to change its shape without fracturing; viscosity gives a material a low value of resistance to deformation. Austenitic steel is ductile but not very viscous. Lead is both ductile and viscous. Metals at temperatures close to the melting point have low viscosity but no ductility (because of the phenomenon of burning) [89]. It should be noted that the above definitions of ductility and viscosity are not generally accepted.

No reliable law for plastic flow of a material has yet been found which satisfactorily correlates with the present experimental results. Existing data on physical processes which occur during plastic flow do not give a complete picture of the mechanical processes involved and of those material constants which would enable one to measure the material's strength and ductility in that state of deformation [90].

Studies of physicochemical transformations and technological capacity for deformation reveal the great importance of the plastic properties of materials and their deformation resistance. It is known that the degree of ductility is determined by the magnitude of permanent strain (in terms of percentage or relative units), whereas strength indices have the dimensions of stress or specific pressure.

The most common strength characteristics are the yield point, ultimate strength or fracture strength, hardness, flow stress, and others; whereas the characteristics of plasticity are lengthening, contraction, size of imprint in hardness tests, decrease in length caused by compression, degree of deformation at a fixed value of the flow stress, and so on. A correct appraisal of material strength can be made by determining the true ultimate strength corresponding to the breaking point and to the actual cross-sectional area at the point of fracture.

A determination of flow stress, as well as other mechanical characteristics, is often of great interest to technologists, because it is indispensable to the computation of the power required by presses for extruding rods, wires, or pipes of a given material [91].

In tension testing, elongation characterizes the capacity of a material to undergo uniform deformation, whereas contraction (in the region of the neck) indicates maximum deformation. Therefore, contraction is a more reliable characteristic of materials which neck than of those which do not; furthermore, contraction is not affected by the length of the specimen tested.

Toughness characterizes the work absorbed per unit volume of metal. Toughness is determined approximately as the product of stress and total elongation. Impact strength is a characteristic of stored energy. In industry, tests of impact characteristics are conducted in addition to static tests in metals. To detect physicochemical transformations in alloys, by contrast, dynamic testing is considered more effective. This effectiveness is evident in cases in which physicochemical transformations increase the brittleness of the material. When comparable data on the effect of static and dynamic forces are computed, the influence of the rate of deformation on ductility and strength should be considered.

Hardness and flow-stress tests are not necessarily carried to failure of the material, whereas in tension, compression, torsion, and bending tests, the ultimate deformation results in fracture (formation of cracks). Compression and torsion are "milder" methods of testing than tension and bending tests. Each of these methods has its own peculiarities. Neck formation occurs when ductile materials are stretched. In compression tests, friction on the bearing surfaces is unavoidable, and only short samples may be used (to avoid lateral bending). Fracture by bending is not possible in a ductile material (contraction of over 50 percent). Twisting and bending produce an irregular distribution of stresses and strains. Compression, especially nonuniform hydrostatic compression as a milder form of stress, permits an appraisal of the mechanical properties of brittle materials that is not feasible in tension testing (of tool steel, for instance) [92]. Torsion is seldom used in mechanical testing of alloys for physicochemical-analysis purposes; however, it has certain advantages such as stability of shape of the tested sample, the possibility of precisely measuring the shear resistance, and so forth. When selecting a method of mechanical testing, one should consider every property mentioned here.

To determine the specimen's range of plasticity, the specimen should be fractured. This procedure may also enable one to determine the rupture strength.

The resistance of a material to external forces is of a dual nature—the resistance to plastic deformation (the strength along slip planes) and the resistance to rupture (determined by intercrystalline and crystalline cohesion). The idea that two types of forces exist was advanced by Davidenkov and subsequently developed by Friedman. Two types of fracture exist: cleavage, caused by normal stresses and resulting in a mirror-like fracture surface along cleavage planes; and shearing, caused by tangential stresses producing a fibrous cleavage along slip planes. These two types of fracture are easily recognized by their external appearance. The fracture plane produced by cleavage is perpendicular to the direction of the greatest normal stress, whereas the fracture plane produced by shear traverses the direction of greatest tangential stress. In most cases a ruptured surface has a combination of both types of fracture—shear and cleavage [93]. Certain metals (particularly α iron and its alloys, which have a body-centered-cubic lattice) fracture by cleavage and shear on various crystallographic planes: in cleavage along a (100) plane, in shear along (110), (112) and (123) planes. Certain face-centered-cubic, non-cold-short metals and alloys (copper and aluminum alloys) fracture exclusively by shearing.

The maximum ductility is related to the nonuniform plastic deformation in the volume of material subjected to deformation. The more brittle the metal, the more heterogeneous its flow. It should be noted that the physicomechanical nature of fracture is not really clear at present, as shown by numerous lively discussions appearing in scientific journals [94]. As a matter of fact, opposite views exist as to the effect of temperature on rupture resistance. Some researchers think that fracture is caused by normal stresses (i.e., by cleavage); others deny the existence of cleavage and ascribe fracture to shearing only.

In any case, when the mechanical method of testing for physicochemical analysis of alloys is used, the dual nature of fracture should be considered, as has rarely been done until now.

A large variety of methods for evaluating the mechanical properties of materials has been accumulated in developing the techniques for testing materials. Such testing procedures and apparatus are appropriately described in various manuals and government publications [5], [7], [9], [12], [40], [45], [81]–[86] and [95]–[106], and we shall not discuss them. We emphasize, however, that it is not sufficient to measure just one property alone, usually hardness; at least two properties should be measured, one characterizing strength or deformation resistance, and the other, ductility. It is advisable to use static as well as impact effects when measuring the influence of the rate of deformation.

Let us now examine the interrelation of distinct mechanical properties, a subject which has not been sufficiently explored in the existing literature. This problem is being studied basically in material-testing laboratories by measuring the strength properties of manufactured articles. Many of the equipments and methods for testing materials may be applied to solving metallographic and physicochemical problems, mainly for an approximate evaluation of metallic-alloy properties of a system.

The possibility of making a quick appraisal of the ultimate tensile strength of an alloy on the basis of its measured hardness, foregoing tension testing, is an interesting proposition. Working on various processes, Minkevich has devoted much thought and effort to showing the relation existing between yield strength, ultimate strength, and hardness in tests utilizing steel balls or cones made of various grades of steel [107].

In 1902, Brinell referred to the empirical relationship between Brinell hardness H_B of steel and the ultimate tensile strength σ_B in the form $\sigma_B = CH_B$, where C is a constant of proportionality; for example, for steels, $C = 0.33-0.36$ [108], [109].

Several attempts have been made to establish a relation between σ_B and H_B for other metals and alloys of industrial importance. It was found that the proportionality between σ_B and H_B for ductile metals exhibiting necking at rupture has a common significance and that only the coefficient C changes somewhat for different metals. Thus, of the annealed metals: for aluminum, $C = 0.27$; for lead and tin, 0.29; for copper, 0.55; for duraluminum, 0.36; for brass, 0.35; for alloys of Cu-Zn-Al, $C = 0.48$, and so forth.

This correlation is used mostly for approximating the ultimate tensile strength by hardness tests in standard production work. The coefficient C for a given metal depends on the mechanical and thermal history, i.e., on the structure, but the relationship itself is observed for hardness that is determined under standard conditions. Other similar types of correlation may be established for other methods of hardness measurement (Fig. 16).

Brittle materials (cast iron, cast aluminum alloys) which do not neck at rupture show a great deal of scatter in the value of C and the equation does not apply for them. This reaction becomes understandable if one keeps in mind that, for brittle materials, the ultimate tensile strength characterizes resistance to fracture but not resistance to deformation. The linear relationship, however, is established for characteristics of similar types only, as, for instance, hardness and ultimate strength of plastically deformable materials. Attempts to compute a correlation of σ_B with H_B result in a very complex situation, because the nature of the stress (form of loading) when a material is indented with a ball is quite different from that when it is stretched. The character and the effect of cold working are also quite different. A peculiar parallelism exists between high elasticity modulus and high Brinnell hardness (and also with melting temperature). This dependence is only generally true and disappears when pure metals are changed to alloys [109].

As stated by Gudtsov, hardness is a manifestation of surface energy [110]. Davidenkov claims that Brinell hardness characterizes the tendency of a metal to work harden [83].

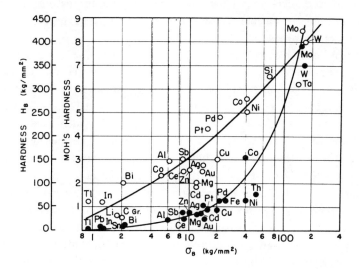

FIG. 16. Relationship of ultimate tensile strength to hardness in common metals in the annealed state.
●-Brinell hardness;   ○-Moh's hardness (Gulyaev).

Rosenberg has suggested a method to determine the elastic modulus from Brinell hardness tests under variable loads [111]. Methods to determine the ultimate strength and reduction in area, based on experimental data obtained from tests with small-diameter perforations in thin-sheet samples, were worked out at the LFTI and at the Institute for General and Inorganic Chemistry, Academy of Sciences, U.S.S.R. [112], [113]. Similar research was conducted at the Institute for Processing of Non-Ferrous Metals [114], [115]. Although the stress condition of a material subjected to impact testing with a punch is complex and does not correspond exactly to the stress condition of a material subjected to simple shear, results obtained from indentation tests with a number of metals have been found to coincide reasonably with the ultimate strength and reduction in area as measured by tension. These results apply to both metals and complex alloys.

A specific method of testing the critical temperature for cold brittleness (suggested by Davidenkov, Zlatin and Shevandin) consists of breaking a set of small, notched, split rings by means of simple hammer strokes and measuring their deformation at the fracture surface over a range of temperatures [116].

Worthy of note is a method developed by Vitman for testing the ultimate amount of plastic flow occurring in materials in the area of the small conical impression [117], [118]. Special apparatus in the laboratory for mechanical testing at the LFTI of the Academy of Sciences, U.S.S.R., was built to determine yield stress and ultimate strength based on hardness tests by indenting cones at various temperatures (up to 600°C) in an evacuated chamber [119].

Several of the tests mentioned may be adapted to testing the mechanical properties of alloys of various compositions by a method suggested by Vekshinsky [120], or by other procedures [121], [122].

Davidenkov and his associates have proved that, for a number of ductile materials, a majority of the ductile characteristics may be measured in tension by means of a special hardness test performed with two cones [123], [124]. Particularly for steel, according to Davidenkov, $\sigma_B = 0.32H_C - 16$ where H_C is the hardness as determined by the cone method. The idea here is to determine the characteristic points of "true stress" in tension. The method is experimentally quite simple; the material is indented with a 90°-apex-angle cone. Unfortunately, as proved by experiments, this method does not apply to all materials; for instance, in steel, the uniform elongation must not exceed 15 percent [119].

A check of existing methods for determining tension characteristics based on hardness tests for stainless steels was made by Sichikov, Zakharov, and Kozlova [125]. It was found that, for these materials, the correlation between ultimate strength and hardness is best determined by the Brinell and Rockwell methods.

The same authors state that a linear dependence is apparently present between the yield stress and the reciprocal of the indentation diameter.

Cone-tested hardness and the true ultimate tensile strength S_C are, according to Pashkov, correlated by the equation $H_C \cong 3S_C$ [90], where H_C is the hardness as determined by the 90°-angle-cone method.

Indices of strength characteristics (mainly of ultimate tensile strength) thus obtained are quite reliable. A fault common to all the above methods, however, is that they result in unreliable data on ductility characteristics.

Extensive compression tests have been conducted by Kuznetzov and his associates, especially Bolshanina [21]. It was found that, in essence, their results would be best described as exponential functions (polytropic curves). The laws governing these functions were also studied under various experimental conditions and with various metals.

The theoretical basis for the conversion of one test method to another is given by the deformation theory in the form of generalized curves of the elementary stress state (generalized flow curve) [90], [126]. No other theory has yet been given.

In this respect it is assumed that basic mechanical characteristics reflect various characteristic points on and sections of the stress-strain curve.

As shown by Ludwig, true stress curves in tension, compression, and torsion will coincide if generalized deformations are plotted along the abscissa and the corresponding stresses are plotted along the ordinate axis. This approach permits a correlation of the data obtained in one experiment with those of another [127], [128].

It is recognized that additional corrections should be incorporated into the existing theory of the generalized curve of strength to take into account the type of test. Experimental data demonstrate that the corrections of the generalized curve are often relatively minor—about 10 to 20 percent. A number of experiments, however, have also shown that stresses found at equivalent deformations in tests under different stress conditions do not correlate for one and the same material. Therefore a single criterion of plasticity, in the form of a generalized flow curve, is considered doubtful by a number of research workers [90].

A simpler way of finding a more reliable correlation between the various mechanical constants is the statistical method, by establishing the coefficient of correlation. In this field, Shchapov and his associates are most prominent, having processed the extensive statistical data of the railway transport system. Shchapov brought to attention the existing correlation between ultimate tensile strength and impact toughness for steel at various temperatures [129].

Davidenkov is credited with a thorough survey of research on mechanical tests conducted in the U.S.S.R. from 1917 to 1947 and also on the interrelationships among these properties [130].

Figure 17 shows the correlation between the fracture strength and the elastic modulus for a number of elements, according to Guliayev [39].

The physicochemical analysis reveals a correlation between hardness and yield stress, since both properties represent the resistance of a material to deformation. The point was first proved in 1908 by Kurnakov and Zhemchuzhny. They found that the numerical value of flow stress is 2 to 2.5 times greater than the Brinnell hardness number for annealed soft metals whereas, for certain salts, this correlation constant approaches 7.5 [9]. The correlation between hardness, flow stress, and internal friction of solids is disputed by some [7], [21].

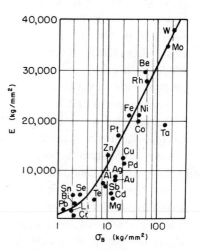

FIG. 17. Relationship between the ultimate tensile strength and the elastic modulus of some common metals.

Using duraluminum as a test material, Gubkin made a detailed study of the existing correlations between yield stress, hardness, and the true stress in uniaxial tension. He found that the magnitude of the coefficient is affected by the conditions of flow, coefficient of external friction, temperature, and rate and degree of deformation [131]. Except for the work of Shchapov, we know of no other studies or published papers on the correlations between various mechanical properties as a function of temperature. In certain metals, including some ductile and especially polymorphous ones, a greater decrease in hardness than in strength is observed with an increase in temperature; the correlation between these properties is therefore of a variable magnitude. In cold-short metals, the yield strength increases at a greater rate than does the ultimate tensile strength with a decrease in temperature.

For these reasons mechanical properties of materials should be tested by indirect as well as by direct experimental methods, especially at various temperatures. A change in the correlation of hardness with strength, of hardness with flow stress, and changes in other correlations may thus be used to determine the temperatures of phase transformations in the solid state.

The above likewise refers to the established correlations of changes in mechanical properties with certain other physical characteristics (for instance, between hardness and electrical resistance, and between hardness and magnetic properties). It should also be noted that, with a rise in temperature, the mechanical and electrical properties of alloys may change in different ways—for example, hardness and strength will decrease, but the electrical resistivity will increase in metals as a function of increased temperature. An interesting fact pertaining to the interrelationships of properties in liquid and solid alloys was observed in the paper submitted by Bobkov and Samarin on chromium and nickel alloys [132]. They found that a decrease of surface tension of melts creates alloys with a higher impact toughness. The correlation of surface tension of melts and the structure and hardness of metals is being successfully determined by Semenchenko and his associates.*

Khotkevich and Golik studied an original research problem on ductility in compression for various pure metals at the temperature of liquid helium and found a correlation between the plastic deformation of the specimen and changes in its electrical conductivity and superconductivity properties [52].

Establishment of a quantitative relationship among various characteristics pertaining to deformation—especially hardness, yield strength, ultimate strength, and flow stress—at various temperatures is a serious problem, the solution of which may help to reduce drastically the amount of work needed for physicochemical research on alloys.

It is now timely to discuss the present status of studies on the mechanical properties of materials observed on microsamples, or the so-called problem of micromechanical testing. The determination of the mechanical properties from experiments with small samples is an old problem. The advantages to be derived from microsamples are obvious, their main merit being the economy of materials used in the experiments. Thus, in static-tension experiments most commonly performed, the samples are usually 10 mm in diameter and 100 mm long. The most commonly used sample in microrupture experiments is of 1-mm diameter with a gage length of 5 mm. An average microsample is 1000 times less in volume than a standard sample. This use of small samples is especially advantageous for numerous tests on rare or expensive metals, in the evaluation of their properties, in experiments on single crystals, and so forth. Further,

---

* See summary of the Third All-Union Conference on Physicochemical Analysis. Academia Nauk, U.S.S.R., 1955.

certain problems are altogether impossible to solve with standard-size specimens, such as studies on anisotropy of mechanical properties of relatively light-gage wire, and tests for mechanical properties (exclusive of hardness) of many manufactured instrument parts and installations, and emergency parts.

The drawbacks of microtesting are that greater precision is required in the preparation of specimens and less precision is attainable in measuring the properties, as the size of the specimen is reduced. These drawbacks apply particularly to ductility characteristics, which are more sensitive to surface conditions.

Roytman and Friedman demonstrated that the size of a sample tested in tension affects mostly the magnitude of relative contraction ψ and the fracture strength S_k, which increase with a decrease in size of the sample.

For steels with a stable structure (heated or annealed at high temperatures), sample size has an insignificant effect; when a 5-mm-diameter sample was reduced to 0.8 mm, the increase in relative contraction did not exceed 6 percent. A considerably greater effect of the scale factor was observed in the nonstable structures of high-hardness steels. In structural steel, after tempering, an increase of 39 to 50 percent in relative contraction was observed when the diameter of the sample was decreased from 5 mm to 0.8 mm [133].

As stated by Pevzner and Yakimova, in their research on 30 KHGSA steel, the size of the sample has no effect on its ultimate tensile strength. The yield strength, fracture strength, and especially contraction, however, are substantially affected by the scaling factor. The significance of these characteristics becomes greater as the size of the sample is decreased [134]. It should be noted here, however, that normal-size samples, in relation to large billets or parts, are, in effect, microscopic samples and, to eliminate any effect of the scale factor, in important cases it is necessary to resort to testing parts as well as samples.

Gagarin, who originally suggested the well-known testing press for comparatively small-size samples as far back as 1895, should be considered as the founder of the method. A reliable diagram of the test can be obtained with his device on samples measuring 5 and even 3 mm in diameter. By reducing the load weight in the force-measuring device of Gagarin's press, Dragomirov and Shaposhnikov in 1912 performed experiments on 2-mm-diameter samples cut from rifle barrels [135]. The first tests on small samples using a specially built device were started by Shchapov and Lorens [136], who suggested the term "micromechanical testing." The basic goal of these tests was to observe, by means of a microscope, structural changes occurring during the process of plastic deformation. Several variations of microrupturing devices have been built recently [137]–[140]. One of these, the machine VIAM designed by Roytman and Friedman for room-temperature testing, is outstanding in obtaining precise results [137].

Averkiev, Kolesnikov, Pavlov, and Yakutovich developed a device for pulling thin wire at various temperatures and various rates of loading [139]. Yuriev,

Rechitskaya, and Mishurinsky have demonstrated that Chevenard's device may be adapted for high-temperature tests [138], [140].

Lebedev and this author have indicated that it is possible to test microrupture samples not only with microrupturing devices, but also with regular low-power testing equipment used for tension as for compression testing [141]. These microrupturing devices have complicated construction features and, in tests at various temperatures and in protective atmospheres, were found difficult to operate. A universal yet simple device was developed in the laboratories for mechanical testing of the Institute of General and Inorganic Chemistry, for tests with microsamples at various load conditions and at various temperatures under atmospheric conditions or protective atmospheres [142], [143]. A description of the device is given in Chapter 2 of this book.

Mechanical Test Methods Applied to Physicochemical Analysis

Approximately 30 physical properties are now measured for a physicochemical analysis. Mechanical properties are more sensitive to molecular-bonding characteristics than to any other property [8].

The precision of measurement and, especially, the sensitivity of the property being measured are of prime importance in the physicochemical analysis. For example, the limit of error in measurement of specific weight may be reduced to 0.001 percent, whereas a change in specific weight when chemical compounds are formed is often so minute as to pass unnoticed. On the other hand, the limit of error from sampling for a hardness measurement is about 5 percent; however, the formation of solid solutions and chemical compounds in metallic alloys is usually accompanied by an increase in hardness of a magnitude far greater than the limit of error for the given experiment [12].

The high sensitivity to physicochemical transformations and the simplicity of determination present an extensive field for the hardness-test method in physicochemical analysis of metallic alloys. Final conclusions on the interaction of components in physicochemical analysis are reached solely on the basis of cumulative data of properties. For this reason measurements should not be limited to hardness alone.

Kurnakov indicated that the development of physicochemical analysis grew from the requirements of practical metallography. The goal of systematic research in metallic systems by methods of physicochemical analysis is the selection of new alloys. The method of mechanical testing as well as other physical research methods may play an important role in achieving this goal; the chemical individuality of any one phase affects all of its mechanical properties, which are so important in the practical utilization of alloys. The above applies not only to metallic systems, but to organic and salt systems as well.

Certain mechanical properties are so sensitive to alloy composition that means of detecting a change in these properties may become a new method of chemical analysis (changes in the hardness of annealed steel with carbon content; sharp increase in the hardness of titanium, molybdenum, beryllium, and zirconium caused by increase of oxygen content, and so on).

It is unfortunate that, even now, research on metallic systems and alloys is inadequate and unsystematic and, thus, alloys sometimes selected for a particular task are not of the highest standard and are inadequate for industrial purposes. In the field of physicochemical testing methods, tension tests were introduced, along with hardness tests, between 1908 and 1913 by Kurnakov and Zhemchuzhny, who developed types of stress-strain curves which characterize the plastic properties of a material as brittle or ductile. They also found the correlation between flow stress and hardness for a number of metals and salts Kurnakov and his students used both methods with good results for research on metallic, salt, and organic systems. Nevertheless, as stated previously, hardness and flow stress are indices of a material's resistance to deformation and do not characterize the property of ductility. Besides, in these experiments, the material is not taken to fracture and, therefore, the maximum strength, not to mention ultimate ductility, cannot be obtained. Later, Urazov, Ageyev, Nemilov, Pogodin, Grigoriev, Gubkin, Kornilov, Shamrai, Rudnitsky, and others achieved excellent results using tension tests together with hardness tests for physicochemical analyses of metallic alloys. New mechanical test methods to supplement the physicochemical analysis were likewise developed.

Kuznetsov and K. V. Savitsky suggested a drill method—a steadily revolving bit is pressed into a sample and, after a predetermined number of revolutions, the resulting hole is measured. This drill-test method was used in experiments with certain metallic and salt systems and the variation in the diameter of the drilled hole in relation to changes in composition was found to conform to the rule for binary systems established by Kurnakov [21]. Kornilov developed a method and a device, based on centrifugal force, for measuring the strength of metallic bodies and is using it now in research on the phenomena of high-temperature strength and on physicochemical transformations in alloys [144].*

Gubkin and this author have suggested that, in compression tests of cylindrical specimens, the amount of deformation achieved at the start of the first crack may be used as a criterion for determining phase boundary regions [146]. Compression tests are simple; they clearly show the influence of the different factors on the ductility of metals and furnish reliable data on technological plasticity, because compression is the basic stress observed in major methods of pressure processing (rolling, forging, extruding) [147]. Smiriagin, Tammann, and others were successful in determining the solidus of certain systems by mechanical testing (loss in strength under tension or torsion) of heated samples [148]-[150].

Bochvar and Novikov measured the mechanical properties of alloys in the solid–liquid state during their solidification with interesting results [151].

---

* *Editor's Note*: Kornilov's technique is described rather fully in a British publication [145, pp. 215-219].

Let us briefly review the more important results obtained from physicochemical analysis of metallic systems by the mechanical test method.

As defined by Kurnakov, the chemical diagram of composition versus property provides a geometrical presentation of transformations occurring in an equilibrium system [8].

In its general form, the chemical diagram shows a property versus any one of a number of equilibrium factors (concentration, temperature, pressure) [152], [153]. Appropriate chemical diagrams adapted to mechanical testing are obtainable from studies of the mechanical properties of systems in relation to composition, pressure, or temperature.

A greater wealth of data is available in studies of mechanical properties in relation to chemical composition. Systematic research on a whole range of physicochemical properties of systems helped Kurnakov and his associates widen our scope of knowledge of matter and arrive at important conclusions of practical value.

Physicochemical analyses of metallic alloys enabled Kurnakov to plot composition-versus-property diagrams for typical cases of metallic interaction, to classify metallic phases, and to determine properties of certain compositions (daltonides) and intermediate compositions (bertholides); these analyses have contributed to the discovery of compounds (of super lattices) formed by solid solutions which, in all fairness, should be called Kurnakov compounds. The laws governing changes occurring in a number of properties at ordinary temperatures in thermodynamically stable binary systems are known as Kurnakov laws. To Kurnakov and Zhemchuzhny we owe the discovery that the formation of solid metallic solutions is accompanied by an increase in hardness and in flow stress in relation to the value of its original components. The variation in hardness and flow stress in a continuous solid-solution system can be described by a continuous curve with a maximum. Hardness and flow stress of a thermodynamically stable system composed of a mechanical mixture of components are linear functions of the composition. The curve of hardness versus composition is analogous to the curve of electrical resistivity and is inverse to the curve of electrical conductivity and to the temperature coefficient of electrical resistivity as a function of composition.

A definite chemical compound is characterized by a single point on the lines of the physicochemical properties. In the great majority of cases, the chemical-compound-formation process, while generating heat, is accompanied by an increase in hardness in relation to the hardness of its components.

Kurnakov and Zhemchuzhny state that when the flow stress is measured the very appearance of the flow diagram is in itself a characteristic which graphically demonstrates the special features of the chemical system and of the molecular structure of the given material [9].

Apparently all the rules governing hardness and measurement of flow stress, relative to the type of diagram as determined by Kurnakov, could also be applied to other characteristics of deformation resistance, such as yield strength and ultimate strength in tension and compression tests. Nevertheless, ductility properties, as a rule, must be inverse to resistance characteristics. It is clear that Kurnakov's laws apply to thermodynamically stable alloys in which the microstructure is described by an equilibrium condition. Systems not in equilibrium are often characterized by higher values of hardness and strength because of high stresses in the crystal structure caused by physicochemical transformations (aging and martensitic transformations). The aging effect—a technically important property of metallic alloys—is detected and measured almost exclusively by changes of mechanical properties and, primarily, by the comparative hardness of aged and annealed alloys. Studies of ternary systems by physicochemical analysis are still in the primitive stage. The laws governing binary systems will facilitate studies of ternary systems; however, greater difficulties are expected in the latter. A number of papers on the experimental correlation of mechanical properties to composition in ternary metallic systems have already been published.

Urazov and Shushpanova [154], [155] think that, from a physicochemical viewpoint, alloys lying on each side of a single cut associated with polythermal lines (i.e., consisting of a solid saturated by two phases) should exhibit optimum mechanical properties as a result of aging. This conclusion is confirmed by experimental measurement of the mechanical properties (ultimate strength and hardness) of alloys obtained by three cuts of the diagram Al-Mg-Si perpendicular to the pseudobinary line Al-Mg$_2$Si (Figs. 18 and 19). In all instances, changes in mechanical properties take place according to the same law—alloys present on the pseudobinary line display minimum strength. Development of maximum strength is clearly observed on both sides of the minimum. Urazov has plotted a schematic diagram for hardness of ternary alloys after aging, in which the base metal A is not only in solution with metals B and C but also with the compound BC [154] (Fig. 20).

A thorough survey of properties of metallic solid solutions and, in particular, a review of hardness variations with various aging treatments are given in Ageyev's "Chemistry of Metallic Alloys" [18].

Nemilov and his associates (Rudnitsky, Vidusova, and others) have used wire samples for testing the ultimate strength and total elongation as well as changes in hardness relative to the chemical composition in ternary systems of precious metals [156–160]. They found that in certain systems (e.g., platinum, copper, nickel) hardness and ultimate strength in ternary solid solutions vary along curves with a slanting minimum instead of maximum; this observation has been made previously about binary solid solutions. Using the X-ray method, Kuznetsov demonstrated that an abnormal deviation from established rules for binary solid solutions was observed in the lattice-parameter–composition curve [161].

Results of studies on hardness in palladium-nickel-chromium and copper-nickel-chromium systems show that the hardness test enables one to determine for

FIG. 18. Diagram illustrating change in the ultimate tensile strength.

○—○, first cut; ×—×, second cut; ●—●, third cut.

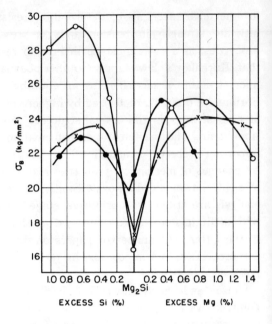

EXCESS Si (%)   EXCESS Mg (%)

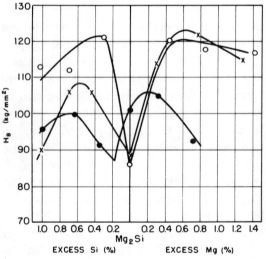

FIG. 19. Diagram illustrating change in hardness.

○—○, first cut; ×—×, second cut; ●—●, third cut.

EXCESS Si (%)   EXCESS Mg (%)

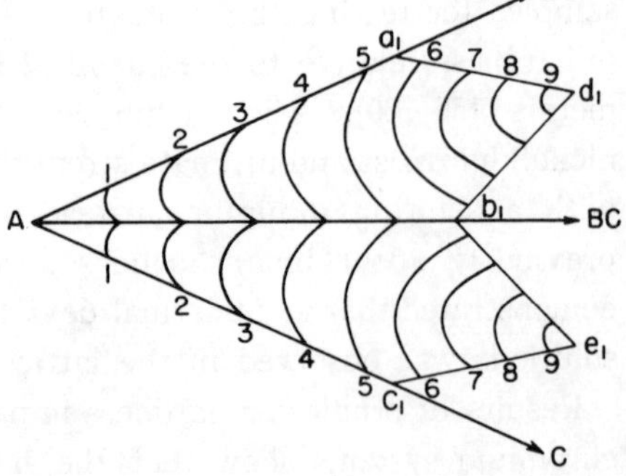

FIG. 20. Diagram of constant hardness in a ternary system.

ternary systems not only the boundaries of heterogeneous and homogeneous fields but also the locations of the eutectic lines. These transitions show up in a less-pronounced way on the curves of the temperature coefficient of electrical resistance and virtually not at all on the electrical-resistance curves. The same authors state that, in a gold-platinum-palladium system, hardness tests enabled them to define the limit of solid solubility with considerably greater precision than was possible with the microstructural method.

Thus through knowledge of mechanical properties it is often possible to appraise thoroughly the structure of a phase diagram and the resulting alloy properties with a greater degree of precision than by other methods.

In the platinum-palladium-nickel and palladium-copper-nickel systems no relationship between hardness and electrical resistance was observed. Nemilov was one of the first to note that the properties of a two-phase mechanical mixture do not always follow the linearity law in a ternary system because the concentration of phases which form the mixture is then changed. Pogodin and his students studied the physicochemical properties of metallic alloys under different conditions (eutectics, solid solutions, intermediate phases) [12], [162, 163]. Of great interest is a method suggested by Petrov to determine the minimum number of cuts needed in ternary systems in order to plot a diagram showing how hardness changes with composition, on the basis of the geometrical properties of such ternary systems [164], [165]. Using the β phase in tests with Ag-Mg-Zn alloys, Petrov and Model found that changes in crystal structure are detected most readily by the hardness test and the position of the solidus. Attention should be directed to a deduction made by Grigoriev and Kudryavtsev that, for thermodynamically unstable alloys, a curve of a given physicochemical property may not coincide with that of another, as in the case of hardness and electrical conductivity in systems of iron-manganese and iron-chromium-manganese [166].

Shamray made a detailed study of the structure and mechanical properties of ternary alloys of lithium with aluminum, magnesium, and zinc [167].

Friedman suggests that the effect of composition on the ductility of solids should be examined by the type of fracture (brittle or viscous) that samples exhibit. An increase in concentration of solid solutions always leads to an increase in the resistance to plastic flow. The ductility is decreased with an increase in the concentration in ductile systems (face-centered metals) but is increased with brittle materials (alloys of zinc and magnesium). This relation does not apply to alloys which rupture along grain boundaries, such as cast alloys [82].

It should be noted that, in mechanical properties of alloys, the correlation of the curve for complex mechanical characteristics (impact toughness, for instance) with that for physicochemical processes in materials may possibly be complex and not well defined [168].

Experimental efforts to find rules for changes in physicochemical properties by altering the composition of materials will continue to be developed and will hasten and facilitate research on the properties of complex systems.

Research on the influence of pressure on the mechanical properties of solids has been the least developed because of immense technical difficulties. The effect of pressure is closely related to the influence of the type of stress on ductility and strength. It is known that a uniform hydrostatic pressure applied to a solid will not cause its fracture (as, for instance, stones on the ocean bottom) or produce plastic deformation; it can only compress. After being subjected to pressure and on assuming a specific form (a spherical one for isotropic bodies) the material will behave as an elastic body and will withstand enormous pressure without fracturing [33], [169]. With an increase in hydrostatic pressure, individual crystals are compressed more compactly and the only possible deformation is by twinning or by slip in individual crystals. Experimental results regarding the influence of pressure on physical and physicochemical processes in solids, as well as the mechanical effects of high pressure are given by Bridgeman [170]. Thus, for instance, it is possible to shorten copper and steel to 1/50 and 1/20 of their original lengths, respectively, by compression.

In an experiment for measuring flow stress, a hydrostatic, nonuniform pressure will be most favorable to ductility conditions with an increase in the amount of plastic flow by slip and a decrease in the amount of intercrystalline slip. In extended experiments, this method has made it possible to achieve plastic flow in a number of such brittle materials as marble, sandstone, metallic bismuth, and others [23], [33]. Kurnakov and Zhemchuzhny were thus able to convert natural and synthetic salts to a ductile condition [9]. In a hydrostatic, non-uniform-compression test, the higher the lateral pressure the lower the inter-crystalline deformation, and the higher the secondary tensile stresses the higher the ductility of the material. Because of increased friction the applied force per unit volume of the formed material is greater, whereas the deformation efficiency is less than in other methods of deformation.

Research by Lepeshkov, Bodaleva, Kotova, and this author on a number of natural salts has revealed that the magnitude of the flow stress is strongly controlled by the friction produced between the surface of a salt sample and the sides of the cylinder used in the experiment. When a metal cylinder is substituted for the salt cylinder, the salt flow increases several times. Results on the flow stress thus obtained in natural salts were in agreement with the regularity of salt deposit observed in a number of salt-dome formations [171]. Analogous tests are also planned on the plastic flow of metals.

Another method which contributes to plastic deformation consists of application of bilateral stress followed by uniaxial compression, but the friction at both ends of the tested sample affects the characteristics of deformation resistance— even the character of rupture is thus affected [172]. Tension stress and especially biaxial and triaxial stresses are the least conducive to plasticity.

TABLE 2

DEPENDENCE OF SOFTNESS COEFFICIENT ON STRESS STATE

Stress State	Softness Coefficient
Triaxial tension	0–0.1
Uniaxial tension	0.5
Torsion	0.8
Biaxial compression	1.0
Uniaxial compression	2.0
Triaxial compression	4.0–∞

A residual change in the form of a solid may be described by three deformations caused by stresses acting in the directions of three mutually perpendicular axes. Friedman surmises that, to characterize the stress state, one should use the "softness" (or "viscous") coefficient, which represents a correlation of the greatest displacement stress to the greatest positive normal adduced stress (Table 2) [85]. Apparently the lower the softness coefficient, the less a given process contributes to ductility. Figure 21 shows the schemes of effective forces under the commonly used loading methods.

Tension stressing facilitates intercrystalline deformation, which greatly lowers the ductility. Significant evidence of intercrystalline deformation indicates the beginning of fracture [173].

All materials subjected to hydrostatic tension will rupture in a brittle fashion, but such loading schemes can be achieved only in a geometrically point-like body. Korneyev studied the influence of the type of stress state in fabrication processes on the ductility of metals and alloys [174].

High pressures have been used extensively in technology in the last 20 years. High pressure has a great effect on matter; it often creates new products and hastens flow reactions. Laboratory experiments conducted at high pressures have disclosed mechanisms that, under ordinary conditions, are not observable. Among those who have done research on high-pressure procedures, Russian scientists occupy a place of honor. In 1833 the compressibility of glass was

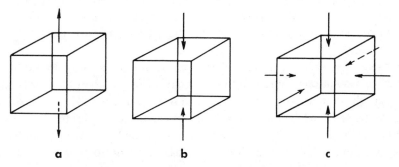

FIG. 21. Schematic diagram showing various stress states.
a. uniaxial tension; b. uniaxial compression; c. nonuniform triaxial compression.

made the object of research at the Russian Academy of Sciences and was also studied by Mendeleyev. An important contribution to the development of theoretical studies on the critical state of matter was made by Stoletov (1892–1894); experimental studies by Avenarius and Nadezhdin (1875–1887) and many other scientists should also be acknowledged. Khvolson in 1881 was the first to observe the effect of pressure on electrical conductivity in metals. Pushkin and Grebenshchikov studied the change in melting temperature and eutectic temperature with increases in pressure up to 4000 atmospheres [173].

Some of the subsequent work by our compatriots on the influence of pressure on the physicochemical transformations in metals and salts are listed below.

Vereshchagin and Likhter, guided by the published experimental data, plotted compressibility of elements as a function of their atomic numbers at pressures up to $100,000 \, kg/cm^2$. These curves are shown in Fig. 22 [174]. Zakharova and Zolotareva conducted studies on the influence of pressures (up to $100 \, kg/mm^2$) on the solid-state solubility of zinc in aluminum, of silicon in copper and of tin in copper [175]. These studies revealed that the higher the pressure of the compression test, the higher the value of maximum concentration. Zakharova also studied the effect of pressure ($10,000 \, kg/cm^2$) on the eutectoid decomposition in copper–aluminum alloys and demonstrated that the pressure effect in the process of tempering after quenching raises the temperature of both the inception and the completion of eutectoid decomposition [176]. Butuzov, Gonikberg, and Smirnov studied the effect of pressures up to $34,000 \, kg/cm^2$ on the melting point of tin and lead [177] and found that at $33,000 \, kg/cm^2$ the melting point for tin goes up to 315°C (instead of 232°C) and to 527°C for lead (instead of 327°C at 1 atm). In gallium and in bismuth the melting point decreases with an increase in pressure. Prosvirin, when investigating the effect of external pressure on phase transformations in steel and cast iron, found that a hydrostatic pressure produces an increase in density in a cast alloy without changing its form, yields a marked improvement in mechanical properties, and eliminates the appearance of anisotropy [178]. He also found that a unilateral (nonhydrostatic) pressure of $12,000 \, kg/cm^2$ exercises a considerable stabilizing effect on internal transformations, which often occur spontaneously in tool steel. Bochvar, developing Chernov's ideas, was highly successful in using air pressure while melting alloys to reduce porosity and to improve the physicochemical properties of cast articles [179].

Konobeyevsky, Zakharova, and Tarasova found that the decomposition of cold-worked solid solutions (caused by directional diffusion when annealed) proceeds faster than the decomposition of undeformed solid solutions [180], [181]. Analogous results were obtained in low-temperature annealing of tin-bronze. Research on annealing of highly cold-worked bronze demonstrated that true solubility of tin in copper is much lower than that previously determined (1 percent instead of 14.5 percent, at 200°C). These findings led to a revision of other, similar phase diagrams (Cu-Zn, Cu-Sb, Cu-Si, Al-Mg, and others).

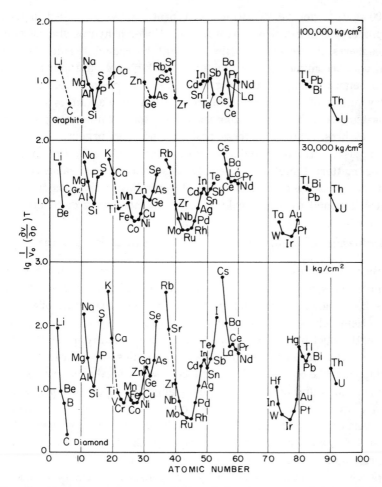

FIG. 22. Dependence of compressibility of the elements on their atomic number.

Berg, Yanatieva, and this author have conducted studies on the influence of mechanical pressure on the interaction of salts in the solid state. Using thermal analysis on pre-pressurized salt mixtures at 6000 atmospheres, they found a 1 to 2 percent formation of new phases in all cases where reactions were accompanied by contraction [182].

Using the process of nonuniform hydrostatic compression (punching the sample through the die hole) Baron, Tylkina, and this author were the first to obtain deformed samples (rods) of pure metallic alloys in magnesium-zinc and magnesium-aluminum systems [183], [184].

Metallic compounds and metal carbides are evidently very sensitive to pressure. Thus, for instance, cemented tungsten carbide (known as Carboloy in foreign literature) is used in the manufacture of parts in apparatus operating at pressures over 100,000 atmospheres. This very tough alloy, able to withstand pressures up to 75,000 kg/cm², yet very brittle when bent and when pulled in tension, undergoes property changes when pressurized. Under a hydrostatic pressure of 25,000 atmospheres it becomes ductile and will withstand tensile stresses of great magnitude, becoming the ideal material for high-pressure apparatus [170].

A physicochemical analysis defining the effect of pressure on mechanical properties by means of a property-composition-pressure diagram is still lacking. Inasmuch as today's technology is compelled to resort to processing at increasingly high pressures, a study of these problems becomes urgent. As proved in a number of cases, pressure produces substantial changes in the mechanical properties of matter; therefore systematic research on the influence of this equilibrium factor on the properties of metals and alloys as well as on mechanical properties is bound to result in important and interesting discoveries.

Influence of Temperature on Mechanical Properties

The number of studies on the mechanical properties of metallic systems at various temperatures has increased sharply in the last few years. A special interest has been shown in the cold-brittleness of steel, the nature of which has not yet been definitely solved [21], [85], [99], [185], and in heat-resistant alloys. Impact strength, ductility, and hardness have been studied most thoroughly. Tests have been conducted to determine the properties of a large number of alloys considered to be of practical importance. Mechanical-property tests under various temperatures and over the complete range of concentrations, even for binary alloys, are few in number. The influence of temperature on the mechanical properties of a number of rare metals has not been studied. A comparison of specific experimental data often becomes difficult because of variations in metal purity and because of different test procedures.

In this province, no law has been as yet established. Kuznetsov, discussing the effect of temperature on the properties of metals, states [21, p. 206]:

"In spite of the importance of the problems and of the numerous tests conducted, this sphere, unfortunately, is still in a very primitive state. It has not been theoretically explored and has been studied experimentally only. This applies both to pure polycrystalline metals, their alloys and to metallic single crystals."

Experimental results show that plasticity in metals is of a dual nature, athermal and thermal. Supporting the existence of thermally independent (athermal) plasticity is the fact that many metals (such as copper, aluminum, and others) preserve their plasticity at nearly absolute zero. The thermal aspect of plasticity is related to the amplitude of thermal atomic vibrations and increases when the material is heated. The influence of temperature is often complex because, besides its purely physical effect, the temperature (especially in the realm of elevated atom mobility) induces various physicochemical processes.

Some of them are precipitation formation and agglomeration, solution of easily soluble components, diffusion of structure-free precipitates, polymorphic transformations, dissociation of chemical compounds, oxidation, and gas absorptivity. The occurrence of softening processes (i.e., recovery and recrystallization) exerts great influence on the physicochemical properties of deformed metals and alloys subjected to elevated temperatures.

Grain boundaries have a considerable effect on the tensile strength of metals at low temperatures and on lowered strength at elevated temperatures [186].

As demonstrated in the experimental section of this book, heating and cooling may cause such great changes in internal structure as to render the same material either brittle or ductile, especially with the application of stress. The mechanical properties of a metal are unquestionably related to its melting point. It follows that tests to correlate temperature effects on the properties of various metals and alloys should be conducted, not at certain constant temperatures, but under conditions of equal atomic mobility—that is, at corresponding temperatures which encompass the whole temperature range of the material in its solid state. This requirement is especially pertinent for materials with different melting points. However, for practical purposes, as a rule mechanical properties are important only at the specific temperatures at which the materials are used; therefore, for testing, the usual temperature range is quite adequate.

In most experiments only the mean statistical temperature of the specimen is measured but local temperatures, especially along slip planes, may increase considerably during the process of deformation. This phenomenon, because of inadequate testing procedures, has evidently been overlooked.

As stated previously, the existing correlation of hardness and electrical resistance with changes in composition at ordinary temperatures disappears with an increase in temperature because then, as a rule, hardness decreases while the electrical resistance increases.

As stated in the introduction to this work, significant contributions have been made by Kurnakov, Zhemchuzhny, Shishokin, Bochvar, Gubkin, Kornilov, and others. We should mention here certain recent studies describing the temperature dependence of physicochemical and mechanical properties of metallic systems.

Classical experiments with flow-stress diagrams of solids conducted by Kurnakov and Zhemchuzhny convinced them that a rise in temperature produced an effect analogous to the lowering of the deformation rate and a simultaneous increase in the ductility of the material [9]. In 1946, Bochvar observed that Kurnakov laws governing mechanical-property changes in relation to the type of phase diagram seem to apply only at low temperatures [187].

Kornilov discovered a rule governing the temperature dependence for diffusion of metals in iron [188]. According to this rule changes in the diffusion of elements in their solid state in the given solvent, depending on temperature, are determined by a relative change of the atomic elements' radii with temperature. This rule was confirmed in experiments with a number of binary alloys. He also examined the basic relations between phase diagrams and heat resistance in metallic systems [144].

Kostenets, of the Institute for Physics and Technology of the Academy of Sciences of the Ukrainian S.S.R., experimented on the fracture of metals cooled to the temperature of liquid hydrogen and found that austenitic steels and face-centered-cubic, non-ferrous metals will not become brittle even at those temperatures [189]. Similar results with liquid helium were obtained by Khotkevich and Golic of the Academy of Sciences, U.S.S.R. [52].

Kolesnikov, Pavlov, Yakovleva and Yakutovich have studied the shapes of stress–strain curves for eight pure metals at various temperatures. They found that, generally speaking, these diagrams belonged to either of the two basic types: "low-temperature type" and "high-temperature type" [190].

Kornilov and Mikheyev have measured the impact resistance of iron-base alloys at various temperatures. They found that the impact-strength–temperature curves of solid solutions of carbon, chromium, silicon, tungsten, and of some other metals in iron are analogous to the temperature curve for the impact strength of pure iron and that the thermal brittleness in these alloys is due to the same cause as for pure iron [191]. The reason for this is not as yet sufficiently clear.

Osipov reviewed the correlation of the melting point to the heat resistance of certain metallic alloys [192].

This author reported that the highest temperature modification of a metal that exhibits allotropy should be the most ductile [193]. A device for observing changes in the microstructure of stressed samples at high temperatures in vacuum or in inert gas was built by Lebedev in 1949 at the Institute for General and Inorganic Chemistry. This device has great promise [194].

Oding and his associates achieved interesting results in grain-boundary shearing in a heated metal. In U-12 steel, the grain boundary sheared at an average linear rate of 0.10 to 0.16 mm/hr, and in tin bronze at 0.30 to 0.40 mm/hr [195].

Soviet scientists have contributed considerably to the knowledge of the effect of temperature on the characteristics of deformation. As demonstrated by Ito in 1923 the temperature dependence of Brinell hardness is described by a diminishing exponential function of a specific type [196]. Pogodin, Shishokin, and Gubkin gave theoretical proof, confirmed by numerous experiments, that this function holds not only for hardness, but also for yield stress [131], [197], [198]. Gubkin proved that the above rule applies to all types of properties related to deformation resistance [131]. Subsequently the effect of temperature on changes in strength was studied in detail by Gubkin and his associates, Zakharov (for brasses), Kutaitsev (for low-melting-point, nonferrous metals), and this author (for magnesium alloys). Their findings confirmed that the established rule was followed in every case [199]–[201].

Work done by Kurnakov's school has reliably established that the effect of temperature on all mechanical properties, which determine the resistance to deformation in metals, can be quantitatively described by

$$M_2 = M_1 \exp\left[-\alpha(t_2 - t_1)\right],$$

where M_1 is a given mechanical property at temperature t_1, M_2 is a given mechanical property at temperature t_2, and α is a temperature coefficient of the property.

Experimenting with duraluminum, Gubkin found various factors affecting the temperature coefficient of the property [126], such as:

1. The type of stress condition (yield, hardness, or uniaxial tension)—therefore it is dependent on the relative values of the principal stresses.
2. The extent of plastic deformation.
3. The rate of deformation—the greater the rate, the lower will be the temperature coefficient (absolute value).
4. The external-friction coefficient—the temperature coefficient in tests with lubrication is different from that in tests without it.
5. The physicochemical condition of the material (solid solution, mechanical mixture, and others).

In the absence of physicochemical transformations in a material, the logarithm of deformation resistance varies linearly with temperature. It was demonstrated by representatives from Kurnakov's school that at phase transformations the temperature coefficient of a mechanical property will change in value and thus bring about a break and consequent change of slope in the logarithmic straight line of a property. The above exponential law for changes in strength with temperature is of great practical importance, providing facilities for reliable technical computations in solving problems in the working of metals. This law is also basic to mechanical testing procedures and is used for physicochemical analysis purposes.

Davidenkov, Vitman, and Zlatin demonstrated recently that, in certain temperature ranges where strain aging takes place, a departure from the exponential laws occurs after cold working of annealed iron and duraluminum [52]. In their study an apparently successful attempt was made to use the exponential function in describing the effect of temperature on the ductility characteristics; we shall have more to say on this later. Incidentally, the exponential law seems to describe quite precisely a number of phenomena and processes, such as passing of atoms from a metastable to a more stable state, formation and growth of new nuclei (recrystallization, solidification, relaxation, diffusion), and so forth.

Supplementing an article by Kurnakov and Zhemchuzhny [9], Gubkin presented the current status of relaxation (stress decrease with time) and described its effect on the softening process (recovery and recrystallization) occurring in a stressed material when heated.

In tests with magnesium alloys Gubkin and this author have observed that no statement should be made about the temperature dependence of plasticity without due reference to the rate of deformation when deciding on the optimum conditions for deformation. A true concept of the nature of the phenomena taking place can be obtained only by correlating the ductility and resistance characteristics with the temperature-rate factor of deformation [201]. Iveronova established X-ray techniques for measuring the temperatures present at the inception and at the end of the recrystallization process in solid solutions based on copper, silver, and aluminum [202].

Gubkin and his associates have conducted research in recent years on the formability of industrial alloys based on copper, nickel, iron, and magnesium, in relation to impurity content, temperature, and rate of deformation [203].

Trusova studied a number of solid solutions based on aluminum and copper in the temperature range from 20 to 500°C to determine the temperature coefficient of hardness [204]. Important research on the correlation of hardness with the elastic modulus for a number of metals and alloys, at elevated temperatures, was done by Fedotov [205].

This review clearly shows that a number of important and pertinent questions, such as the temperature effect on the plasticity of polymorphous metals and metallic alloys, have been completely unexplored. In the following chapters we will examine the influence of temperature on the mechanical properties of single, binary, and, occasionally, ternary systems, mainly on the basis of the author's experimental data. Because of lack of published reference material, this experimental, methodical presentation has proved to be a voluminous job. As planned, it started with simple objectives, passing to other more complex ones, as from single to binary systems.

Our research involved mainly the crystalline structures and the chemical nature of metals and alloys. The first metals studied were those devoid of transformations in the solid state; single-component systems and metallic phases were studied next. Because of impurities, a number of so-called pure metals are not pure—they are just low-concentration alloys. In order to avoid such handicaps in our research on single-component systems, we made every effort to deal with metals of the highest purity obtainable.

We did not set before ourselves the goal of making a complete survey of all published information on the mechanical properties of a certain metal or alloy at various temperatures. It was rather our purpose to find out and to clarify the characteristic features of temperature dependence in properties of typical metals and alloys.

2

Equipment and Techniques

General Basis of Experimental Work

The greatest possible variety of test methods was used in conducting the test program in order to obtain the maximum amount of information on the properties of the materials investigated and on the changes occurring therein. The type of data gathered on the characteristic properties and the equations for their computation are shown in Table 3 [100].

Tests were conducted to determine the strength and ductility characteristics of each material. Data from tension, compression, and flow-stress tests were used to prepare stress–strain diagrams which were later converted into curves of true stress. Experiments were conducted with standard equipment for measuring hardness and microhardness—with Gagarin's press, with the universal 7- and 35-ton testing machines, and with pendulum and vertical-ram-impact machines. Only short-duration tests of the application of force were made. Whenever possible, all the tests were run at a uniform rate of deformation. Both static and dynamic tests were run, as a rule, on materials in ample supply for microsamples. For tests on samples of rare metals, special techniques and equipment were devised; however, for brevity no description of equipment for testing microsamples is given here. The test equipment was modified to prevent heat-induced oxidation of samples; these modifications made it possible to conduct static experiments in argon atmospheres or in vacuum. Figures 23 through 26 show some of these installations; Fig. 27 shows equipment to measure yield stress.

Tests were conducted on the following single-component metals: Cu, Al, Cr, Ca, Sr, Ba, In, Zn, Cd, Mg, Ge, Sn, Fe, Mn, Co, Ti, Zr, La, Ce, and some others. Similar tests were conducted on the following metallic compounds: Mg_2Si, $NiSi$, Ni_2Si, $CuSi_3$, $CoSi_2$, $MgZn$, $MgZn_2$, $MgZn_5$, $MgCd$, Mg_3Cd, $CuAl_2$, $CuMg_2$, β and α phases in the Al-Mg system, and others. For binary systems, studies were conducted on the following alloys: Cu-Ni, Ni-Re, Mo-Re, Cu-Zn, Al-Mg, Mg-Zn, Mg-Cd, Mg-Si, Al-Si, Cu-Al, Cu-Mn, Mg-Ge, Cu-Si, Ni-Si, and Co-Si.

TABLE 3.
BASIC MECHANICAL TESTS

Test	Resistance to Plastic Deformation — Type of Test	Resistance to Plastic Deformation — Associated Equation (kg/mm²)	Parameter	Associated Equation
Hardness	Brinnell Hardness (ball hardness)	$H_B = L/S$	Diameter d, area F, and surface S of imprint	$F = \pi d^2/4$ (mm²); $S = (D^2/2) - \pi d^2/2\sqrt{D^2 - d^2}$ (mm²)
	Meyer Hardness	$H_M = L/F$	Depth h and volume v of imprint	$h = D/2 - \frac{1}{2}\sqrt{D^2 - d^2}$ (mm²); $v = 1/6 - \pi h(3r^2 - h^2)$ (mm²)
	Cone-Indentation Hardness	$H_c = L/F$	Same	$S = (4 \sin\psi/2)/\pi d^2 = 1.11\,d^2$ (mm²)
	Same	$H_c = L/S$	Same	$S = (2 \sin\psi/2)/d^2$ (mm²)
	Vickers Hardness (pyramid hardness)	$H_p = L/S$	Diagonal d and surface S of imprint	
	Microhardness (impact by tetra-hedral diamond pyramid)	$H_\square = L/S$	Surface impression S of imprint	$S = (2 \sin\psi/2)/d^2$ (mm²)
Flow (extrusion)	Flow Stress	$K = L_{st}/F_0$	Relative decrease in sample area a	$a = [(F_0 - F_c)/F_0]\cdot 100$ (%)
Tension	Yield Strength	$\sigma_{0.2} = L_{0.2}/F_0$	Transverse contraction ψ of sample	$\psi = [(F_0 - F_c)/F_0]\cdot 100$ (%)
	Ultimate Strength in Tension or Fracture Strength	$\sigma_B = L_{max}/F_0$	Relative elongation δ_n	$\delta_n = [(l_k - l_0)/l_0]\cdot 100$ (%)
	True Ultimate Strength in Tension	$\sigma_p = L_{rr}/F_c$		
Compression	Ultimate Strength in Compression (resistance to fracture)	$\sigma_{compr} = L_{max}/F_0$	Relative contraction ϵ_{st} of sample in uniaxial static compression	$\epsilon_{st} = [(h_0 - h_c)/h_0]\cdot 100$ (%)
			ϵ_{dyn} as in uniaxial dynamic compression	$\epsilon_{dyn} = [(h_0 - h_c)/h_0]\cdot 100$ (%)
Notched Impact			Specific impact resistance a_o	$a_o = A/F$ (kg·m/cm²)

Symbols:

Hardness: L—force of indenter (kg); D—ball diameter (mm); d—diameter of imprint (mm); ψ—angle of cone (90° or 120°) or angle of pyramid (136°).

Flow: L_{st}—applied force in steady-state flow.

Tension: $L_{0.2}$—load causing elongation of 0.2 percent; L_{max}—maximum load (kg); L_{rr}—fracturing load; F_0—initial cross-sectional area of sample (mm²); F_c—cross-sectional area of sample (mm²) in fracture area; l_0—gage length of sample prior to testing (mm); l_c—gage length of sample after rupture (mm).

Compression: h_0—height of sample before compression (mm); h_c—height of sample after compression (mm).

Notched Impact: A—work done to fracture sample (kg·m); F—transverse cross-sectional area of sample (cm²) prior to test (at notch).

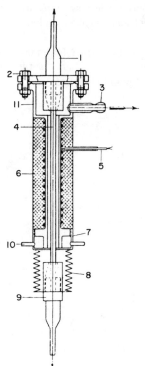

FIG. 23. Schematic diagram of apparatus for testing wire at high temperatures under vacuum.

1-upper grip; *2*-tightening bolt; *3*-to vacuum pump; *4*-specimen; *5*-thermocouple; *6*-furnace; *7*-cooling jacket; *8*-sylphon bellows; *9*-lower grip; *10*-water-cooling chamber; *11*-chamber.

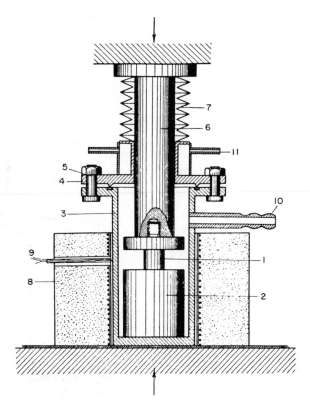

FIG. 24. Sketch of apparatus for compression testing at high temperature in protective atmosphere.

1-specimen; *2*-base; *3*-container; *4*-container cover; *5*-tightening bolt; *6*-punch; *7*-sylphon bellows; *8*-furnace; *9*-thermocouple; *10*-vacuum outlet; *11*-water-cooling chamber.

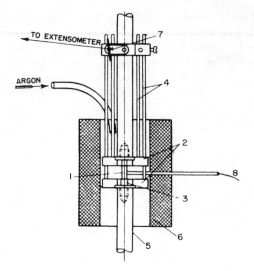

FIG. 25. Sketch showing apparatus for measuring elastic modulus at high temperatures.

1-specimen; *2*-collars; *3*-fulcrum bearings; *4*-extension arms; *5*-grip; *6*-furnace; *7*-mirror; *8*-thermocouple.

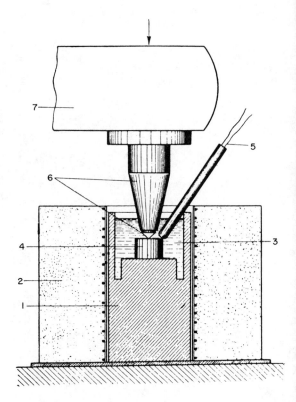

FIG. 26. Sketch of a hardness-testing machine using a protective medium.

1-container; *2*-furnace; *3*-protective medium; *4*-specimen; *5*-thermocouple; *6*-pobedit cone; *7*-press crossarm.

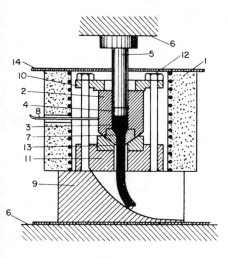

FIG. 27. High-temperature apparatus for measuring flow stress.

1–furnace; *2*–container; *3*–test bar; *4*–punch tip; *5*–punch; *6*–press crossarm; *7*–die; *8*–thermocouple; *9*–support; *10*–cover; *11*–base of apparatus; *12*–tightening bolts; *13*–block; *14*–asbestos.

In ternary systems, research was conducted along cuts of the Cu-Zn-Al system (region of high copper concentration) and on the Mg-Al-Zn system (region of high magnesium concentration). In the presentation of the experimental data, the purity of the metal used is specified for each individual case.

Tests were made on both cast and deformed samples, the latter being given preference. Wherever possible, standard samples were used. For tension experiments, samples were normally of a gage length ten times the diameter [206]. Tension tests at elevated temperatures were conducted on specimens with threaded heads [206], [207].

Moreover, a number of tests were made with Gagarin quintuple specimens. Specimens for microrupture tests were of 1-mm diameter and 5-mm gage length, and of 2-mm diameter and 10-mm gage length. Cylindrical specimens with a gage length not over $1\frac{1}{2}$ times the specimen diameter (to avoid lateral bending) were also used in compression tests [208]. In a number of cases, for various reasons, specimen diameters of 15, 10, 8, 7, 5, 3, 2, and 1 mm were used. For determination of toughness, GOST advises the use of prismatic specimens a square cross section of 10-mm per side, with one side notch in the form of a 2-mm-deep groove [209]. Such specimens involve difficulties of preparation as they require bench and milling-machine processing. Experiments on magnesium alloys (conducted by Kurova and this author) and on brasses (by Stepanova and this author) demonstrated that these specimens can be successfully replaced by cylindrical specimens of 11-mm diameter (to preserve the standard specimen volume) with a circular groove 2 mm deep; the latter are considerably easier to prepare [210]. For this reason cylindrical specimens were used. Flow stress was also measured on cylindrical specimens of 20-, 15-, 10-mm lengths, roughly equal to $1\frac{1}{2}$ times the respective specimen diameters. At least two or three specimens were used for each determination.

Tests Conducted

Hardness

Hardness was tested in conformity with the existing standards [211], [212]. Kubasov tested hardness by means of a pobedit* 90°-angle cone. Measuring hardness with a cone has an advantage in that, at sufficiently heavy loads, hardness does not depend on the value of the applied loads because the resulting imprints are similar; this advantage does not apply to ball testing for hardness. The cone method is particularly good because of its simplicity and high sensitivity. With a rise in temperature, the resistance of a material decreases, hence it is sometimes necessary to measure hardness at various loads; this procedure is acceptable in cone tests. For ductile materials, Kubasov hardness is distinctly related to total elongation and ultimate strength.

Hardness testing was conducted on a 7-ton machine (scaled to 1400 kg). A ball or cone was specially mounted and fastened to a moving crossarm and heated in a furnace together with the attached specimen (Fig. 26). Testing at various temperatures was usually done under 50-to-100-kg loads. Microhardness tests were conducted on apparatus PMT-2 and PMT-3 built by IMASH of the Academy of Sciences, U.S.S.R. [213], [214]. For microhardness tests at elevated temperatures (up to 450°C), a special unit was assembled (Fig. 28).

Cooling and Heating

Tests were conducted over a wide temperature range—from the boiling point of liquid nitrogen (−196°C) up to temperatures approaching the melting point of the given metal or alloy. As a rule, the furnace or the refrigerator was an integral part of the testing unit and specimens were tested in it. In impact tests this procedure was not always feasible as the furnace was adjacent to the a ram-impact machine. Moving a specimen from the furnace to the ram-impact machine took from 3 to 5 sec. Tests revealed that in this time interval, depending on the initial temperature, the temperature of the specimen dropped between 15 and 30°C. To compensate for this loss, the specimen was preheated to a correspondingly higher temperature. Specimens were heated to 1000°C in resistance furnaces and to higher temperatures in induction furnaces. Alloys of copper-zinc were heated up to 500°C in saltpeter baths while magnesium-cadmium alloys were heated up to 300°C in castor oil. To prevent oxidation at high temperatures, specimens for impact-bending and impact-compression tests were heated and tested in evacuated, sealed, quartz ampules.

Samples were cooled to −60°C in dry ice, to −183°C in liquid air, and to −196°C in liquid nitrogen.

The temperature was measured to within ±5°C by mercury thermometers and various thermocouples, mostly platinum–platinum-rhodium, attached to potentiometers. In all the experiments the mercury tip of the thermometer or the soldered joint of the thermocouple was adjacent to the specimen. In view

---

* *Editor's Note*: Pobedit refers to a series of tungsten-carbide-titanium-carbide alloys.

FIG. 28.   Apparatus for testing microhardness at high temperatures.

of the comparatively small size of specimens, exposure to heat during the experiment was of 30-min duration as a rule.

Stress in Tension

The theory of true-stress curves, especially as related to the mechanical processing of metals, was extensively developed by Gubkin [16], [18].

A curve for true stress is obtained by relating the load at a given instant to the specimen area at the same instant. To this end a diagram of applied stress versus elongation should be plotted. Elongation data, which are related to the area of the specimen and to its contraction, determine the effective area. These correlations are based on the constant volume of the specimen, both before and after elongation. True-stress curves may be plotted in coordinates of stress-elongation or stress-contraction. The degree of deformation is expressed in terms of either elongation or contraction. The extent of deformation may likewise be expressed as the logarithm of the ratio of initial to actual area, but here the construction becomes more complex.

Curves obtained from stress-elongation diagrams are the most precise. It is unfortunate, however, that for tension a true-stress curve may be reliably plotted only up to the point of necking; beyond this point the stress condition ceases to be linear, becoming multiaxial, complex, and, as yet, not completely understood. Much light, however, has been thrown on the subject by Davidenkov [215].

It is expedient, therefore, to substitute for the curve of true stresses its tangent at the point of necking and to plot the so-called "orientation straight lines" of true stresses* which encompass the whole range of the specimen's stress. Such substitution permits one to retain the linear relation between stress and strain. Check tests proved that the resulting error is negligible in practice, but only at room temperature. In the room-temperature case, orienting straight lines of true stresses were plotted. The two following forces were first determined: σ_n, true stress at the moment of neck formation in the specimen, and σ_f, stress at fracture. Determination of σ_n was made by Eq. (1)

$$\sigma_n = \frac{L_{\max}}{F_n} \quad \text{or} \quad \sigma_n = \frac{\sigma_B}{1 - \psi_n}, \tag{1}$$

where ψ_n is the cross-sectional contraction of the specimen area at the moment of neck formation. On the other hand, $\psi_n = (F_0 - F_n)/F_0$, where F_0 corresponds to the cross-sectional area of the specimen. F_n was determined by measuring the cylindrical part of the fractured specimen because elongation is concentrated at the point of neck formation, while the cylindrical part remains unaltered. Equation (1) shows that the stress in the necked region differs from the ultimate tensile strength only in that the maximum load is not related to the initial area of the specimen but to the area existing at the moment of neck formation. The magnitude of the true fracture resistance σ_f (also designated as S_e) is likewise defined by the formula $\sigma_f = L_f/F_e$, where L_f is the load at fracture and F_e is the neck area of the fractured specimen. The true stress σ_n or σ_f, together with the ultimate strength σ_B may be used to compute the capacity of the test equipment by appropriate equations based on plastic-deformation theories. In conformity with the properties of true stress curves, σ_u was also calculated from the equation $\sigma_u = 2\sigma_n$, in which σ_u denotes ulimate stress as it corresponds to an infinite degree of deformation when the specimen is strained to zero area, i.e., to the ideal point.

A schematic aspect of an orientation straight line is shown in Fig. 29, in which the straight line is plotted between the two points σ_n and σ_u. Inasmuch as the extreme right abscissa represents an ideal case, where $\psi = 1$, all real cases of tension (contraction of area less than 100 percent) will coincide with the orientation straight line.

Orientation straight lines are also important because they permit a determination of temperatures where softening processes (recovery and recrystallization)

---

* *Editor's Note:* Orientation straight lines are not used by American or British scientists, but appear to be extensively used by the Russian scientists and engineers (see Fig. 29).

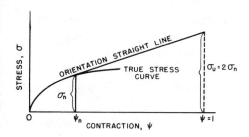

FIG. 29. Construction of the orientation straight line.

begin. In conformance with the theory of deformation, the slope of the orientation straight line indicates the metal's tendency to harden. At higher temperatures, the magnitude of σ_n will naturally decrease; this decrease will lead to a decrease in ultimate stress $\sigma_u = 2\sigma_n$. This equality applies only to a case of deformation by cold working [216]. With an increase of temperature in the experiment, the slope of the orientation straight line will decrease. During hot deformation it is possible to remove the effects of cold working by the mechanisms of recovery and recrystallization. Under such conditions, σ_u approaches σ_n and the straight line will be virtually parallel to the abscissa.

To determine the temperature at inception of the softening process in the tested metal, we proceed as follows. Orientation straight lines should be plotted for each temperature test, in conformity with the equation $\sigma_u = 2\sigma_n$; in other words, we assume that the mechanism of cold deformation is operative at all temperatures. To determine the temperature at which deviation from the mechanism of cold deformation begins, it suffices to show the corresponding values of the true ultimate strength σ_f on the plotted orientation straight lines. This magnitude must coincide with the orientation straight line only if the cold-deformation mechanism is present, because only then does $\sigma_u = 2\sigma_n$, whereas all the intermediate stresses always coincide with the orientation straight line connecting σ_n with σ_u. Should the magnitude of σ_f be below the orientation straight line, the cold-deformation mechanism will be absent and the magnitude of the deviation will conform with the degree of recovery or recrystallization at the given temperature and rate of strain.

The method for measuring the temperatures at which softening begins, on the basis of the data furnished by the orientation straight lines, was tested in our experiments on magnesium and its alloys as well as on other metals; the results obtained compared favorably with X-ray data [216]. Figure 30 shows magnesium.

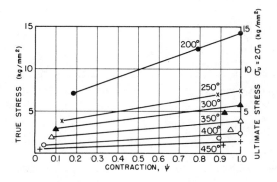

FIG. 30. Orientation straight lines of true stress for magnesium.

orientation straight lines for true stresses of magnesium tested to fracture at various temperatures. On each straight line the first point from the left corresponds to the necking stress σ_n, the second to the true ultimate strength σ_p. True ultimate stress σ_u is placed on the right ordinate, which corresponds to $\psi = 1$. As can be seen in the figure, it appears that the softening process is already present in tension tests with magnesium at 300°C, because σ_p is below the orientation straight line.

It would be interesting to determine, at some future date, the influence of phase-transformation processes on the behavior of the orientation straight lines and on the state of σ_p and whether there would be, in this instance, an analogy to the softening process.

True Stresses in Static Compression

By means of a plotter or by recording readings with a dynamometer in deformation tests, diagrams were made in coordinates of load versus decrease in height of the deformed specimen. These diagrams served to establish the true stresses σ_x in compression, i.e., the ratio of the value of the load L_x at a given deformation to the true cross-sectional area F_x of the specimen, at the same amount of deformation:

$$\sigma_x = L_x/F_x .$$

Tension tests differ from compression tests, since in compression no necking is present and true-stress curves can be plotted for the whole range of deformation. In compression tests, friction on the bearing surfaces of the specimens contributes to measurement of the true stress; thus, for the same degree of deformation, compression tests will show somewhat higher stresses than tension tests.

Calculations were made as follows. The cross-sectional area of the deformed specimen may be computed at any stage of deformation by using the law of the constancy of volume before and after plastic deformation of the specimen,

$$V_0 = V_{\mathrm{con}} = V_x = \mathrm{const.},$$

and for cylindrical specimens,

$$F_0 h_0 = F_{\mathrm{con}} h_{\mathrm{con}} = F_x h_x ,$$

where h_0 is the initial height of the compression specimen and h_x is the height of the compressed specimen at any stage of deformation; thus $F_x = V_x/h_x$. The value of h_x may be determined by the following equation for computation of the extent of deformation in compression:

$$[(h_0 - h_x)/h_0]100 = a ,$$

where a is the percent of deformation. Thus $h_x = h_0(100 - a)/100$.

The value of the load L_x required for computation of the true stress σ_x is shown by the ordinate of the test diagram which corresponds to the abscissa value h_x. True-stress measurements may be taken at any point on the deformation curve. Stress measurements were obtained at 10-percent intervals of the deformation curve; this interval was found to be convenient and precise for the computation of deformation characteristics. The required true ultimate stress for rupture was usually noted. The curves of true stress, determined as described above, were plotted as stress versus deformation. In experiments with a number of metals and alloys, curves were plotted at various temperatures. A comparison of curves plotted at various temperatures clearly shows the tendency of a material to deform plastically and the resistance of the material to plastic deformation under various conditions of test. The angle of the curves in relation to the abscissa indicates the presence or absence of softening processes (Fig. 31). When complete softening occurs during flow, the curve is virtually parallel to the abscissa. The following is an example of a computation of the true stress, in a magnesium specimen 15 mm in diameter, 20 mm high, required to contract by 4 mm (or by 20 percent) at room temperature.

$$V_0 = F_0 h_0 = (\pi 15^2/4)20 = 3533 \text{ mm}^3 .$$

Height of a 20-percent-deformed specimen is equal to

$$h_{20} = 20[(100 - 20)/100] = 16 \text{ mm} .$$

It follows, therefore, that the area at this stage of deformation is

$$F_{20} = 3533/16 = 221 \text{ mm}^2 .$$

The compression diagram (Fig. 32) shows that the load at $h = 16$ mm (after deduction of elastic deformation) will be equal to 2660 kg. The true stress for this case is, therefore,

$$\sigma_{20} = (L_{20}/F_{20}) = 2660/221 = 12.0 \text{ kg/mm}^2 .$$

Plasticity and Resistance to Deformation

The theory of physicochemical analysis states that a correct concept of transformations of matter under certain conditions may be obtained solely on

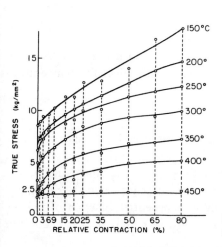

FIG. 31. True-stress–strain curves for slow compression of magnesium specimens.

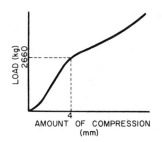

FIG. 32. Compression stress-strain diagram of a magnesium specimen at 20°C.

the cumulative data of changes occurring in several physical properties rather than on the data relative to a change in any single property. Naturally this restriction also applies to the method of mechanical tests. A final conclusion on the brittleness or ductility of matter is possible only when it is based on findings covering several mechanical properties.

To this end, so-called ductility diagrams were prepared as far back as 1941 [217], [218]. Ductility diagrams show all the numerical values of the metal's plasticity characteristics in the form of temperature functions obtained under various mechanical tests. These curves illustrate graphically the influence of the temperature–strain-rate dependence on the ductility properties for a particular state of the material investigated. Besides their scientific value, the ductility diagrams are of great practical importance, as they help to determine the optimum conditions for hot working [57], [218]. This subject will be discussed in greater detail in Chapter 6.

The first ductility diagrams of magnesium and its alloys (Fig. 33) were plotted by Gubkin and this author [57], [216]. We used elongation and reduction of area in tension testing, impact strength, and relative contraction in slow compression as well as in impact compression, as indices of ductility. Test results will be given in related sections of this study. When the indices of resistance to deformation as obtained by various test methods are plotted as a function of temperature, then, by analogy with the ductility diagram, this summary of data may be considered the resistance diagram. We plotted and used such diagrams in a series of experiments to determine the temperature dependence of strength characteristics of materials. We made good use of ductility and resistance diagrams in studies on transformations occurring in metals and alloys. The next step in this direction is to plot compre-

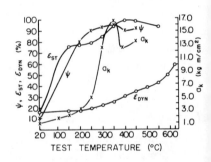

FIG. 33. Ductility diagram for magnesium (nomenclature as defined in Table 3).

hensive diagrams of ductility and of resistance in coordinates of: ductility-composition-temperature; ductility-resistance-temperature; ductility-temperature-rate of deformation; and so on.

Logarithmic Analysis of Changes in Ductility

The term "logarithmic analysis" which is introduced here describes correctly, in our opinion, the procedures used to determine the ductility of materials.

As pointed out earlier, Soviet scientists Shishokin, Pogodin, Gubkin, and others should be credited with the discovery of the dependence of the resistance-to-deformation characteristics on a diminishing exponential function of temperature. It seems that we were the first to undertake a similar task—determining the temperature dependence of ductility characteristics—and we have also surmised that this dependence, within limits, may be described by an increasing exponential function as follows:

$$P_2 = P_1 e^{\alpha(t_2 - t_1)} \, ,$$

where P_1 is the ductility of the given material at temperature t_1; P_2 is the ductility of the material at temperature t_2; and α is the temperature coefficient.

As will be shown later, this assumption was proved to be correct in many instances and is very useful in determining the characteristic temperatures for polymorphic and other phase transitions.

When a ductility diagram is plotted in semi-logarithmic coordinates, the exponential curves for plasticity exhibit straight lines. Since different phases have different temperature coefficients for each property, every individual phase is characterized by a straight line with a definite slope. The points at which these straight lines intersect for different phases show the temperature of the phase transition. This temperature value becomes pronounced when the values of α for different phases are distinctly different and, therefore, are characterized by a contrasting difference in the slopes of the straight lines.

It thus becomes possible to determine the temperatures of allotropic transformations, recrystallization, abrupt changes in solubility, and so on. The more acute the angle formed by the intersecting logarithmic lines the more accurate will be the temperature determination. By means of logarithmic analysis and extrapolation it is possible to evaluate the magnitude of mechanical properties, particularly ductility, for metals and alloys at absolute zero, which is difficult to achieve experimentally. Because of the imperfection of the extrapolation method itself, such an evaluation becomes extremely approximate.

The temperature coefficient of mechanical properties was computed by the formula

$$\alpha = (\log M_1 - \log M_2)/(t_2 - t_1) \, ,$$

where M_1 and M_2 are numerical values which characterize the corresponding mechanical properties at temperatures t_1 and t_2. A further development of the logarithmic-analysis method is necessary, as we do not yet know the equations describing in a precise manner the temperature dependence of complex mechanical properties—for example, impact strength. They could possibly be described by equations which do not represent straight lines when plotted logarithmically. We know that only the exponential and logarithmic functions are straight lines in the semi-logarithmic scale [219]–[221]. The application of the exponential function is the first approach in this case, whereas the temperature dependence of mechanical properties will probably be better defined by analyzing the data with a logarithmic or some other function. In any event, a logarithmic analysis of ductility characteristics has as much physical basis as a logarithmic analysis of strength characteristics.

Equipment and Techniques for Micromechanical Testing

Along with the development of test equipment for macrospecimens, a great deal of effort was expended on the satisfactory development and utilization of special apparatus for micromechanical testing. At first, experiments were conducted to substitute shear tests for tension tests since the former can utilize small samples that are easily prepared. A special device for punching 2-mm-diameter holes in plates 0.5 mm thick was built at the LFTI, AN, U.S.S.R., to obtain a diagram of the shearing; to this end changes in the position of the die in relation to the applied load were recorded. The resulting data were used to compute the basic stress characteristics [112].

Our first step was to determine if, in our physicochemical analysis, we could use the device built by the LFTI. Tests run on copper-nickel and on some magnesium alloys gave positive results [113]. However, this device had the following shortcomings:

1. It required an additional, special, and somewhat complex apparatus suitable to only one kind of test.
2. It had insufficient shear area (3 mm²), in which only a negligible number of grains and inclusions could be observed, so that resulting data were unsatisfactory.
3. Tests had to be interrupted for load recording.

It was therefore decided to use Gagarin's press for shear testing; thus the complex apparatus was eliminated, the specimen's shear area was increased (50 mm²), and a stress-strain diagram was automatically recorded [113]. For shear-stress testing we used the attachment shown in Fig. 34. A 2-mm-wide specimen (1) is placed in the die (2), tightened by a nut (3), which has an axial opening for an 8-mm-diameter punch (4). The assembled attachment is placed on the bench of Gagarin's press and an 8-mm hole is then punched (5).

The following stress characteristics were determined: proportional limit, ultimate strength, true ultimate strength, and contraction. The derived data were obtained by conversion of data recorded on the press diagram of shear force versus deformation, using simple equations [113]. Check tests conducted on samples of copper-nickel, copper-zinc, and magnesium alloy (over 100 samples were used) proved that for ductile alloys the correlation of shear tests to tension tests, especially with reference to ultimate strength, is fairly satisfactory.

The value of reduction of area was found to be lower for shear-stress tests than for tension tests of magnesium alloys which are brittle at ordinary temperatures. In experiments with 60 alloys of Cu-Zn-Al, the correlation coefficient was 0.93 and the correlation of the mean ultimate tensile strength in tension tests to ulitimate punch strength was 0.63. Data obtained on experiments with copper-nickel alloys forming a continuous series of solid solutions are shown in Fig. 35.

It should be noted that all the samples used in Gagarin press testing of 11 copper-nickel alloys had an aggregate weight of only 175 gr, whereas the standard

a

FIG. 34. A supplemental attachment to Gagarin's press for shearing tests.

a. As assembled.   *b.* Disassembled.

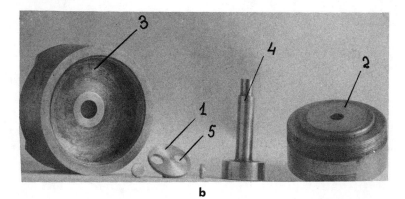

b

procedure in tensile tests requires at least 4 kg of sample material. A correlation of ultimate tensile strength to Brinell hardness was determined for forged and annealed copper-nickel alloys; the mean proportionality coefficient in this case was 0.54, with 0.6 for copper and 0.5 for nickel. For alloys of this system, a normal elastic modulus was obtained by Rosenberg's method [111] or ball indentation at various loads (Fig. 36). Data obtained by both methods was found to be fairly comparable.

In the second stage of this research, we examined the possibilities of testing samples for microfracture with standard testing equipment [141]. To obtain a more precise determination of load, low-capacity machines are advisable. For a machine used only for tensile tests, a special clamping device should be made for holding the specimen in place. Equipment used exclusively in compression tests (Gagarin press, for example) may be adapted to tensile testing with the aid of a Gagarin-type reverser, proportionally reduced in size. In the absence of test machines, the specimen may be loaded either by sand, water, or shot, by means of a special device (Fig. 37). This procedure is quite adequate, as the maximum fracture load for steel samples (1-mm diameter) at room temperature is usually under 50 or 60 kg.

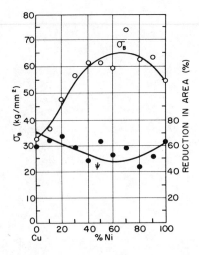

FIG. 35. Fracture strength and reduction of area of copper-nickel alloys (Savitsky and Slavina).

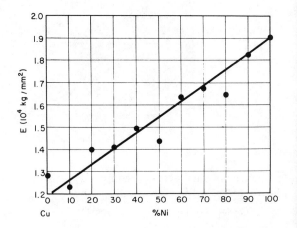

FIG. 36. Average modulus of elasticity for copper-nickel alloys.

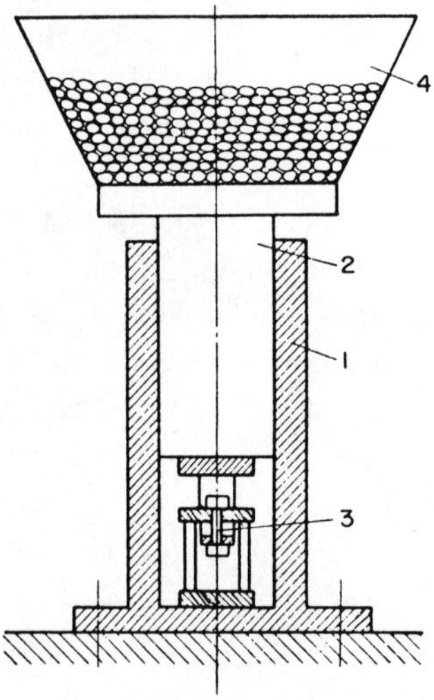

FIG. 37. Apparatus for fracture tests of microsamples (Savitsky and Lebedev).

1-cylinder; *2*-punch; *3*-reverser and sample; *4*-loading pan.

A Universal Device

Years of experiment with microsamples have enabled us to develop and perfect a simple yet universal device for micromechanical testing by all the basic methods for axial loading at ordinary, high, and low temperatures, either in air, vacuum, or protective atmospheres [142], [143]. The device shown in Fig. 38 consists of a block (1), a hollow cylinder (2) in which is set a polished, cylindrical anvil made of tempered steel or of pobedit (3), and a punch (4) with a removable upper platen (5) adjustable to various load conditions. The specimen (6) is placed between the upper platen and the anvil. The vertical motion of the punch (4) is measured to a precision of 0.01 to 0.001 mm by an optical indicator connected to its tip. For visual observation of the process of deformation, the cylinder should be transparent. Friction arising between the punch and the walls of the cylinder may be reduced by ribbing the punch. This device may be used for testing microspecimens as well as macrospecimens. The size of the tested specimen is limited only by the height and diameter of the cylinder, which may be of fairly large dimensions. Both metallic and non-metallic (plastic and other) specimens may be tested by the device.

We have intentionally excluded loading attachments of any sort in order to keep the device simple and inexpensive, because existing and available equipment in laboratories in various institutes is quite adequate for experiments conducted under a wide range of loading.

To load the specimen and measure the deforming load during the experiment, the device should be placed between the blocks which operate the compression phase of the testing press, so that the punch platen is adjacent to the upper block while that part of the block to which the cylinder is fastened rests on the lower block. Low-capacity machines are to be preferred for testing microsamples in order to enhance the precision of load determinations. In the absence of low-capacity machines, tests can be run either on a Gagarin press or on IM–4A or IM–4R machines. When a machine has been designed for tension tests, it is necessary to place the device in a regular reverser to convert elongation to contraction. If necessary, a test chart based on

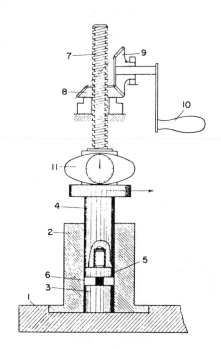

FIG. 38. Sketch of universal apparatus for testing at various temperatures.

1-base plate; *2*-cylinder; *3*-anvil; *4*-punch; *5*-punch tip; *6*-specimen; *7—10*-loading mechanism; *11*-dynamometer.

readings of the load gage and the device indicator may be plotted in the usual way. If no test equipment is available, the device may be loaded with the aid of the simple modification shown in Fig. 37.

A modified loading procedure (shown in Fig. 38) is more convenient, especially in tests requiring heavier loads (e.g., compression tests at ordinary temperature). The load is imposed by a manually operated screw (7) with the aid of nut (8), conical gear (9), and handle (10). The load is measured by a dynamometer (11) set between the base of the bolt and the head of the punch. Elastic (spring) dynamometers of 100-, 200-, and 300-kg capacity are best suited for this purpose. It is thus possible to relate loading not only to ultimate strength but also to yield point and to fracture resistance.

Static- as well as impact-loading experiments may be conducted with this device, with which it is possible to run virtually any basic mechanical test (compression, tension, hardness, bend, shear, warp, torsion, punch, and so on). It may also be used for industrial testing and for preparing microsamples.

Changing from one experiment to another is very simple. Switching from a compression to a hardness test, for instance, requires only substitution of the flat platen fastened to the bottom part of the punch by a plate with an attached ball (Brinell hardness test), cone (Rockwell or Kubasov hardness test), or pyramid (Vickers hardness test). Other test methods (tension, bend, shear, and so on) will require the installation of a simple attachment for clamping the specimen within the working area of the cylinder. In some experiments, changing the punch platen is also required.

Compression Tests

The compression-test procedure is clearly demonstrated in the sketch of the device (Fig. 38). The test specimen (6) is placed on the polished anvil (3) set in the cylinder (2). The specimen is deformed by impact with the punch (4) and is measured by the indicator. The upper platen (5) is flat, polished, and made of tempered steel. The specimen may be loaded and the load may be measured by any of the methods described above.

For testing brittle materials by a nonuniform hydrostatic method the sample must first be compressed into a bushing made of a more plastic material [92].

In compression tests, the sample may be of any form. For best results, however, the usual practice is to use cylindrical specimens with a height-to-diameter ratio of 1.5 to 2.5. Spherical specimens may also be used, but they are more difficult to prepare.

Compression tests offer the advantage of using specimens of any size, as they require no special attachments to hold them in place since the specimen retains its position between the punch and the anvil by virtue of external friction. It should be noted that when very small samples are used, because of the increase of relative surface, the role of surface energy is enhanced and the values of hardness and plasticity, as compared with those observed in larger samples, are greater. It follows, therefore, that in compression tests specimens should be not less than 1 mm in diameter. For best results testing should be stopped at the sign of the first crack in the specimen; this crack serves as a criterion for establishing the maximum hardness and ductility of the material.

Compression (or impact) experiments permit immediate distinction between a brittle and a plastic material. Specimens of very brittle materials (manganese, quartz, and others), when experimentally subjected to a certain degree of loading, suddenly crumble into powder. At this point the needles of the load indicator of the machine and of the indicator return to zero, sometimes accompanied by crackling sounds in the device.

More ductile materials (such as magnesium, cast iron, and others) on reaching a certain level of loading and deformation in compression are known to cleave at an angle of 45° to the specimen's axis. Plastic-material specimens (copper, aluminum, Armco iron, and others) assume a disk form when compressed. The greater the plasticity of the material, the greater will be its resistance to crack formation on the edges of the resulting disks.

The quantitative importance of plasticity and strength of microspecimens is computed by the usual equations.

Hardness Tests

The above-described device allows one to determine the hardness of a material by any of the methods based on the depth of penetration by an indenter made of a harder material (steel, tungsten carbide, diamond).

The prevalent methods of testing hardness (Brinell, Rockwell, and Vickers hardness tests) are based on this principle. As already stated, a reconstruction of the device for testing hardness amounts to a change of the indenter. In a hardness test, any specimen with two parallel surfaces (one of which is protected) and of a size to fit the cylinder's work area will do.

A major defect of existing devices for testing hardness is that tests may be conducted only at a specified range of loading for each device. This defect is eliminated in the apparatus described above and hardness can be tested at any magnitude of loading applied to the punch. In an experiment, the depth of the indentation (which, to a certain degree, is the criterion of plasticity for the material) may be measured by the indicator in relation to the applied force. The indenter's diameter or the length of its diagonal is measured at the completion of the experiment by ordinary means, with Brinell's magnifier or by a measuring microscope. The value of the hardness of a material measured by either method is computed by standard equations or taken from tables.

Tension Tests

Microspecimens are simply tested in tension with the universal device (Fig. 38) by using a Gagarin-type reverser reduced in size to fit the test (see Fig. 37). In this case the reverser with the inserted microspecimen is placed in the chamber of the device, between the punch and the anvil. A flat punch tip is used.

Testing is conducted as usual, and the value of the applied load is recorded from readings of the machine's load gage and the magnitude of deformation (elongation) is obtained from readings of the device's indicator. Furthermore, the computation of deformation (the relative elongation and transverse contraction) is done with the usual equations, on data of the specimen's dimensions both before and after fracture. Specimens should be measured with a measuring microscope having precision to 0.01 mm. If necessary, diagrams for true stress may be plotted as in compression tests.

The heads of microfracturing specimens most commonly used have a working-surface diameter of 1 mm and a gage length of 5 mm. If necessary the specimen, even without a head (in the form of wire), can be clamped to the reverser; this procedure requires an alteration of the reverser's clamping chucks, as in a chucking lathe, or by addition of notched blocks.

A device has been designed to pressure-process microsamples for tensile testing. It eliminates the loss of material that is inevitable with the sawing method. To prepare a microsample, both ends of a uniformly cylindrical wire are flattened axially in the device. The contours and sizes of all the punches should correspond to the form and size of the microsample's head.

A microspecimen can also be made by a somewhat different method. Material, in either powder or bar form, is placed in the cylinder (Fig. 39) and is processed into wire. The resulting waste end material may serve as one of the heads of the microtensile specimen. To obtain the other head, the length of wire should be turned 180° and flattened by the punch (2) at the other end. For better results, the specimen and the waste end should first be placed in a suitable die.

In a check test on steel, copper, aluminum, and some nonferrous alloys, the characteristics of strength and plasticity for microsamples were 5 to 10 percent greater than those for standard-size samples. This discrepancy may be explained by the scaling factor and usually occurs in micromechanical experiments [137].

Bend and Shear Tests

Bending tests (with one or two points of support) are easily performed with the device. A reverser, similar in type but smaller than a Gagarin reverser for bending tests, should be used to facilitate fastening the specimen. An appropriate punch should be inserted for bending the microspecimen. Readings taken from the device's indicator will clearly be related to the magnitude of the deflection of

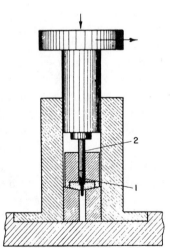

FIG. 39. Sketch of device for determination of flow stress.
1-tailing; *2*-punch.

the specimen. The magnitude of the bending moment may be easily determined from the machine's load-gage readings. The described attachment, somewhat modified, may be used for cutting the specimen into sections. In bilateral shear tests, a special attachment for holding the specimen in the working area of the device should be used. The specimen should be either cylindrical or prismatic in form. The punch should be fitted with a tip appropriate to the experiment.

Punch and Warp Tests

For this type of experiment, a special miniature attachment should be inserted into the working area of the cylinder. Holes may be punched in sheets and the applied force and the resulting deformation may be measured with this device. Warp tests, in which a die is substituted for a flat anvil, may also be conducted. Whenever necessary it is possible to correlate the data on the punchability with the mechanical characteristics of the material under stress, as recommended by some authors [112]-[115]. In this case, the size of the specimen is controlled only by the diameter of the punch tip and of the die and this, in turn, depends exclusively upon manufacturing techniques for punches and dies of very small diameter (e.g., 0.1 mm). A 1-to-4 ratio of punch diameter to specimen thickness is recommended.

Determination of Flow Stress

The principle of this test is demonstrated by Fig. 39. To minimize the waste of material in short supply it is best to use a demountable die and to compress additionally by means of a conical indenter.

Torsion Tests

The universal device may also be adapted to torsion tests (Fig. 40). The specimen (1) is cylindrical, threaded at both ends for securing in the anvil (2) and in the upper platen of the press (3). Other methods of fastening the specimen may be worked out. To prevent slipping, a gasket should be mounted on the prongs (5) imbedded

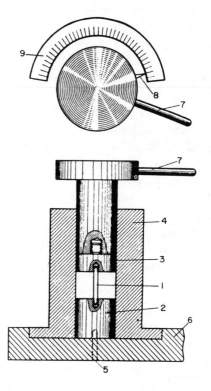

Fig. 40. Sketch of apparatus for torsion testing.

1-specimen; 2-anvil; 3-punch tip; 4-cylinder; 5-prong; 6-bottom plate; 7-hand lever; 8-pointer; 9-scale.

in the cylinder's base (4) or in the bottom plate (6) of the device. The specimen is loaded manually with the hand lever (7) attached to the head of the punch. The angular adjustment of the punch is controlled by the pointer (8) and the graduated scale (9).

Unfortunately, in its present form, this device is not quite adequate for measuring torque. Under these conditions, the torsion test becomes virtually a technological experiment. Inasmuch as torsion tests are infrequent and are run only in special cases, the need for a specially built device for measuring torque is questionable; however, it is feasible if it should be considered indispensable. The problem of measuring torque was studied by Novokreshchenov and Markova, who successfully conducted highly precise measurements of torque by the electromagnetic method [222].

Pressure Determination for Compressing Powders

The universal device may be used for compressing powders while recording the applied force necessary to form them properly. Such experiments may prove valuable in the development of production techniques for articles made of rare and expensive powdered metals by the methods of powder metallurgy. Powders are compressed by the device in the same manner in which compression tests are conducted. When the powder is in short supply, it should not be placed directly in the cylinder, but in a special, smaller, cylindrical container. For more convenient operation, the cylinder should be made without a bottom or with a demountable bottom. The diameter of the punch tip, naturally, should conform to that of the small container, which is then placed on the anvil of the cylinder. The compression volume may be determined from readings of the press load gage. To measure the magnitude of stress in the compressed material, the maximum pressure is divided by the cylinder's working area covered by the powder. Valuable information on the properties may be obtained by examining the compressed specimen. By using a modified version of the device adapted for high-temperature work, it is possible to anneal (bake) the formed powder conglomerate or to compress it at elevated temperatures.

The device thus provides the means to develop the most favorable technological conditions (of temperature and pressure) for processing by the powder-metallurgy method with an outlay of only a fraction of a gram of material. The basic tests which may be performed with this device prove its unrestricted versatility. Other tests, not described here, may also be performed by other methods, requiring no substantial changes in the structure of the device.

Modifications for Special Test Conditions

Proceeding now to a description of a modified device for testing at elevated or at low temperatures, in protective atmosphere, or in vacuum, we note that all that has been said about the various test methods at room temperature is valid for the tests listed below. Special punches and adjustments are not necessary.

High Temperatures. Those who work in material testing know the equipment complications which take place in high-temperature tests. No equipment or procedures have yet been developed for certain kinds of high-temperature testing (such as torsion tests, bending tests, and so on).

The outstanding merit of the universal device is the ease with which high-temperature tests may be performed. It is necessary only to place the cylinder with the enclosed specimen and punch into the furnace. It is expedient that the cylinder be in the form of a spool to facilitate coil winding, which will convert it to a heater. The modified device for high-temperature tests is shown in Fig. 41. To enhance the precision of temperature measurement, a thermocouple (2) may be inserted into a specially designed opening through the furnace and cylinder walls to the space between the upper and lower platens. A water-cooled leader bushing is necessary to prevent jamming of the punch when it becomes heated.

The cylinder should be of stainless steel and the upper platen and anvil of pobedit. In an experiment at high temperatures, the maximum temperature is limited solely by the heat-resistant properties of the parts of the device. The experiment is conducted as follows: the device is assembled as usual and the electric furnace is switched on; after the specimen is heated and exposed to a given temperature for the necessary length of time, the indicator needle is set at zero and the experiment can be started.

It should be noted that, with samples of adequate size, this modified device may be used as a dilatometer, because any change in length of the specimen

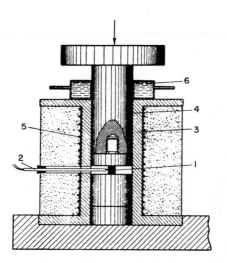

FIG. 41. Modified apparatus for testing at high temperatures.

1-specimen; *2*-thermocouple; *3*-cylinder; *4*-punch; *5*-electric furnace; *6*-leading bushing.

caused by heating or cooling (not under stress) will be readily observed from indicator readings (to a precision of 0.01 to 0.001 mm). Further, the device will measure factors which apparently have not been evaluated until now; it measures quantitatively the amount of internal pressure which develops in phase or other transformations caused by changes in volume of the material (allotropic or other transformations) [223]. The device and the sample are heated in the test apparatus with the platens placed adjacent to it. Heating of the specimen, especially at temperatures where some transformation occurs, will result in its expansion. This tendency, however, is checked by the upper platen, which presses against the punch. The expanding specimen will therefore transmit pressure by way of the platen and the punch to the dynamometer, which will record the load. The apparatus enables one to study the influence of one of the most important environmental factors, temperature, on the mechanical properties of materials as well as on the phenomena which occur in the solid state. The device can evaluate the influence of stress on the tranformations taking place in the solid state at various temperatures.

Low Temperatures. The low-temperature version (Fig. 42) differs from the high-temperature one shown in Fig. 41 in that the space surrounding the cylinder (1) is filled with dry ice or some cooling liquid such as liquid nitrogen. Depending on the cooling liquids now obtainable, testing at temperatures as low as −200°C is possible with this device.

Protective Liquid Media. Certain materials (for instance alkaline materials and alkali-earth metals) are readily oxidized by contact with air and can be tested

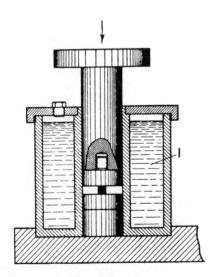

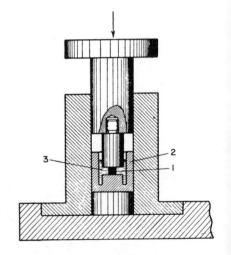

FIG. 42. Modified apparatus for testing at low temperatures.

1-liquid coolant.

FIG. 43. Modified apparatus for testing in protective media.

1-specimen; 2-container; 3-protective fluid.

only under special protective conditions. We found that experiments with such materials may be conveniently and reliably conducted in transparent protective media, neutral to the test material. Such liquids as toluene (methyl benzene) and kerosene are used. Aluminum and copper alloys may be tested up to 450°C in potassium nitrate (saltpeter). A number of other materials will not oxidize at high temperature if they are placed in solutions of molten salt mixtures consisting of chlorides and fluorides of certain alkali metals. The device differs from the others in that the specimen is placed in a container filled with a protective fluid. The punch platen should be of a diameter to fit the container (Fig. 43).

The container may be placed into and removed from the cylinder by means of a special tool adapted to fit into the openings of the upper part of the container.

The use of protective media has enabled us to determine, for the first time apparently, the mechanical properties of certain metals such as alkali earth metals and to establish that they are classified in the following order as to strength: calcium, strontium, barium. The order is reversed for ductility properties.

Figure 44 shows the true stress curves in compression tests for these metals conducted at room temperature. Our compression tests were made with cylindrical specimens (1 by 1 mm) in toluene. Cone hardness was 13.2 kg/mm² for calcium and 5.5 kg/mm² for barium. Using a protective medium at ordinary temperature, it has been possible to extrude calcium into a wire about 15 mm long and 1 mm in diameter. The flow stress at 75-percent deformation was about 90 kg/mm².

When a protective fluid that will not interact with the tested material is not available (and such media for high-temperature testing are not readily found) the test should

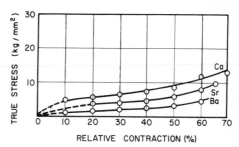

FIG. 44. Stress–strain curves in compression for a number of alkali earth metals.

be carried out in an inert gas (for example, argon or helium) or in a vacuum.

Vacuum or Inert-Gas Atmosphere. This modification is different from the one shown in Fig. 41 (for tests in air) only in that the work chamber is located in a hermetically sealed steel jacket (Fig. 45).

Besides sealing, which is a standard requirement in all vacuum installations, no other material changes in construction of the device have been made, except for sylphon bellows (1) and springs (2). Using the sylphon bellows solves the problem of transferring the motion of the punch into the vacuum chamber without reducing the vacuum. Other methods of solving this problem may well be found, such as rubber and metal gaskets. In our experience, however, the

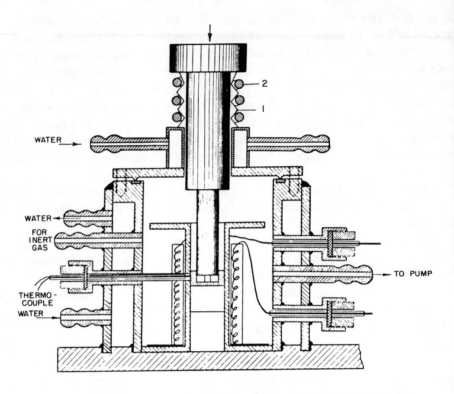

FIG. 45. Modified apparatus for high-temperature testing in vacuum or inert-gas atmosphere (Savitsky).

sylphon bellows proved to be very good. The spring (2) is needed to compensate for atmospheric pressure which would otherwise cause the sylphon to contract and the tightened corrugations would then interfere with the free movement of the punch. An external cooling jacket is required for the rubber packing which insulates the conductor wires and the thermocouple; otherwise, the sides of the device, heated by the furnace, would burn the rubber. For experiments in vacuum, the shell of the electric furnace should be made of quartz, because any ceramic material when heated will generate gas, thereby lowering the vacuum. By using vacuum and diffusion pumps, it is comparatively easy to reach a vacuum in the order of 10^{-4} to 10^{-5} mm. In certain instances, when the possibility of oxidation is to be eliminated to a still greater degree, burning of a getter (strontium, barium, and others) may be utilized.

The vacuum device described above may be used not only at temperatures attainable with the average furnace (nichrome, No. 2 alloy) but also for higher-temperature tests in which the furnace elements are made of tungsten, molybdenum or tantalum. In these cases additional measures to safeguard the heaters from oxidation are superfluous. When a conventional furnace is used, the vacuum chamber may be reduced in size. As a result, the arrangement is considerably simplified (Fig. 46) and the degree of the vacuum is increased.

In vacuum experiments, the tare weight of the punch should be calibrated and the value of the applied force should be subtracted from the recorded load-gage values.

A shift from vacuum to inert-gas experiments greatly decreases the demands for packing, cooling of the shell of the device, and other precautions. The spring (2) becomes unnecessary, but one more opening is needed in the external jacket for a gas outlet. Less stringent packing techniques will produce only a slightly higher inert-gas leakage.

The procedure in experiments with inert gas or vacuum is as follows: the specimen is placed in the cylinder chamber. The upper part of the device (consisting of a lid with a cooling muff and of a punch with sylphon bellows) is bolted to the cylinder. The vacuum pumps are next activated and the inert gas is introduced. The electric furnace is then turned on to heat the specimen to a predetermined temperature. After the required exposure, both the device and the specimen are ready for the test. Further procedure is identical with that pertaining to testing at room temperature. Figure 47 illustrates the vacuum modification of the device, complete with loading attachment.

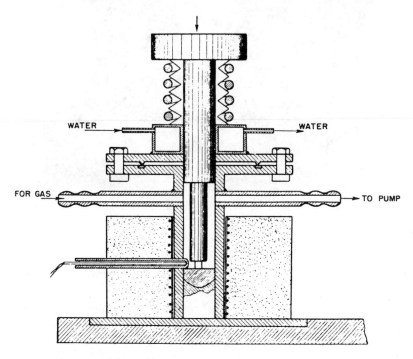

FIG. 46. Another modified apparatus for micromechanical testing in vacuum or inert-gas atmosphere (Savitsky).

FIG. 47. General view of apparatus with loading attachment (vacuum modification).

Some Experimental Data

Of the mass of experimental data obtained we shall mention here test results on the mechanical properties of copper-nickel alloys.

As we know, copper and nickel are completely soluble in both the liquid and the solid states. Data which characterize the mechanical properties of these alloys, as obtained from experiments with microsamples, are shown in Fig. 48.

Kurnakov and Rapke measured these alloys for Brinell hardness and found that the hardest alloys of the system are in the weight range of 40–60 percent nickel [9]. Our tests with these alloys, using microsamples and the cone-

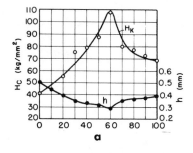

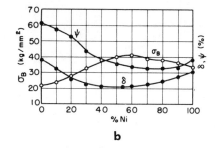

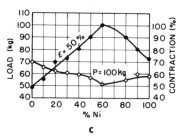

FIG. 48. Mechanical properties of alloys
in the copper-nickel system.

a. Hardness: H_c, cone hardness; h, depth
   of penetration of cone.

b. Mechanical properties in compression.

c. Mechanical properties in tension.

hardness test method, have enabled us to determine this hardness with a greater
degree of precision: the hardest alloy is one containing 60 percent nickel.

Compression tests with microsamples of the same alloys show that deformation and ductility curves are analogous. We measured deformation resistance
by the weight of loading required to compress a microsample of cylindrical form
(1 mm both in diameter and height) by 50 percent in height; ductility was
measured by the relative contraction of the sample in a compression test under
a 100-kg load. It should be mentioned that in compression tests with 11 alloys
of this system, only 0.2 g of net weight of the samples were used.

Tests with microfracture samples likewise confirmed the behavior of curves
for hardness, strength, and ductility in the above deformation tests. Addition
of nickel to copper, or vice versa, increases the strength and decreases the
ductility of the resulting alloy. A 60 percent nickel alloy has the highest
ultimate strength. The microfracture specimens made of different grades of
nickel-copper alloys weighed 1.5 g.

Gathering reliable data on all of the basic mechanical properties (hardness,
ductility, and strength characteristics in compression and tension tests) of the
whole system required only 2 g of net weight of samples.

Inasmuch as a universal device in the form described above was developed
only recently, practically speaking, its possibilities have not been fully ex-
ploited.

3

Monomorphic Metals

We first studied the influence of temperature on single-component metallic systems, plotting diagrams for mechanical property versus temperature for pure metals.

The grouping of metals by type was based on their crystal structure (cubic and hexagonal). This method of grouping is justified because crystal structure is the foremost factor determining the metal's behavior in deformation (Fig. 49). Data on the crystal structures and melting temperatures of monomorphic metals are given in Table 4.

The influence of temperature on the mechanical properties of two-component systems is examined in relation to the type of equilibrium diagram, which is determined by the physicochemical nature of the reacting components.

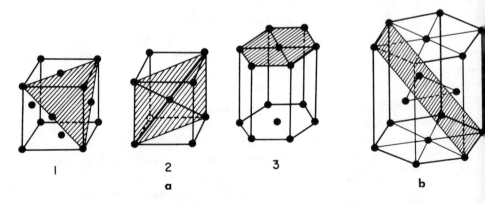

FIG. 49. Planes in typical metallic lattices.

a. Slip planes: *1*-face-centered-cubic lattice; *2*-body-centered-cubic lattice; *3*-hexagonal lattice. b. Twinning plane in hexagonal lattice.

Cubic Metals

In this section we shall examine the mechanical properties of typical cubic metals such as copper, aluminum, indium, chromium, and barium. A trait common to the first three is that they crystallize in lattices of cubic symmetry (type K12) which have the greatest number of slip systems (four planes and three directions in each plane, i.e., 12 slip systems) and an absence of tranforsmations of the crystal structure right up to the melting point. The other face-centered-cubic monomorphic metals—silver, nickel, gold, platinum, palladium and others—are analogous and, therefore, will not be examined independently [52], [185], [189], [190], and [225]-[231]. Of the body-centered-cubic metals, chromium and barium will be used as examples.

All metals, when heated, display changes within their crystal structures; such changes include increase in lattice parameters, appearance of new slip planes, recrystallization, and dissolution and diffusion of impurities. In discussing the absence of transformations in the crystal structure of monomorphic metals, we wish to emphasize that the type of crystal lattice and its individuality remain unchanged by temperature.

In all such metals, when heated, the crystal lattices increase in size, the force of cohesion diminishes, and, consequently, the metal softens.

Copper

The mechanical properties of copper at both ordinary and elevated temperatures have been thoroughly explored in studies by Gubkin, Zakharova, Zakharov, Bobylev, and Chipizhenko [126], [199], [232], [233]. Gubkin and his associates have measured the hardness, flow stress, impact, and compression strength; Bobylev and Chipizhenko worked on creep. These studies demonstrated that the mechanical properties of pure copper change smoothly with temperature. Changes of curvature in the property-temperature curve may develop only because of the recrystallization phenomenon or the appearance of the so-called brittle zone in insufficiently deoxidized copper at about 500°C (Fig. 50). Gubkin and Zakharov attribute this phenomenon to incomplete recrystallization. In slow-rate tests, the brittle zone broadens out [232] from 450 to 900°C (Fig. 51). This change is apparently connected with oxidation, i.e., with a deterioration of grain boundaries under atmospheric conditions.

This viewpoint is supported by the fact that the brittle zone appears only in tests where tensile stresses (rupture, impact strength) are present; they determine the strength of the crystal boundaries. In other methods of loading (in compression tests and especially hardness tests by indenting) the brittle zone does not appear.

Intensive studies have been made recently on the existence of viscous flow along the grain boundaries in heated copper.

Our wire-testing experiments in vacuum (see Fig. 24) have demonstrated that, in the absence of oxidation, no brittle zone occurs in copper. Bobylev and

TABLE 4

CRYSTAL STRUCTURES AND MELTING TEMPERATURES OF MONOMORPHIC METALS[a]

Cubic and Closely Related Structures				Hexagonal Close-Packed and Related Structures		Low-Symmetry Structures	
Body-Centered, K8	Melting Temp. (°C)	Face-Centered, K12	Melting Temp. (°C)	G12	Melting Temp. (°C)	Rhombohedral	Melting Temp. (°C)
Cesium	28.5	Indium (tetragonal lattice)	156.4	Cadmium	320.9	Gallium (rhombic lattice)	29.8
Rubidium	38.5	Lead	327.4	Terbium	327±5	Mercury	−39.0
Potassium	62.3	Aluminum	659.7	Zinc	419.5	Bismuth	271.3
Sodium	97.5	Silver	960.8	Magnesium	651.0	Antimony	630.5
Lithium	186.0	Gold	1063.0	Scandium	1200.0	Arsenic	814.0
Radium (tetragonal lattice)	700.0	Copper	1083.0	Beryllium	1278±5		
Barium	725.0	Nickel	1455.0	Gadolinium	1350.0	Diamond	
Europium	1150±50	Palladium	1549.4	Yttrium[b]	1490.0	Germanium	958.5
Vanadium	1710.0	Platinum	1773.5	Dysprosium	1500.0	Silicon	1420.0
Chromium	1890.0	Ytterbium	1800.0	Holmium	1500.0		
Niobium	2500±50	Thorium	1845.0	Erbium	1550.0		
Molybdenum	2620±10	Iridium	2454.0	Thulium	1600±50		
Tungsten	3370.0			Lutecium	1700±50		
Polonium (simple cubic lattice)	····			Ruthenium	2450.0		
				Technetium	2600±100		
				Osmium	2700		
				Rhenium	3167±60		

[a] Editor's Note. Melting-point values in the original book have been checked against values in the 41st Edition of the Handbook of Chemistry and Physics and, where significantly different, have been changed accordingly.

[b] Melting-temperature data of rare-earth metals of the yttrium subgroup are taken from Spedding and Daane [224].

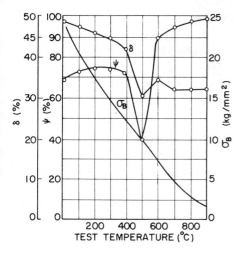

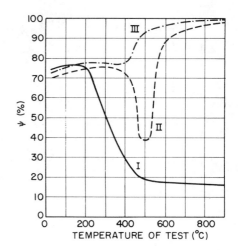

FIG. 50. Changes in mechanical properties of M-1 copper at elevated temperatures (Bobylev and Chipizhenko).

FIG. 51. Reduction in area of M-1 copper with respect to test temperature and rate of strain in tension (Bobylev and Chipizhenko). I-1 mm/min; II-20 mm/min; III-300 mm/min.

Chipizhenko determined that the brittle zone is absent in oxygen-free copper tested with generator gas.

A clear discontinuity at 500°C in the hardness curve (Fig. 52) is apparently related to the recrystallization temperature. This assumption is confirmed by the shape of the true-stress–strain curves when the samples are compressed (1×1 mm) in the universal device (Fig. 53, curve for 500°C). Diffraction spots on X-ray photographs of copper samples deformed at 500°C at a rate of 10 mm/min have been detected by Gubkin and Zakharova; these spots indicate the in-

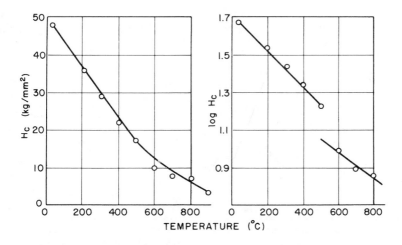

FIG. 52. Effect of temperature on the hardness of copper.

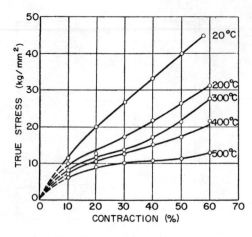

FIG. 53. True-stress curves in compression of copper specimens.

ception of recrystallization and also substantiate the above assumption. The same authors plotted true-stress curves for uniaxial and plane-parallel deformation of copper specimens at various speeds. They found no structural changes caused by heat except recrystallization.

Table 5 gives the mechanical properties of copper at low temperatures [234] and shows that, in spite of a pronounced increase in strength (especially σ_B), copper, even at very low temperatures, does not become brittle; this fact is directly related to its face-centered-cubic structure.

TABLE 5

CHANGES IN THE MECHANICAL PROPERTIES OF ELECTROLYTIC COPPER
AS A FUNCTION OF TEMPERATURE

Temperature (°C)	Hardness H_c (kg/mm²)	Ultimate Tensile Strength (kg/mm²)	Elongation δ (%)	Reduction in Area ψ (%)	Yield strength $\sigma_{0.2}$ (kg/mm²)
−180[a]	....	40.8	58	77	8.0
−120	....	28.8	45	70	7.5
− 80	....	27.0	47	74	7.0
− 40	....	23.6	47	77	6.4
− 20	....	22.0	48	76	6.0
− 10	....	22.4	40	78	6.2
+ 20[b]	48.0	19.0	36	67	...
100	47.0	....	..	..	...
200	36.0	....	..	..	...
300	28.8	18.3	42	62	...
400	22.3	15.0	43	74	...
500	17.5	13.0	45	75	...
600	10.0	11.5	37	65	...
700	8.0	....	..	..	...
800	7.4	....	..	..	...
900	3.5	....	..	..	...

[a] Data on subzero temperatures from [234].
[b] Data on above-zero temperatures from experiments with wire specimens of 5-mm diameter, 160-mm length.

The author's experiments, together with data found in the literature on the subject, lead to two conclusions. First, mechanical testing is sufficiently sensitive to detect and to determine the temperature of recrystallization and other physicochemical transformations caused by heat. Second, the heat-caused changes in the mechanical properties in face-centered-cubic metals (of which copper is typical) occur smoothly. The effects related to recrystallization and to the appearance of a brittle zone in insufficiently pure metals tested under atmospheric conditions are disregarded.

Lead

Lead is a face-centered-cubic metal and is typical of ductile materials. Because of its low melting point, lead recrystallizes at room temperature and hence is not subject to work hardening. Figure 54 shows that the mechanical properties of heated lead change smoothly [234].

Kutaitsev, who studied the hardness and yield strength of lead at various temperatures, has likewise not been able to detect any changes of curvature in the curves as plotted [200]. It should be noted that the reduction in area under tensile stress charac-

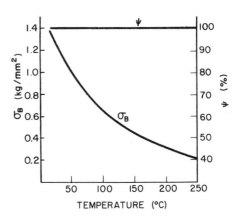

FIG. 54. Changes in the mechanical properties of annealed lead in relation to temperature.

terizes rather well the ductility of lead at all temperatures, in this instance close to 100 percent. Lead remains ductile even at very low temperatures; however, its ultimate strength then becomes at least twice as great as at high temperatures [234], [235]. Because the ductility of lead has been extensively studied, it is unnecessary to dwell further on this subject.

Aluminum

Aluminum is also a face-centered-cubic metal and its mechanical properties react to temperature in the same manner as do those of copper and lead (Fig. 55) [234].

Figure 56 shows true-stress curves obtained in compression experiments with microsamples (2×2 mm) of aluminum (99.7 percent) at various temperatures. Figure 57 demonstrates changes in the hardness of aluminum as a result of temperature changes.

From the data submitted it is evident that the mechanical properties of heated aluminum change smoothly. The temperature coefficient of aluminum hardness in the range 20 to 500°C is -2×10^{-3}. The true-stress–strain curve at 400°C indicates that, in compression tests of technical aluminum at this temperature, recrystallization processes occur even at high degrees of deformation. Superpure aluminum (99.9995 percent) recrystallizes even at −50°C.

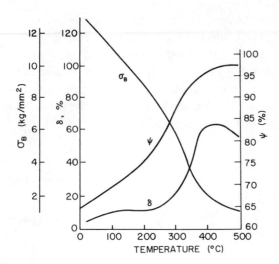

FIG. 55. Changes in the mechanical properties of aluminum at elevated temperatures.

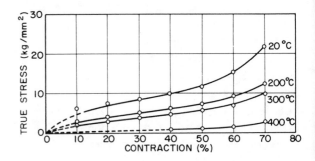

FIG. 56. True-stress curves of aluminum.

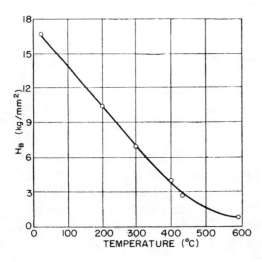

FIG. 57. Influence of temperature on the hardness of aluminum.

We know that aluminum retains its high ductility down to nearly absolute zero; but in this state, its strength is increased (about 2.5 times) [234]. As a rule, as the temperature is decreased below room temperature, the yield stress increases at a slower rate than the ultimate strength in face-centered-cubic metals with faultless grain boundaries. These metals do not become brittle at any low temperature. In certain metals (nickel, copper) the yield stress remains constant at low temperatures, whereas an increase in ultimate tensile strength is observed and, consequently, the spread $\sigma_B - \sigma_S$ widens. Thus it appears that these metals, when cooled, become less brittle [21].

Indium

Indium does not really belong in the cubic-structure column of Table 4 [236]; its structure is face-centered-tetragonal, but its axial ratio is nearly one ($c/a = 1.08$). This ratio leads to the assumption that the ductility properties of this metal will differ only slightly from those of cubic-type metals; thus it can be included in this group.

An evaluation of the mechanical properties of indium has confirmed this assumption. Indium is easily melted (its melting point is approximately 156°C) and it is very ductile. Its ductility properties are comparable to those of lead or thallium, whereas its resistance to deformation is lower.

With 20 g of the metal at our disposal, we conducted tests on the mechanical properties of indium of 99.85 percent purity. The hardness was measured in the temperature range 20 to 120°C. Up to 100°C the specimens were heated in water and, for higher temperatures, in oil. Hardness was measured with a pobedit cone, using a special device with a 2-kg load. The results obtained are presented in Table 6.

The hardness of indium at room temperature is 1.14 kg/mm². With a rise in temperature hardness decreases and, at 120°C, becomes 0.56 kg/mm². An increase in hardness observed at 50°C leads to the assumption that some kind of transformation occurs in indium at this temperature.

TABLE 6

HARDNESS OF INDIUM AT VARIOUS TEMPERATURES

Temperature (°C)	Indentation Diameter (mm)	Hardness H_c (kg/mm²)
20	1.26	1.14
30	1.33	1.01
40	1.45	0.85
50	1.26	1.14
60	1.52	0.84
70	1.59	0.71
80	1.63	0.68
100	1.75	0.59
120	1.80	0.56

Specimens for tension and compression tests were prepared by extrusion. A wire 3 mm in diameter was extruded from a 10-mm block under a 420-kg load. The flow stress was 5.4 kg/mm^2. Tension testing was performed at room temperature. The results were: ultimate tensile strength $\sigma_B = 0.3$ kg/mm^2, elongation $\delta = 40$ percent, and reduction in area $\psi = 99.5$ percent. Samples for compression testing in the Gagarin press were extruded into 5-mm-diameter rods. It was found that indium can be compressed close to 100 percent of its length without fracturing. Further, an industrial test with bending and twisting was performed; in this experiment, a 5-mm-diameter indium wire withstood more than ten 180-deg bends without fracturing. Data in the literature indicate that indium retains its ductility even at the temperature of liquid helium [52].

Chromium

Chromium is widely used in industry as a component in various steels, as a resistant alloy, and as a material for chrome-plating metallic objects. The melting point of chromium depends on the purity and is between 1800 and 1950°C [230]. Chromium is a body-centered-cubic metal, an isomorphic structure like α Fe, Mo, W, V, and Ta.

By the nature of its crystal structure, chromium should be a ductile metal. Nevertheless, industrial chromium obtained by either the aluminothermic, the hydride, or the electrolytic method is brittle, evidently because of the presence of small quantitites of impurities, such as hydrogen, oxygen, nitrogen, and carbon, that are virtually insoluble in chromium. However insignificant their content, these impurities create new phases (oxides, nitrides, carbides, hydrides) that, as a rule, form along grain boundaries and impart brittleness to the chromium.* In this brittle state, chromium cannot be processed at either high or low temperatures.

However, chromium is apparently a ductile metal, even at room temperature, when produced under certain conditions (such as soaking in hydrogen, degasifying, melting in an inert atmosphere, wrapping specimens with iron in heating, and producing by the iodide method) that contribute to a sharp lowering of oxygen content and of other impurities [238]–[242]. The transition of chromium from a brittle to a ductile condition occurs within a definite temperature range which depends on the purity of the metal and the method of processing the samples. In the opinion of some researchers, the brittle behavior of chromium should be viewed as an individual case of brittleness in body-centered-cubic types of metal (α Fe and others)[243]. The basis of this behavior is not yet clear; studies would be desirable to determine whether brittle fracture is due to the properties of the body-centered lattice or to a certain proportion of impurities. The problem may also be approached by searching for some purifying additives. No element, however, has so far been found to lower the critical transition temperature

---

* Of all gases, nitrogen is apparently the most harmful [237].

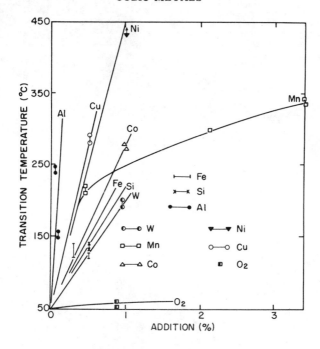

FIG. 58. Effect of additives on the brittle-to-ductile transition temperature in chromium (Sully).

(Fig. 58) [241]. Nevertheless, despite numerous studies on the nature of brittleness in chromium, no proven specimens of ductile chromium suitable for use in industry have yet been produced. When this problem is solved, chromium, being a heat-resistant, acid-proof, high-melting-point, and available metal, may acquire a special importance in industry, both in its pure form and as an alloy for parts to be used at high temperatures.

Comparative experimental research was conducted on the mechanical properties of aluminothermic, hydride, and electrolytic chromium in the temperature range −196 to 1300°C, and a graph was prepared showing the process of recrystallization in chromium.

Figure 59 shows the microstructure of the chromium investigated. In its initial state, aluminothermic chromium has a coarse-grained structure with light-yellow inclusions between the grains. The microhardness within the grain was 145 kg/mm² and that of the grain-boundary inclusions was 260 kg/mm². Remelted chromium has a finer-grained structure with narrower grain boundaries. A considerable number of pores is found in chromium hydride prepared by powder-metallurgy methods. The purity of aluminothermic chromium is 98.9 percent, that of hydride chromium is 98.5 percent, and that of electrolytic chromium 99.5 percent. Experimental data on the effect of temperature on the hardness of chromium are given in Table 7 and in Fig. 60a.

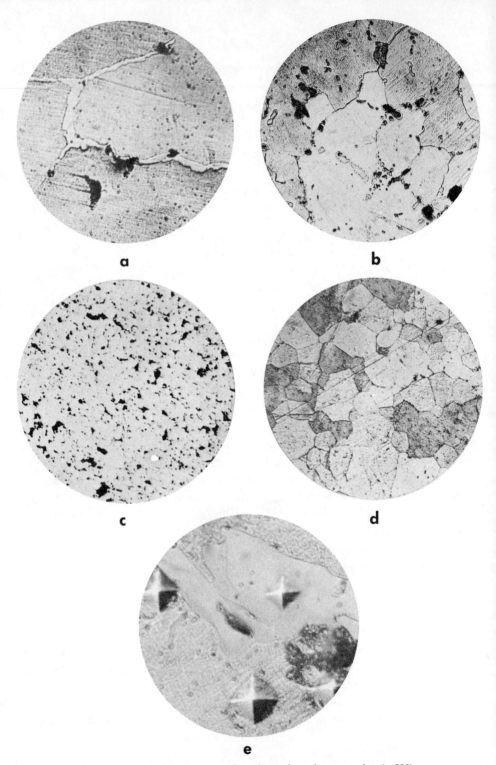

FIG. 59. Microstructures of various chromium samples ($\times 200$).

a. aluminothermic chromium, initial state; *b.* aluminothermic chromium, remelted; *c.* hydride chromium, initial state; *d.* electrolytic chromium, remelted in vacuum; *e.* microhardness impressions of aluminothermic chromium ($\times 500$).

TABLE 7

HARDNESS OF CHROMIUM AT VARIOUS TEMPERATURES

Temperature (°C)	Hardness H_c (kg/mm²)		
	Aluminothermic	Hydride	Electrolytic
−196	220	...	...
− 60	210	...	...
+ 20	201	104	105
100	190	99	102
200	185	96	94
300	167	92	91
400	164	82	82
450	...	95	94
500	169	95	91
600	153	84	79
700	132	75	70
800	100	69	..
900	90	..	66
1000	63	60	..

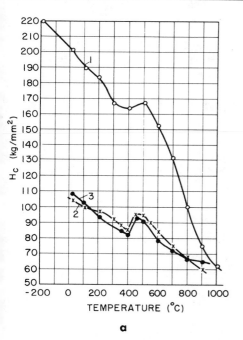

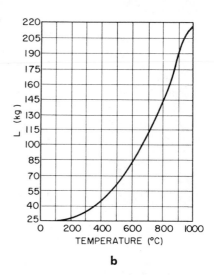

a

b

FIG. 60. Effect of temperature on chromium.

a. Hardness of: 1-aluminothermic remelted chromium; 2-chromium hydride (prepared by powder-metallurgy methods); 3-electrolytic chromium (remelted in vacuum). b. Internal pressure changes in heated aluminothermic chromium (cylindrical specimens, $d = 10.5$ and $h = 28$ mm).

Experiments show that up to 800°C aluminothermic chromium is about twice as hard as hydride and electrolytic chromium, the latter two differing very little in hardness.

With an increase in temperature, chromium of all types softens. At 1000°C the hardness of all types is on the order of 60 kg/mm²; at 20°C it is 200 kg/mm² for aluminothermic chromium and approximately 100 kg/mm² for the other types of chromium. As shown in Fig. 60a, an increase in hardness is observed in all types of chromium between 400 and 500°C; this increase is apparently caused by a certain kind of age-hardening process and diffusion of impurities. We did not fully investigate the nature of this transformation.

Measurement of the magnitude of internal pressure in aluminothermic chromium (measured by the method described on page 123) showed that in the temperature range 20 to 1000°C no abnormal change in volume on the resulting pressure occurs (Fig. 60b).

Because of the excessive brittleness of aluminothermic chromium at room temperature, we were unable to prepare standard specimens with grips suitable for tension experiments. We used chromium specimens in the form of rods of 7 × 100 mm, obtained by suction-feeding molten chromium into porcelain pipes. Special cam-chuck-type clamps were built to hold the specimens. Average results of several experiments are shown below.

Temperature (°C)	Ultimate Tensile Strength σ_B (kg/mm²)	Relative Elongation $\delta(\%)$	Reduction in Area $\psi(\%)$
20	4.7	0	0
1100	10.0	1	1

Gagarin-type specimens made of remelted electrolytic chromium were formed with great difficulty. Average experimental results for fracture tests are summarized below.

Temperature (°C)	Ultimate Tensile Strength σ_B (kg/mm²)	Reduction in Area $\psi(\%)$
20	17.5	1
500	28.0	21
700	21.0	26

These tests have shown that aluminothermic chromium cannot be deformed in tension; even at 1100°C, its elongation and reduction in area are minor. Remelted electrolytic chromium is considerably stronger and above 500°C it becomes quite ductile in tension.

It is noteworthy that the ultimate strength of aluminothermic chromium at 1100°C is more than twice that at room temperature (from 4.7 to 10 kg/mm²).

Remelted electrolytic chromium heated to 700°C also shows an increase in strength, to 8.2 kg/mm².

This strength increase in chromium at elevated temperature, although unusual for plastic metals, conforms to the general rule for brittle materials under ordinary conditions. As we shall mention later, we observed this phenomenon jointly with Terekhova and Baron in germanium, silicon, and intermetallic compounds [244], [245]. The ultimate strength of aluminothermic chromium in compression tests also increases with an increase in temperature; at −196, +20, and +200°C, the respective strengths of cylindrical samples of 9-mm length and 6-mm diameter were 70, 97, and 113 kg/mm².

The brittle-to-ductile transition temperatures in static compression are 500°C for aluminothermic chromium, 350°C for hydride chromium, and 200°C for electrolytic chromium. In static compression tests above 1000°C, specimens of aluminothermic and remelted hydride chromium pressed into steel containers showed a reduction in height of over 90 percent. The ductility–temperature curve for chromium in static compression showed a bend at 400 to 500°C as in hardness tests.

Tests for dynamic deformation of aluminothermic and hydride chromium were conducted on a vertical-ram-impact device. The specimens used were 15 mm long and 10 mm in diameter. These fractured in a brittle fashion, by cleavage, up to 400°C and in a ductile fashion at 500°C and higher. At 1300°C an aluminothermic chromium specimen withstood a deformation of 87 percent without fracturing; deformation was caused by a single impact with a ram-impact machine of 100-kg capacity.

Chromium toughness was tested on cylindrical, unnotched specimens 10 mm in diameter and 60 mm long (Table 8).

TABLE 8

IMPACT TOUGHNESS OF CHROMIUM AT VARIOUS TEMPERATURES

Temperature (°C)	Toughness a_k (kg m/cm²)			Remarks
	Aluminothermic Chromium	Hydride Chromium	Electrolytic Chromium	
20	0.25	0.3	0.2	A ductile type of fracture is observed in electrolytic chromium at 500° and 700°C
700	0.3	...	7.0	
900	0.5	...	3.0	
1000	1.2	0.6	2.5	
1250	1.8	1.2	3.0	

A summary of experiments performed leads to the following conclusions:

1. The various types of chromium tested, although brittle under ordinary conditions, become ductile with increase in temperature and deform, especially under static-compression conditions. Aluminothermic chromium, even when highly impure, will withstand a 90 percent reduction in length

when compressed at 1000°C. The strength and ductility of chromium depend to a great extent on the method of production of the metal and on
its purity.

2.   Chromium is very sensitive to the type of deformation; tension stresses
      (tensile deformation, impact bending) induce brittleness, whereas compres-
      sion stresses induce ductility. This finding suggests that the brittleness
      of chromium is related to the condition of the crystal boundaries, since
      tension testing is primarily a measure of the strength of the boundaries.
      Chromium is especially sensitive to the rate of deformation; when the
      rate is lowered, the temperature limit of its brittleness is likewise lowered—
      from 500°C in dynamic tests to 200°C in static tests on electrolytic chro-
      mium.

3.   A bend is observed at about 500°C for a whole range of mechanical-prop-
      erties–temperature curves for chromium. The physicochemical nature
      of this phenomenon is still unsolved; however, it is known that the purer
      the metal the lower the transition temperature. This fact definitely sup-
      ports the viewpoint that the brittle behavior of chromium is related to
      its impurity content.

The diagram in Fig. 61 shows that the recrystallization of remelted chromium
takes place at about 1000°C when it is annealed after being cold worked up to
any degree of deformation, within the limits of 0 to 40 percent [246].

Barium

Figure 62 presents the experimental data we obtained on the mechanical properties of cast barium (99.9 percent pure) [247]. Barium, having a body-centered-
cubic lattice, is characterized by a high degree of ductility at any temperature,
low resistance to deformation, and absence of polymorphic transformations.

The hardness of barium at 20°C is 5 kg/mm^2 and at 600°C is 0.5 kg/mm^2. The
ultimate strength of barium at 20°C is 1.3 kg/mm^2 and is less when the material
is heated.

Tension tests were conducted with 3-mm Gagarin samples. The lower ductility
of barium at temperatures above 400°C is apparently due to oxidation since the
experiments were conducted in industrial argon.

General Conclusions on Cubic Metals

From known data on the crystalline structure of metals, it has been reliably
determined that approximately 25 metals belong in the cubic-symmetry group.
Of these, Li, Na, K, Rb, Cs, Ba, Eu, V, Nb, Ta, Cr, Mo, and W have a body-centered-
cubic lattice with a coordination number of 8 (type K8, Table 4). All high-melting-point metals of this type tend to be brittle, but this tendency declines sharply
as the purity of the metal increases. Both K12 and K8 lattices are typically
metallic.

Other monomorphic metals of cubic symmetry—a great majority of which are
heavy metals—have a face-centered-cubic lattice with a coordination number of 12
(type K12); Al, Th, Ni, Pt, Pd, Cu, Ag, Au, Pb, Yb, and Ir belong to this group.

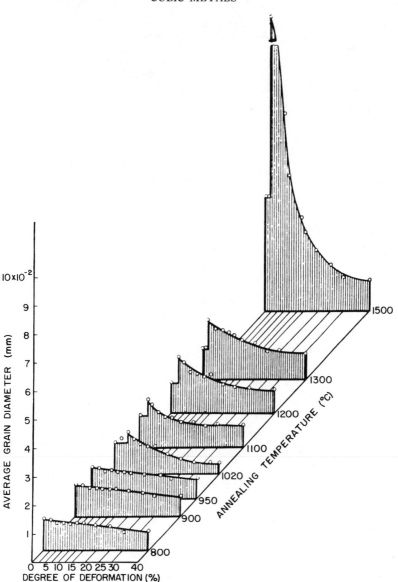

FIG. 61. Recrystallization diagram of electrolytic chromium subsequent to cold deformation and annealing (Savitsky, Terekhova, Kholopov).

Crystalline structures observed in certain electrolytically precipitated metals and other structures (e.g., hexagonal nickel, chromium, molybdenum, and tungsten) will not be discussed here. They may be classified as pseudo-polymorphic and are often related to the precipitation of hydrogen (formation of hydrides) caused by electrolysis.

That the majority of metals of cubic symmetry are highly ductile is widely known (Na, K, Nb, Ta, V, Al, Ni, Cu, Pb, and the noble metals). Industrial chromium is an exception because of impurities. Iodide chromium, however, exhib-

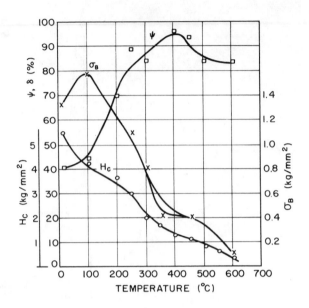

Fig. 62. Effect of temperature on the mechanical properties of (sublimated) barium.

its ductility similar to that of metals of cubic symmetry [248], [249]. Metals with a face-centered-cubic lattice (such as Ag, Al, Cu, Ni, and Pb) not only retain but increase their ductility at −196 and −253°C [21].

These findings justify the assertion that high ductility and smooth curves of mechanical properties versus temperature are the general rule for all pure, monomorphic metals of cubic symmetry. Differences in the nature of packing are not of major importance because even the K8-type lattice has a sufficient number of slip planes. Consequently, the crystal structure (in the form of a face-centered- or body-centered-cubic lattice) insures the retention of ductility in cooling, provided the intercrystalline phase of the given metal or alloy is not sensitive to low-temperature brittleness. The causes of low values of reduction in area in tension tests with molybdenum at low temperatures observed by Kostenets [189] are not clear. The metal apparently was not sufficiently pure.

The above conclusions, in our opinion, warrant the assumption that studies of new monomorphic cubic metals and alloys (whose mechanical properties are yet unknown) will reveal that they too are ductile. Ductility should not be confused with resistance to deformation, which in the same metal at certain temperatures may be of the same high order. Examples of such metals at ordinary temperatures are tantalum, molybdenum, nickel, and tungsten. From data obtained in the mechanical processing of foil and wire made of tungsten, tantalum, and niobium, it is known that a number of metals become ductile and adequately withstand working only in the absence of impurities. The quantitative dependence of mechanical properties on temperature, for metals of a given symmetry, is based mainly on their melting point. There is every reason to believe that a direct dependence exists between the melting temperature and the temperature coefficients of mechanical properties; the former characterizes the lattice's resistance to thermal vibration; the latter, resistance to mechanical effects (Fig. 63).

It is possible that changes in slip mechanisms at very high or very low temperatures are characteristic for a number of metals. Thus, in face-centered-cubic

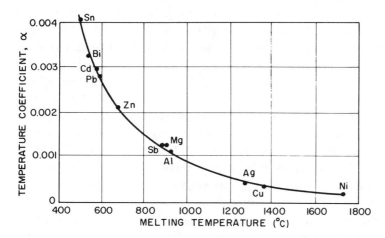

FIG. 63. Relationship between the temperature coefficients of hardness and the melting temperatures of metals (Ito).

metals, slip occurs along (111) planes at low temperatures and along (100) planes at high temperatures. The slip direction [110] remains unchanged. Published data indicate that a relationship exists between the direction of slip planes in body-centered-cubic metals and the corresponding temperature T/T_M, where T is the absolute temperature at which slip occurs and T_M is the melting temperature. The correlation between these two factors is shown below [250].

Metal, Alloy	T/T_M	Slip Plane
W, Mo, Na	0.08–0.24	(112)
Mo, Na, β brass	0.26–0.50	(110)
Na, K	0.80	(123)

Existing data suggest that new slip planes develop in K12-type lattices at elevated temperatures [22]. It has not been explained why this development occurs expressly at 450°C, regardless of the nature of the metal.

Slip planes may apparently be changed with comparative ease by a change in temperature, chemical composition, and pressure. Changing the direction of slip, however, is much more difficult.

In spite of its importance, no systematic research on the relationship of the phase diagram to changes in slip planes has as yet been undertaken.

Hexagonal Metals

The hexagonal close-packed lattice of the G12 structure is another typical metallic lattice. The following monomorphic metals crystallize in this structure: Be, Mg, Zn, Cd, Y, Re, Ru, Os, Tc, and the rare-earth metals Gd, Tb, Dy, Ho, Er, Tm, and Lu [38], [231], [251].

No reliable data appear to be available on the presence of polymorphism in beryllium [252], [253]. Smooth changes in the hardness of beryllium with temperature indicate that at least up to 800°C no transformations occur in the crystal structure of beryllium [254] (Fig. 64).* It is worth noting that, while the axial ratio c/a in the unit cell of magnesium is 1.624, which is close to 1.633 (a figure corresponding to the close packing of hard spheres), the figure for beryllium is markedly lower ($c/a = 1.568$), so that the unit cell of this metal is flattened in the direction of the c-axis. In zinc and in cadmium this ratio exceeds 1.8, their unit cells being elongated vertically. Consequently, of the 12 adjoining atoms surrounding each atom in a zinc or cadmium crystal, six located in the same plane (0001) are the nearest and the other six (three in each of the two parallel layers) are about 10 percent farther away than their nearest neighbors. In beryllium, however, the nearest neighbors, by contrast, are the six atoms located in the neighboring layers [44].

This difference in crystal structure naturally creates a certain divergence in the mechanical behavior of these metals. Beryllium in pure form, because of its low atomic volume, has a greater hardness than do the other hexagonal metals. Slip mechanisms in the deformation of a beryllium crystal under uniaxial com-

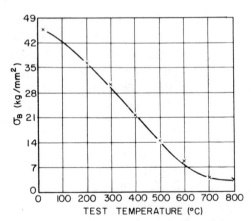

FIG. 64. Effect of temperature on the ultimate tensile strength of hot-pressed and annealed beryllium [254].

---

* *Editor's Note*: Recent work by Martin and Moore suggests that beryllium transforms to a body-centered-cubic structure near its melting temperature [255].

pression in the temperature interval 253 to 800°C have been described by Garber *et al.* [256].

In all hexagonal metals one plane has the densest atomic packing—this is the basal plane. Therefore, at ordinary temperatures, slip takes place in this plane alone (see Figs. 8 and 49). Resistance to deformation is related to the degree of coincidence of the direction of the shear stresses with the active slip planes. Deformation occurs most easily when the shear stress is parallel to the slip plane. Slip will not take place along a plane which is perpendicular to the direction of the shear stress [257].

Under ordinary conditions hexagonal metals are more resistant to deformation then cubic metals. For example, slip occurs in a plane perpendicular to the diagonal of the cube in a face-centered-cubic lattice (Fig. 49). There are four such planes in a cubic crystal. In the presence of this variety of possibilities for slip, the probability of coincidence in any of the crystal planes with the direction of the shear stress is high and, therefore, deformation will easily occur. Deformation of a polycrystalline metallic sample with a hexagonal lattice, which will deform only along the basal plane, presents a different situation. In some favorably oriented crystals, deformation will occur easily; in other crystals, because of improper orientation, deformation will not take place and the body as a whole will strongly resist deformation. Because of this situation, objects manufactured from hexagonal metals possess a high anisotropy of properties in various directions in relation to the force applied in processing them. Thus, for example, the yield strength may vary by as much as a factor of six [22].

Metals with a hexagonal lattice have a tendency to deform through another mechanism, twinning; this tendency is probably due to their limited capacity to deform by slip. For this reason one will always find traces of twins (which disappear after annealing) in the micro-structure of deformed and unannealed metals with hexagonal lattices (Fig. 65). By contrast, in metals of cubic symmetry (K12), twins appear only as a result of annealing (see Fig. 13).

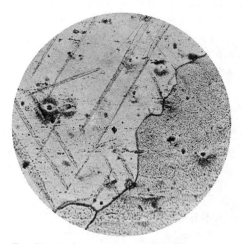

In Chapter 1 it was stated that, according to published data on the properties of single crystals [22], atomic planes other than the basal plane participate in the slip process in magnesium, cadmium, and zinc at 225°C. Apparently the $(10\bar{1}1)$ plane, which ranks second in density of atomic distribution, is the second to participate. This explanation, however, is not sufficiently clear. Does

FIG. 65. Deformation by twinning in magnesium. ×90.

the participation occur at a well-defined temperature and, if so, why does it take place at 225°C in the three different metals even though they differ in their physicochemical nature as well as in their melting points? The above statement of fact has been accepted at face value in the Russian technical literature and is quoted without reservation in a number of textbooks, reference books, and articles, especially with regard to magnesium [258], [259].

It seems more natural, however, to assume that, depending on the physicochemical nature of the metal and its melting point, an increase in temperature would cause a change in the *c/a* ratio and, as the possibility of slip along the basal plane disappeared, other planes, next in line by density of packing, would participate. Evaluation of important experimental material gathered in the course of our studies on the mechanical properties of hexagonal metals indicated that a continuous increase in ductility is obtained with an increase in temperature. These results have confirmed that our assumption is correct, at least with respect to magnesium. Furthermore, it should be borne in mind that, in line with the contemporary outlook on the nature of plastic deformation, changes in shape, especially at high temperatures, will take place not only by slip, but also by other means—for example, by diffusion or by grain-boundary shearing.

At any rate, the abrupt heat-induced increase in the ductility of metals of the hexagonal type is a fact firmly established by experiments. At sufficiently elevated temperatures, Mg, Be, Zn, Cd, and Re are in no way less ductile than metals of the face-centered-cubic type. Experimental data on hand concerning the influence of temperature on the plasticity properties of yttrium, ruthenium, osmium, and some rare-earth metals are inadequate. In our opinion, however, it is reasonable to assert with full confidence that their behavior in this respect is analogous to that of magnesium and the other metals that have been amply studied. In metals with a higher melting point softening will naturally begin at correspondingly higher temperatures.

To illustrate the findings reported above, we present below our experimental data on the plasticity of monomorphic metals of the hexagonal system at various temperatures.

Magnesium

A thorough study of the mechanical properties of commercially pure magnesium (99.7 percent Mg) and of its alloys in relation to various processing factors and, mainly, to temperature, was undertaken in the period 1938 to 1941 under the supervision of Gubkin. Inasmuch as many of our papers were published on the subject, we shall not recount here all the experimental results obtained [146], [147], [201], [210], [216]–[218], and [260]–[265]. It will suffice to quote only the most pertinent information.

A diagram of the ductility of magnesium (Fig. 33) shows that the ductility of magnesium, whether under slow or impact conditions, increases intensively yet smoothly when the metal is heated. This behavior is especially true for reduc

ion in area and for ductility characteristics in compression. A bend in the
impact-toughness–temperature curve at approximately 300°C is evidently related
o a phase of this complex characteristic in the same way as impact toughness
s sensitive to the grain size. The strength decreases as the temperature is
increased and this occurs in a monotonic fashion (Fig. 66) as in the case of the
ductility curves.

We conducted experiments on the mechanical properties of magnesium over a
wide temperature range of −180 to 625°C. No abrupt changes in the property–
temperature curves were observed. Curve 2 (Fig. 67) shows changes in the hardness of magnesium in the temperature range of 0 to 600°C. Magnesium at low
temperatures retains the low ductility which typifies the metal at ordinary
temperatures.

A high degree of ductility was observed in magnesium at elevated temperatures, at which the metal could be easily deformed to a required shape. High
ductility in magnesium is confined to the range 300 to 600°C. The same type
of ductility is also found in magnesium solid solutions. A specimen of MA-3
magnesium alloy with 6 percent Al and 1 percent Zn, fractured in a Gagarin
press test, appears in Fig. 68a. It shows that the contraction in the neck, caused
by tension, reaches 100 percent, which is characteristic of highly plastic metals
such as lead. A notched sample of this alloy will not fracture even when both
halves are brought together as shown in Fig. 68b.

At slow rates of deformation, high ductility at high temperature is likewise a
characteristic of the other worked magnesium alloys, even when in the cast state

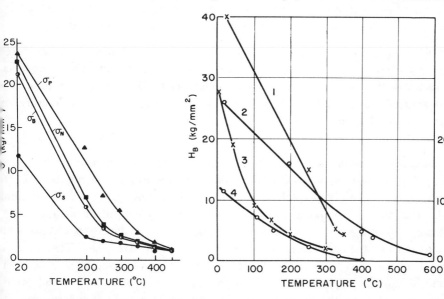

IG. 66. Effect of temperature on the
strength characteristics of magnesium.

FIG. 67. Effect of temperature on the hardness of
zinc (1), magnesium (2), and cadmium (3) and on the
ultimate tensile strength of zinc (4).

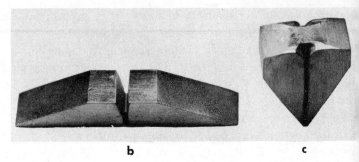

FIG. 68. Samples of MA-3 magnesium alloy.
a. Region of fracture in Gagarin sample at 350°C (×2).
b. Sample prior to bend test in Gagarin press.
c. Sample subsequent to bend test at 350°C.

FIG. 69. Samples of as-cast MA-2 magnesium alloy deformed by compression at 450°C.
a. Original state. *b*. 50-percent deformed. *c*. 75-percent deformed.

(Fig. 69). Fracture of magnesium alloys by compression at low temperatures occurs by cleavage at a 45-deg angle and at high temperatures by the appearance of cracks on the side surface of the samples. It would be desirable to verify the magnitude of ductility at 20°C and to check the mechanism of fracture of superpure and degasified magnesium.

Zinc

It should be considered as definitely proved that zinc is a monomorphic metal [230]. Transformation points in the solid state (discussed in a number of research papers) have been explained as an effect of alloying, primarily of cadmium [266]. The strength of polycrystalline zinc is strongly dependent on grain size. Cast polycrystalline zinc exhibits considerably more resistance to compression than to tension, the latter causing fracture with comparative ease. The fracture strength of cast zinc is between 2 and 7 kg/mm^2, that of wrought zinc between 10 and 22 kg/mm^2, depending on the degree and rate of deformation and orientation. All data on the anomalies of zinc properties at high temperatures reported by various authors [266] should be viewed with caution, because many such anomalies may have been caused by impurities, to which zinc is very sensitive. Thus, for instance, additions of Pb, Fe, Bi, Sb, and As are detrimental to the technological properties of zinc. For all practical purposes, these elements in their solid states are not soluble in zinc. Tin is soluble in zinc in insignificant quantities only and, when its content reaches a few hundredths of 1 percent it is precipitated in eutectic form, which melts at 200°C; when both tin and lead are present in zinc, a ternary eutectic develops with a melting point of 150°C. Distributing itself along the boundaries of the zinc, the eutectic disrupts their solidarity and, as a consequence, makes heat treatment and especially rolling impossible. When the iron content in zinc is greater than 0.02 percent, a brittle compound $FeZn_7$ is formed. Cadmium and copper have no detrimental effect on zinc [234].

In single crystals of zinc favorably oriented in relation to the applied stress, the magnitude of ductility may attain several thousand percent. Single crystals of zinc (also cadmium), even at the temperature of liquid air, register an elongation of approximately 100 percent [186].

Pure polycrystalline zinc hot rolled at 150 to 170°C withstands up to 95 percent deformation. According to Ludwik, a relative elongation of zinc at 180°C exceeds 150 percent [266]. It would be desirable to check if this fact has any relation to the findings reported by Bochvar and Sviderskaya on a so-called super-plasticity property of aluminum alloys with 75 to 85 percent zinc content [267].

In tests for impact toughness below room temperature, zinc behaves in a brittle manner. According to Gubkin, brittleness in zinc appears at temperatures below 100°C [16].

Figure 67 shows that the hardness and ultimate strength of heated zinc undergo rapid but smooth changes with temperature.

Kutaitsev has made a thorough research of the temperature effect on the mechanical properties of zinc (hardness, yield stress, characteristics of creep). He has found that all these mechanical characteristics change smoothly when the zinc is subjected to heating [200].

Cadmium

Cadmium is similar to zinc. It is also monomorphic. Shishokin has studied the yield stress of cadmium at various temperatures [14]. The effect of temperature on hardness and ultimate strength of cadmium was investigated by Kutaitsev [200]. These studies have proven the monotonic decrease in resistance to deformation characteristics with a temperature increase which follows an exponential law (see Fig. 67, curve 3).

Semimetals

Monomorphic, low-symmetry elements such as Ge, Si, Ga, Hg, As, Bi, Sb, and, apparently, Sm, belong to the so-called semimetals or nontypical metals, which have poorly defined metallic qualities. Silicon and germanium have a diamond structure with 34 percent density of packing. Gallium has a rhombic structure

[38]. The other metals mentioned above crystallize in rhombohedral lattices with coordination number 3 (Fig. 70). These structures impede plastic deformation and the metals are brittle under normal conditions. Studies on bismuth and antimony at room temperature have shown that tensile deformation takes place without slip, only by twinning [52]. In compression or tension tests at elevated temperatures, however, slip is apparent.* The above-mentioned elements, with their complex crystalline structure, may be plastically deformed when placed under certain conditions favorable to deformation (high temperature, triaxial compression stresses, slow rates of deformation). Slip traces along octahedral planes have been recently discovered even in diamond [268].

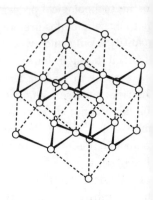

FIG. 70. Crystal structure of antimony.

We have found that at temperatures above 800 to 1000°C silicon can be plastically deformed by compression. The ultimate strength of technical silicon in compression in the temperature interval between 20 and 1000°C increases by a factor of more than 10 (from 1.7 to 21.8 kg/mm²) and in tension it increases by a factor of more than 2 [269]. This phenomenon is apparently related to the well-known increase in the conduction electrons of silicon at elevated temperatures [270].

Detailed studies were made of the influence of temperature on the mechanical properties of germanium (99.99 percent pure), which has a melting point of 958°C.

Germanium, because of its semiconductor capabilities, has acquired a great importance in the realm of radio engineering. Its physical properties are similar to those of diamond and silicon. The mechanical properties of germanium have not been fully investigated, probably because its hardness and brittleness impede handling. Germanium does not lend itself well to machining and for this reason it is melted into blocks and cut by the electrofusing method or with a diamond cutter. Germanium will not oxidize at normal temperatures and in atmospheric conditions, but when heated (especially to temperatures above 700°C) will interact with oxygen from the air. Practically all metals alloy readily with germanium producing eutectics with fairly low melting points [271, page 121]; this capability creates difficulties in the selection of materials suitable for tools in high-temperature experiments with germanium. Hardness tests at high temperatures were conducted with the universal device, purified argon, and magnesite packing

---

* It is of interest to note that, like ice, the low-symmetry elements decrease in volume upon melting (their crystallites swim in the melt); their electrical conductivity in the liquid state is higher than in the solid state.

The microhardness of germanium was found to be 385 kg/mm² at 20°C. It was not possible to measure its hardness by means of a pobedit cone at temperatures below 600°C because the samples would crumble even at low loads. At temperatures above 600°C a brief contact of the cone with the specimen produced no chemical interaction and the impressions were proper in form. Data on the influence of temperature on the hardness of germanium is recorded in Table 9 and is plotted in Figure 71 (curve 1).

TABLE 9

HARDNESS OF GERMANIUM AT VARIOUS TEMPERATURES

Temperature (°C)	Hardness H_c (kg/mm²)	Temperature (°C)	Hardness H_c (kg/mm²)
600	176	900	32
650	150	910	27
700	83	900	30
750	80	940	29
800	50	950	24
850	37	...	..

The bend in the temperature flow of hardness as illustrated on semi-logarithmic coordinates suggests that a certain kind of structural transformation occurs in germanium (appearance of new slip planes, recrystallization) at 650°C; its nature, however, should be determined by X-ray structural analysis. The hardness of germanium at 850°C is comparatively low (37 kg/mm²) and shows little change at higher temperatures. The results of static deformation of germanium are shown in Table 10 and in Fig. 71. The specimens for static-deformation

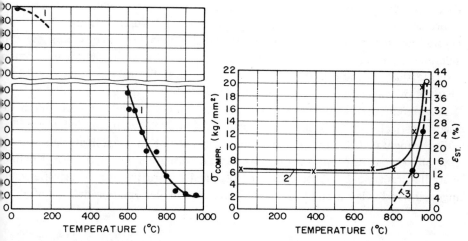

FIG. 71. Effect of temperature on the mechanical properties of germanium: (1) hardness, (2) crushing strength, (3) ductility in static compression.

tests of germanium were cast in a graphite mold in an argon atmosphere. The final specimens measured 6 mm in diameter and 8 mm in length. Tests were made with the Gagarin press.

TABLE 10

MECHANICAL PROPERTIES OF GERMANIUM IN STATIC
COMPRESSION AT VARIOUS TEMPERATURES

Temperature (°C)	Ultimate Strength σ_{compr} (kg/mm²)	Relative Contraction ε_{st} (%)	Type of Fracture
20	6.9	....	Brittle
400	6.1	....	Brittle
700	6.7	....	Brittle
800	6.5	....	Brittle
920	12.4	12.5	Ductile
940	19.5	23	Ductile
940[a]	....	42	Ductile

[a] After 20-hr annealing at 900°C.

Table 10 and Fig. 71 show that at 800°C and lower the samples of germanium in compression tests fracture in a brittle fashion and have nearly identical values of ultimate strength. Above 900°C, hardness and plasticity increase. Crushing strength at 920°C is twice that at 20°C and at 940°C is three times greater [244]. The abrupt increase in the compression strength of germanium at high temperatures, seemingly a paradox, may be explained by its normal tendency to deform plastically under such conditions. Slip along atomic planes in the crystal lattice of germanium is apparently impossible at low temperatures; application of external stresses of low magnitude will cause the metal to fracture in a brittle fashion. In static compression at temperatures above 900°C, polycrystalline germanium will fracture in a ductile fashion and will show considerable decrease in length. Data on hardness and compression of germanium indicate that, at 930 to 940°C, the metal becomes sufficiently plastic to withstand changes of considerable magnitude in shape [244].

Data from recent publications indicate that single crystals of germanium deform plastically at 600°C in bend tests [272] and at 670°C in tension tests [273].

Experiments with silicon and germanium show that even materials with a crystalline structure unfavorable to plastic deformation and with poorly defined metallic properties, may be deformed plastically at temperatures near the melting point, provided a suitable method and rate of deformation are followed.

4

Polymorphic Metals

Mechanical Properties

The phenomenon of polymorphism was discovered in the first half of the last century. Of the more than 70 known metals, more than 20 have temperature allotropy; i.e., they may exist in different crystalline forms at different temperatures. In some metals—such as Bi, Sb, Cd, Li, Rb, Hg, Ba, Ga, and Zn—such changes may be brought about through high hydrostatic pressure, but these changes are reversible and disappear with reduction of pressure [52], [170]. It is also possible to prevent the appearance of polymorphic modifications (which normally are formed under atmospheric conditions) by applying external pressure.

Certain authors explain the polymorphism of metals as a result of the presence of impurities which create a high internal pressure at the time of melting (like carbon in iron) or by the combined action of temperature and impurities [47, 274–276]. An opposite viewpoint is that polymorphism under these or other conditions is inherent in every metal [277].

It should be said that no convincing theory presently exists which would eliminate the possibility for elements to acquire several crystalline forms. This question should be determined for each individual metal separately, by experimentation with pure samples.

Most of the known polymorphic metals belong to the transition group in the Mendeleyev periodic table. The polymorphism of metals has a great scientific value and is a very important technical property. It characterizes the behavior of metals when processed at high or low temperatures and, in general, exercises a major influence on the physicomechanical properties of the metal (ability to dissolve other elements, behavior in thermal processing and corrosion, and so on). The exact number of polymorphic metals has not yet been determined because different viewpoints exist on the presence of polymorphism in some of them. A compilation of metals which exhibit temperature polymorphism is given in Table 11 [38], [236], [250], and [278–284].

Certain metals (tungsten, chromium, nickel, and others) when electrolytically treated exhibit an unusual type of lattice [38], usually hexagonal. There is reason to believe that some of these crystalline structures really correspond to those

TABLE 11

THE POLYMORPHIC PHASES OF METALS

Metal	Melting Temp. (°C)	Crystal Structure of Phases			Transformation Temp. (°C)
		α	β	γ	
Tin	232	Complex cubic (diamond)	Complex tetragonal	. . . .	13–18
Thallium[a]	303	G12	K12	. . . .	230
Plutonium[b]	637 ± 5	Monoclinic	Complex, unknown	Orthorhombic face-centered δ–K12 δ–tetragonal, face-centered ε–K8	119, 218, 310, 472
Neptunium	640	Rhombic	Complex tetragonal	K8	278, 540
Strontium	770	K12	G12	K8	248, 614
Cerium	815	G12	K12	. . . .	380–480
Calcium	851	K12	G12	K8	350, 450
Lanthanum	875	G12	K12	. . . .	600–650
Praseodymium	940	G12	K12	. . . .	600
Neodymium	1020	G12	K12	. . . .	850
Uranium	1133	Rhombic	Complex tetragonal	K8	660, 760
Scandium	1205	G12	K12	. . . .	. . . .
Manganese	1260	Complex cubic	Complex cubic	K12 (δ–K8)	742, 1080
Samarium[c]	1350	Rhombohedral	Near K12	. . . .	917
Cobalt	1490	G12	K12	. . . .	350–470
Iron	1530	K8	K8	K12 (δ–K8)	910, 1405
Titanium	1660	G12	K8	. . . .	885
Thorium[d]	1750	K12	. . . .	. . . .	. . . .
Zirconium	1857	G12	K8	. . . .	862
Rhodium	1960	K8	K12	. . . .	1030
Hafnium	2230	G12	K8	. . . .	1310

[a] *Editor's Note*: Thallium actually transforms from a hexagonal-close-packed to a body-centered-cubic structure at 230°C.

[b] Smith, *Phys. Rev.*, **94**, 4 (1954) [285], [286]. Also *Problems of Contemporary Metallurgy*, **2** (1957).

[c] X-ray investigations have shown that samarium at room temperature has a rhombohedral structure. At 917°C, the lattice becomes close packed, approaching the cubic structure [287].

[d] It has been recently reported that thorium transforms at 1400 ± 25°C from face-centered cubic to body-centered cubic [288].

of the hydrides of metals. Therefore, these modifications have not been included in table 11, which lists polymorphic phases arising from the effect of temperature. Metals which acquire polymorphism from high-pressure effects have likewise been excluded.

Body-centered-cubic alkaline metals under pressure and at low temperatures, apparently have a tendency to become face-centered-cubic [38], [278].

Crystal-structure modifications in lithium, cobalt, and cerium were observed in recent experiments at extremely low temperatures [278 and 289–292]. It is characteristic that at extremely low temperatures the transformations do not go to completion. As a result, a combination of two modifications is frequently observed in metals. These transformations have a martensitic character and localize at separate regions in the sample.

Transformation in lithium may be caused by plastic deformation at extremely low temperature and is accompanied by cracking, similar to twinning in magnesium and zinc or in the formation of martensite [292].

In certain metals, because of their capacity to dissolve impurities, a polymorphic transition will occur, not at some definite temperature (as it should for the case of invariant equilibrium), but in a certain temperature range. In the course of a transformation, hysteresis is often observed because of supercooling.

The high-temperature modifications of metals of the transition groups usually have the structure which is characteristic for the neighboring elements with a fuller electron shell. For example, β titanium and β zirconium have the same body-centered-cubic lattice as vanadium and niobium, which follow the first-named elements in the periodic table; γ iron and β cobalt have a face-centered-cubic lattice, the same as that of nickel and copper [44].

The phenomenon of polymorphism is associated with a certain change in volume at the time of transformation and is frequently accompanied by an abrupt decrease in the metal's resistance to chemical action.

Various crystalline structures found in different modifications of polymorphic metals have a significant bearing on changes in their physicomechanical properties, especially those of ductility and strength. A case in point is tin, which, in its gray modification, is brittle and crumbles spontaneously into powder, whereas white tin, as we know, is highly ductile. For this reason the mechanical method of testing, although indirect, is one of the more sensitive methods enabling us to determine the absence or the presence of thermal polymorphism in a metal and also to define the temperature range of polymorphic transformations.

In contrast to monomorphic metals, which exhibit uniformity of properties as related to temperature, polymorphic metals display abrupt changes in mechanical properties during transformations caused by temperature changes. Thus, for instance, the transition from a hexagonal to a cubic lattice takes place with an abrupt change in the curve relating ductility to temperature. The temperature dependence of mechanical properties of polymorphic metals has as yet been insufficiently studied. Of the 20 polymorphic metals listed in Table 11, reliable and systematic data on their mechanical characteristics at various temperatures have been published on only three (iron, tin, and thallium). The great scientific and practical importance of this question has prompted us to concentrate our efforts on experimental studies of the effects of temperature dependence on the properties of polymorphic metals. The data obtained for the various polymorphic metals are analyzed in the following section.

Effect of Temperature

We shall first examine the three metals—thallium, tin, and iron—on which the published data are considered reliable. We shall then submit our experimental data on the temperature dependence of the mechanical properties of polymorphic metals for which there is practically no information in the published literature —Mn, Ca, Sr, Co, La, Ce, Pr, Ti, and Zr.

Thallium

This metal has only one allotropic transformation that causes the hexagonal-close-packed lattice of the low-temperature modification to be replaced by a face-centered-cubic lattice of the high-temperature phase. The fact that the transformation occurs with a high degree of linear growth has prevented the study of its kinetics.

The results of Shishokin's study on the temperature dependence of the mechanical properties of thallium (long-duration hardness and yield stress) are given in Fig. 72 [14]. In this particular case the hardness method to determine polymorphic transformations proved more sensitive than electrical-resistance measurements.

The author found that the hardness curve exhibits a break in continuity at the transformation temperature of thallium; at the same time the high-temperature modification has a higher temperature coefficient of hardness than does the low-temperature modification. The yield-stress curve exhibits an abrupt

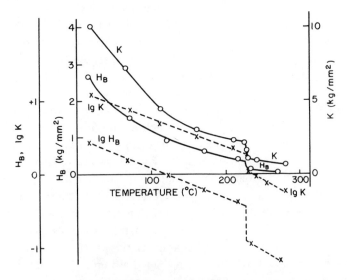

FIG. 72.   Temperature curves of prolonged hardness of flow stress *K* of thallium (after Shishokin).

drop between 226 and 230°C, corresponding to the polymorphic transformation. A similar abrupt change is likewise observed in a logarithmic presentation of the data, but here it is more pronounced. The curve during the cooling of a melted thallium specimen showed that allotropic transformation occurred at 228°C. The author states that the thallium specimen used was not completely pure. Thallium is analogous to lead in its other mechanical characteristics, except that it is softer. At ordinary temperature thallium has an ultimate strength of 1 kg/mm² and a contraction of about 100 percent [266].

Tin

The conversion of white to gray tin was known to Aristotle and was observed in the temples' organ pipes; the nature of this transformation was then not clear. As we know it, white tin (β) with a tetragonal lattice and coordination number of 6 transforms at 17°C to gray tin (α) with a diamond-cubic-type lattice and a coordination number of 4. This transformation is accompanied by a 25.6 percent increase in volume and causes internal stresses in the metal resulting in cracking ("tin plague"). Such sudden changes in volume, producing great internal stresses, impede the process of transformation, which occurs essentially on the surface of the metal. Transformation takes place at an irregular rate and in different directions. The transformation of gray tin to white (induced either by heating or by compression at ordinary temperatures) occurs rapidly, whereas the inverse process is slow and requires supercooling. Most recent data indicate that, under normal conditions, the transformation takes place at 13.2 rather than at 18°C [12].

Addition of small quantities of Zn, Al, Co, Mn, Te, and, to a lesser degree, Fe and Au, hastens the transformation process of white tin to gray [293], [294]. An analogous effect results from addition of Sb-In alloys and Cd-Te alloys, which are closely related to tin with respect to their lattice parameters [295]. The polymorphic transformation is retarded by Bi, Sb, Pb, Cd, Ag, and, to a lesser degree, by Ni and Cu. The influence of the additives mentioned above is observed at negligible concentrations—in the range of 0.001 to 0.01 atomic percent for aluminum and of 0.001 to 0.1 atomic percent for bismuth.

Semenchenko, using the concept of generalized moments, pointed out that elements which decrease the surface tension of liquid tin will retard the formation of α-tin crystals, whereas elements which increase its surface tension will contribute to the transformation of white tin to gray [293].

Gray tin is extremely brittle as a result of its nonmetallic crystal structure and the presence of certain nonmetallic (semiconductor) properties. The predominating cohesion in gray tin is covalent and in white tin, metallic [44]. The high ductility of white tin is universally known. Nothing is known of attempts made to determine the mechanical properties of gray tin in extruded form. The transformation of white tin to gray is a vivid example of the radical change which occurs in the mechanical and other physical properties of a metal as the result of a change in its crystal structure and in the type of cohesion. This change in mechanical properties is so obvious as to eliminate the necessity of conducting mechanical experiments. Existing data on the mechanical properties of tin at various temperatures pertain to white (β) tin. In this respect, its behavior when heated is analogous to that of other monomorphic metals [235], [266]. The hypothesis that at 200°C white tetragonal tin is transformed to a third modification, rhombic gray tin, has not been verified. At any rate, this third modification is unlikely at pressures not exceeding atmospheric pressure.

We present here data obtained in tests on the influence of longtime soaking at −50°C on the Brinell hardness of tin [296] (Fig. 73). Our purpose was to test the possibility of using the short-duration hardness for determining the time of transformation of tin from white to gray. Two grades of tin were used: grade 01 (99.9 percent Sn) specially "plagued" by rubbing powdered mixtures of antimony and indium into the metal, and grade 02P, which is immune to plaguing because it has an elevated concentration of bismuth (0.03 percent) and antimony (0.05 percent).

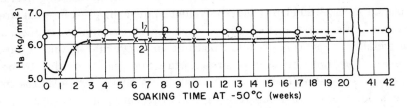

FIG. 73. Effect of soaking at −50°C on the hardness of tin of various purities. *1*-tin of 02P grade; *2*-tin of 01 grade.

As shown in Fig. 73 (curve 1), no change in hardness occurred in the tin which had not been plagued, even after being maintained for nearly a year at −50°C. On the other hand, tin which was subject to transformation showed a 5.5 percent decline in hardness after a week-long exposure (incubation period). Thereafter, the hardness began to increase and, after three weeks, the hardness reached a permanent level, which was 13 percent greater than the original value. It is worth noting that microscopic examination revealed the first traces of transformation (tin plague) only after the eleventh or twelfth week of exposure at −50°C. The increase in hardness of grade 01 is explained by the creation of internal stresses, which appear in the metallic crystal lattice during allotropic transformation. These internal stresses, which may be likened to work-hardening effects, increase the hardness of the metal. Thus an increase in the hardness of tin may serve as an index of the beginning of transformation (tin plague).

Consequently, the hardness-test method provides an earlier warning of the beginning of transformation than does the microstructural method. Other methods such as X-ray analysis may also be used, but they are more complex.

The above-mentioned studies permit the assumption that periodic hardness tests may be used successfully for timely detection of the transformation process of warehoused tin.

It is generally believed that, basically, transformation occurs on the metal's surface. The change in hardness of tin when transformation sets in, however, testifies to the fact that it affects not only the surface layers but the underlying ones as well.

Iron

A great amount of research has been devoted to the properties of iron, yet it may be said that the researchers dealt not with pure iron but mostly with its industrially important alloys, steel and cast iron. Pure iron (the highest purity achieved is about 99.99 percent) has a melting temperature of approximately 1530°C (1528 to 1535°C as variously recorded) [297]. In its solid state, iron is known to exist in several allotropic forms. Iron's polymorphism was first discovered by Chernov. Up to 910°C iron has an α body-centered-cubic lattice. At 910°C α crystals are transformed into γ crystals having a face-centered-cubic lattice. The γ crystals remain unchanged up to 1405°C; beyond this temperature they revert to crystals with a body-centered-cubic lattice, usually known as δ crystals. The latter, in essence, are in no way different from α crystals and their new designation is only to distinguish them from crystals with an identical lattice formed in the temperature range below the γ phase. Crystals of α iron are ferromagnetic at temperatures below 770°C. At 770°C ferromagnetism vanishes. It was formerly thought that this phenomenon proved that iron existed in two forms, one above and the other below 770°C.

A suggestion was made to identify the condition of iron at a temperature above 770°C as the β phase. It was proved, however, by means of X-ray examination that β crystals are in no way structurally different from α crystals. Consequently, in spite of the existing difference in the magnetic properties of β and α crystals, there is no valid reason to consider β crystals as having an independent allotropic form or phase. Both β and δ designations should be preserved, however, to provide a concise way of referring to the paramagnetic condition of crystals at temperatures above 770°C [186]. A schematic representation of the allotropic transformations which occur during the heating and cooling of pure iron is shown in Fig. 74 [172]. Figure 75 illustrates a differential curve of change in length of a heated iron specimen [298].

The density of the γ crystals is more than 2 percent higher than that of α crystals. Therefore, at the point of transition from one form into another, a rather abrupt change in volume takes place. Under rapid cooling, high stresses are created that may surpass the elastic limit, and fracture may even occur.

The influence of alloying on the polymorphism of iron has been examined in a series of papers [12], [34], [186]. The temperature dependence of the mechanical and technological properties of industrial iron (approximate carbon content 0.1

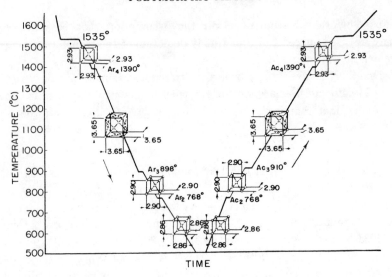

FIG. 74. Schematic representation of allotropic transformations in pure iron during heating and cooling.

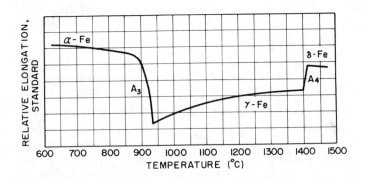

FIG. 75. Differential curve for changes in the length of an iron sample during heating.

percent) and of Armco iron (carbon content 0.02 percent) has been fairly well studied but that of the purest iron (0.001 percent carbon content) and of carbonyl iron (approximately 0.0001 percent carbon content) has not. Research on the properties of noncarbide iron is of great interest, as some authors attribute iron allotropy to the influence of carbon [274–276].

A specific feature of iron allotropy is that each of its polymorphic modifications contributes favorably to the plasticity of the metal. Consequently, when mechanical-property changes caused by temperature take place, allotropic transformations, naturally, are not clearly observed. The effects of additives (mainly oxygen and sulfur) on mechanical and industrial properties of iron are much more pronounced because these elements form oxides and sulfides, which spread themselves along grain boundaries and weaken the metal. Three zones of brittleness are observed in the impact-strength–temperature curve for Armco iron and for carbon steels (Fig. 76) [299].

The diagram in Fig. 76 shows three distinct minima: below 0°C, the 350 to 450°C range, and the 900 to 1000°C temperature range. These three minima correspond to the three types of iron brittleness: low-temperature brittleness, blue brittleness, and hot shortness. The original properties are restored at normal temperatures. The nature and the conditions under which zones of brittleness occur in iron are totally dissimilar. Low-temperature brittleness supposedly is a manifestation of the true physical brittleness of iron, which is dependent on the crystallographic character of fracture and is often accompanied by a special crystalline glitter observed on the fracture surface [300].* Some additives (oxygen) raise the ductile–brittle transition temperature of iron, others (carbon, manganese) lower it [243], [302]. When in a brittle state, iron is very sensitive to all kinds of notches as well as to any abrupt change in shape. Consequently, at low

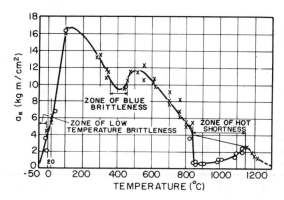

FIG. 76. Impact strength of Armco iron at various temperatures (Gallay and Zolotnikov).

temperatures parts often become damaged or break because of their brittle condition. As pointed out by Dobrovidov, the number of damaged and replaced rails on the Tomsk railway varies in strict relation to atmospheric temperature; it is a minimum in summer and a maximum during the cold winter months [303]. By replacing the standard steel rails with chrome-nickel-steel rails, the fracture problem in winter months was eliminated [304]. In spite of the extensive research done on the low-temperature brittleness of iron, the study is yet incomplete [21].

Davidenkov expresses the opinion that blue brittleness, because of its physical nature, is equivalent to aging after cold working; as in all aging processes it is related to the precipitation from a solid solution of some compound in a high state of dispersion; precipitation progresses so sluggishly as to require a prelim-

---

* Nevertheless, according to Allen and others [301], single crystals of pure iron (99.96 percent) even at −124°C are highly ductile ($\psi \approx 100$ percent).

inary plastic deformation in order to be stimulated [300]. These compounds are probably oxides, carbides, and nitrides.

Hot shortness, which is the third minimum in the diagram for impact strength, appears to be the property of a metal rendered impure by sulfur and oxygen [300].

In presenting the data on the mechanical properties of iron under stress, it

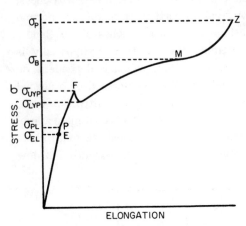

FIG. 77. Diagram of stress-strain in tension for iron.

should be mentioned that its stress–strain curve is extraordinarily characteristic, showing a sharply defined yield point. The stress–strain diagram is shown schematically in Fig. 77. The elastic limit σ_{EL} corresponds to point E at which the first permanent elongation is observed; through point P, which corresponds to the proportional limit σ_{PL}, the stress is proportional to the elongation. The metal begins to yield at point F; σ_{UYP} designates the upper yield point and σ_{LYP} the lower yield point. The stresses associated with points M and Z correspond to the ultimate tensile strength and the true fracture strength respectively.

Lashko, Petrenko, and Slobodyaniuk performed rupture tests with Armco iron in the temperature range 600 to 1100°C [305]. The resulting graph on the temperature dependence of ultimate tensile strength expressed in semilogarithmic coordinates has the appearance of separate straight-line sections confined within the limits of the α, β, and γ phases (Fig. 78). Nevertheless it is not clear why the β phase, which has the same type of lattice as the α phase, should have mechanical properties so different. Pavlov submitted a diagram of deformation

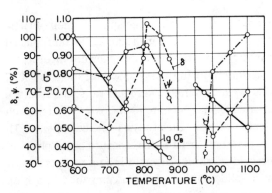

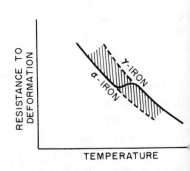

FIG. 78. Relation of mechanical properties to temperature in Armco iron (Lashko, Petrenko, and Slobodyaniuk).

FIG. 79. Schematic representation of resistance to deformation in α and γ iron (Pavlov).

resistance for α and γ iron (Fig. 79). This diagram indicates that at a given temperature γ iron has a greater resistance to deformation than α iron [89].

It is known that blue brittleness and hot shortness of iron are also observed in rupture tests in which the ultimate tensile strength showed an increase, whereas the elongation and the reduction of area were decreased [266]. The temperatures of these zones, however, may differ somewhat from temperatures shown by impact-strength tests.

Rudbakh, in experimenting on the tensile strength of iron with 0.04 percent carbon content in the temperature range 800 to 1100°C [306], observed an abrupt decrease in elongation and contraction at Ac_3 (935°C). At 1100°C Armco iron was found to be very ductile (125 percent elongation and 98 percent reduction in area). Studies by Vratsky and Frantsevich on the properties of certain alloyed steels at high temperatures disclosed that, in the zones of critical points, ductility decreases [307]. The same authors consider the β phase as being qualitatively distinct from the α phase. In their opinion this modification should be viewed as a zone which facilitates the transformation of iron into the γ phase [308].

Our experimental data on the effect of temperature on the mechanical properties of Armco iron (0.025 percent carbon) are shown in Fig. 80.

Tests for tensile strength were conducted with the aid of a special device, 8-mm specimens, and a 7-ton machine with a 40-mm working range and a speed of 16 mm/min. Cylindrical specimens (20 mm long and 15 mm in diameter) were used for compression tests. The capacity of the ramming device in dynamic deformation was about 60 kg. Static deformation was effected under the 7-ton load on the same specimens, the experiments being conducted in a furnace. As may be seen in Fig. 80, the curves show that the ranges of blue brittleness and

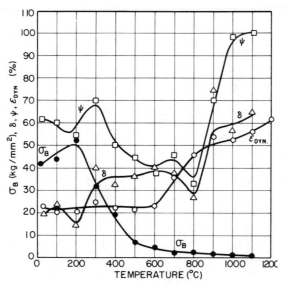

FIG. 80. Mechanical properties of Armco iron at various temperatures.

of hot shortness are characterized by a decrease in ductility and by an increase in strength. Polymorphic transformations in this case are not clearly observed by mechanical testing methods. High values of ductility (the reduction in area reaches 98 to 99 percent at 1000 and 1100°C) and low values of ultimate tensile strength (at 1100°C, $\sigma_B = 1.7$ kg/mm^2) characterize γ iron.

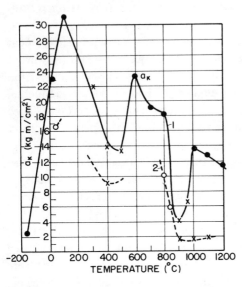

FIG. 81. Effect of temperature on the impact strengths of irons of various purities.

1–pure iron; 2–Armco iron; x–sample fractured.

Ductility curves in dynamic compression rise smoothly with temperature, showing no abrupt dips. This behavior indicates that the physicochemical processes apparently change the condition of the grain boundaries in the temperature range of blue brittleness and hot shortness. These undesirable characteristics are detected only in experiments involving tensile stresses (impact strength, tension) and are not noticed in compression tests.

The impact strength of 99.99-percent-pure iron was compared with that of Armco iron at various temperatures. The specimens were heated and tested in evacuated quartz capsules. Testing was conducted with standard prismatically notched samples. The energy of the impact ram was 30 kg m (Fig. 81, Table 12).

TABLE 12

IMPACT STRENGTH OF IRON AT VARIOUS TEMPERATURES

Temperature (°C)	Impact Strength a_k (kg m/cm^2)		Temperature (°C)	Impact Strength a_k (kg m/cm^2)	
	Pure Iron	Armco Iron		Pure Iron	Armco Iron
−180	2.4	..	650	24.0[a]	....
+20	>24.0	>16[a]	700	19.0	....
100	>31.0[a]	..	800	>18.0[a]	>10.0[a]
200	>36.0[a]	..	850	>15.0[a]	>6.0[a]
300	22.0	..	900	4.0	....
400	14.0	9	950	6.7	1.3
500	13.5	..	1000	>14.0[a]	1.2
550	11.0	..	1050	>12.0[a]	....
600	>23.0[a]	..	1100	>13.0[a]	1.7
			1200	>11.0[a]	....

[a] Specimens were not fractured.

The brittle zones apparently remain, but in pure iron, especially at higher temperatures, the absolute values of impact strength are considerably greater than those of Armco iron.

To conclude, we are submitting here the results of experiments (which we were apparently the first to evaluate) on the magnitude of internal pressure developed in iron specimens as a result of thermal expansion and polymorphic transformation during heating [223]. The universal device for compression experiments (Fig. 82) was used for these tests. Samples were 30 mm long and 15 mm in diameter. After being installed on the 7-ton testing machine (scale, 1400 kg) the device was heated and supporting blocks were placed adjacent to it. By pressing against the punch, the heated expanding sample transmitted the pressure to the load gage of the machine. The punch was made of non-polymorphic material—stainless steel or stellite.

Prior to testing, a dummy run was made to determine the expansion of the punch because of heating. The noted expansion was subsequently subtracted

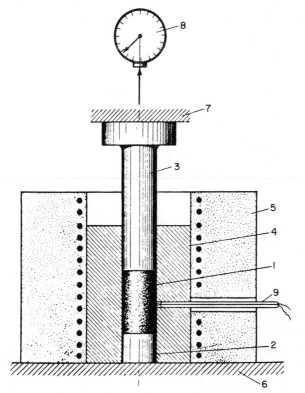

FIG. 82. Schematic illustration of a device for evaluating the internal pressure of metals during heating (Savitsky and Terekhova).

1-sample; 2-anvil; 3-punch; 4-cylinder; 5-electrical furnace; 6-lower supporting block; 7-upper supporting block; 8-load gage; 9-thermocouple.

from the results obtained. On completion
of the experiment, the length of the
sample was usually found to have decreased
by 0.2 to 0.3 mm, with practically no change
in the diameter of its central portion.

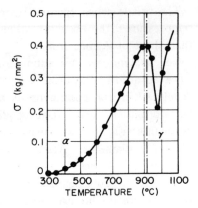

Results on experiments with Armco iron
are presented in Figure 83. The curve has
several regions. The first corresponds to
the pressure observed during heating of the
α phase and rises monotonically up to 920°C;
the maximum value of pressure at 900°C is
0.4 kg/mm². No magnetic transformation is
observed from the slope of the curve. In
the transformation zone $\alpha \rightarrow \gamma$, the internal
pressure shows a decrease of 50 percent
(from 0.4 to 0.2 kg/mm²). The process of

FIG. 83. Effect of temperature on the
magnitude of internal pressure in Armco
iron (sample: $d = 15$ mm; $l = 30$ mm).

expansion of the newly formed γ phase then follows and the magnitude of the
internal pressure increases (up to 0.45 kg/mm²). The slope of the curve is steeper
for the γ phase then for the α phase.

The low absolute magnitude of pressure developed in the specimen is worth
noting. The magnitude of the internal pressure was computed by dividing the
load by the cross-sectional area of the sample. It should be mentioned that,
in this particular case, the pressure magnitude characterizes only the sample
of a given size, because the magnitude of pressure in the heated specimen depends
on its length—the longer the sample the higher the stress. A test run on
Armco–iron samples 20, 40, and 60 mm long showed an analogous slope in the
temperature–pressure curves; the magnitude of the pressure, however, was different for each sample. Pressure may be measured not only during the heating
but also during the cooling process and in compression as well as in tension
testing. For instance, tensile testing with cooled Armco–iron samples (14 mm
in diameter and 100 mm long) showed that during transformation from γ to α
an abrupt increase in internal pressure takes place (from 2 to 15 kg/mm²).

Apparently the technique described above is sensitive and may become one
of the new methods for detecting and accurately evaluating the temperatures
of polymorphic and probably other phase transformations; it may also serve for
evaluating the quantitative magnitudes of internal pressures which develop in
a specimen of a given size. Furthermore, such tests apparently contribute to
the experimental determination of the magnitude of the external pressure (stress)
required for slip or to suppress transformations.

Tamman states that an increase of 1 kg/cm² in pressure will lower the $\gamma \rightarrow \alpha$
transformation temperature by 0.009°C [309]. Roberts-Austen claims that a
4700 kg/cm² pressure will lower the critical temperature of 0.09-percent-carbon

steels to 560°C. Computations show that the pressure required for lowering the critical temperature by 130°C should be approximately 24,000 kg/cm^2; thus the lowered critical point observed by Roberts-Austen is roughly five times greater than that arrived at by calculation [178].

The use of our method to determine internal pressure should yield more precise data. The first requirement is to eliminate all possible thermal expansion of parts of the testing equipment; plastic deformation of the sample and frictional effects against the sides of the cylinder should also be taken into account.

The data obtained should be examined in the light of a strict thermodynamic interpretation. Meanwhile, they should be viewed as being preliminary.

Manganese

In Mendeleyev's periodic table, manganese is classified as a transition element and, like a majority of them, it is allotropic. Zhemchuzhny, in 1906, was the first to discover the polymorphism of manganese [310]. Further studies corroborated the existence of three allotropic modifications—α, β, and γ; these modifications are stable in certain temperature ranges and possess individual crystal structures [38], [311]. According to the latest data available, the α phase is stable below 705°C, the β phase exists between 705 and 1090°C, and the γ phase is stable above 1090°C. Certain authors, after experimenting with alloys of manganese and other elements (copper, palladium, carbon) came to the conclusion that the γ manganese lattice does not remain unchanged to the melting point (1260°C) but transforms into another phase, that of δ manganese [312–315]. The phases, crystal structures, and mechanical properties of manganese are summarized in Table 13.

TABLE 13

PHASES AND THEIR RELATED CRYSTAL STRUCTURES IN MANGANESE

Phase	Crystal Structure	No. of Atoms in Unit Cell [250]	Distance to Nearest Atom (A)	Mechanical Properties
α	Cubic, complex	58	2.24	Brittle
β	Cubic, complex	20	2.37	Semi-brittle
γ	Face-centered-cubic	4	2.67	Ductile
δ	Body-centered-cubic	2	2.90	Ductile

Manganese has a very complex crystal structure. The lattices of the various phases of manganese resemble the crystal structures of a number of intermetallic compounds but not those of pure metals. The lattice of α manganese has a very complex structure which belongs to the cubic system of a 58-atom unit cell (see Fig. 3); such a lattice is similar in structure to those of some intermetallic compounds, of which γ brass is typical. The lattice of β manganese has the complex cubic structure of a 20-atom unit cell similar to that of the

β phase of the Cu–Si alloy system. The face-centered-tetragonal lattice of γ manganese is slightly compressed along the c axis and is analogous to the structure of the compound AuCu, a solid solution of copper and gold [44]. It is considered possible that the γ phase of manganese normally has a face-centered-cubic lattice and that the tetragonal lattice is formed during annealing [316]. The δ phase of manganese crystallizes into a type K8 crystal lattice with a lattice parameter of 3.08 kx [317].

No systematic research has yet been conducted on the effect of temperature on the mechanical properties of pure manganese, probably because of the brittleness of the metal, which greatly hampers the preparation and testing of samples. The brittle behavior of manganese at room temperature is well known. Rolling of samples of vacuum-distilled manganese preheated to 1150°C has been attempted [318]. It has been reported that γ manganese obtained by electrolysis of aqueous solutions is more ductile than α manganese. Apparently γ manganese is stabilized by hydrogen, which is formed in large quantities during the electrolytic process. The conversion of γ manganese into stable α manganese under normal conditions is a slow process (from 14 to 17 days).

Our research was directed toward a systematic study of the influence of temperature on the mechanical properties of manganese. Because impact testing is an exceptionally sensitive method for determining the brittle-to-ductile transition temperature, our main endeavor was to determine the mechanical properties (especially those of ductility) through impact-testing experiments. The impact characteristics examined were the magnitude of contraction, the magnitude of impact toughness, and the type of fracture (brittle or ductile) in the process of impact bending of unnotched samples. The hardness tests were conducted with a pobedit cone having a 90° apex angle.

Electrolytic manganese was used as a starting material. The samples were cast in cylindrical form in preheated metallic molds. The material was melted in a high-frequency electric furnace in corundum crucibles. To prevent cracking, the cast samples were placed in a preheated furnace to cool. Measurements of samples for impact-bending tests were $l = 60$ mm, $d = 9.5$ mm; for impact-compression tests $l = 28$ mm; $d = 18$ mm; and for hardness tests $l = d = 10$ mm. Impact-compression tests were conducted with a vertical drop hammer with 30 kg m capacity. Impact-bending tests were performed by means of a pendulum with a work capacity of 6 kg m. The temperature range was -195 to $+1240$°C.

Experimental data on the mechanical properties of manganese at various temperatures are shown in Fig. 84 and Table 14. The mechanical properties of the α, β, and γ modifications of manganese differ considerably, particularly the α and γ phases. The α manganese has a high degree of hardness (approximately 400 kg/mm^2 at 20°C) and remains brittle in the entire temperature range of its existence. For this reason, even under small impact loads samples of manganese fracture in a brittle fashion not only at low or room temperature but also, for instance, at 700°C.

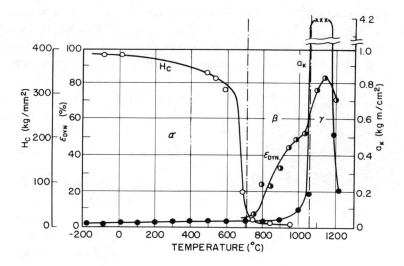

FIG. 84. Effect of temperature on the mechanical properties of manganese.

TABLE 14

EFFECT OF TEMPERATURE ON THE MECHANICAL PROPERTIES OF
ELECTROLYTIC MANGANESE

Temperature (°C)	H_c (kg/mm²)	ε_{dyn} (%)	a_k (kg m/cm²)	Temperature (°C)	ε_{dyn} (%)	a_k (kg m/cm²)
−180	....	....	0.01	1000	47.0	0.10
− 70	388.0	....	0.02	1050	52.0	....
+ 20	384.0	....	0.02	1060	....	0.18
500	336.0	....	....	1080	48.2	4.20
550	324.0	....	....	1120	62.5	4.20[a]
600	300.0	....	....	1140	87.0	4.20[a]
620	....	....	0.02	1150	....	4.20[a]
650	290.0	....	....	1180	72.2	....
700	73.0	....	....	1190	....	0.50
720	....	....	0.03	1200	....	....
750	16.0	5.5	....	1220	....	0.19
800	9.8	25.0	0.03	1240	....	0.03
850	6.6	22.0	....			
900	1.1	32.2	....			
920	....	....	0.04			
950	1.0	44.0	....			
960	....	....	0.04			

[a] Sample did not fracture.

Gamma manganese remains ductile at all temperatures and deforms extensively (up to 90 percent) in impact compression; it does not fracture under impact bending but will plastically deform (Fig. 85). Samples of manganese plastically deformed at elevated temperature often exhibit cracks after cooling as a result of high-compression stresses arising from a decrease in volume during

$\beta \rightarrow \alpha$ transformation (the density of α manganese is 7.46 g/cm³ and that of β manganese is 7.24 g/cm³). As stated by Zhemchuzhny [310] and confirmed by our own findings, the addition of 3.0 percent of copper will produce γ manganese in samples preheated to 1050 to 1100°C and quenched in water at room temperature.

FIG. 85. Manganese sample bent by impact at 1100°C.

We obtained a similar effect in experiments in which Fe, Ni, Cr, Zn, N, Ge, Ca, Ga, Co, and certain other elements were added. Additions of As, Sb, Sn, In, Si, and Al stabilize the β phase of manganese [316].

On the basis of its mechanical properties, the behavior of the β phase lies somewhere between that of the α and γ phases. In the temperature range bordering the α phase, β manganese is predominantly brittle; it is predominantly ductile in the temperature range that borders the γ region. The transformation of $\alpha \rightleftarrows \beta$ is clearly detected by an abrupt decrease in the hardness of the specimens. As mentioned previously, α manganese is characterized by a high degree of hardness, whereas the hardness of β manganese at 750°C is only 16 kg/mm². At higher temperatures its hardness is further decreased—at 950°C it drops to 1 kg/mm². The transformation $\alpha \rightleftarrows \beta$, as measured by other mechanical characteristics, is less distinct because of the extreme brittleness of the samples in this temperature range.

The $\beta \rightleftarrows \gamma$ transformation temperature is clearly observed by the nature of fracture occurring in the samples in impact tests, since the brittle type of fracture in the β-phase region changes into a ductile type of fracture in the γ-phase region (see Fig. 85). Manganese samples at temperatures over 1180 to 1200°C again become brittle. This may be due to the premelting phenomenon and, mainly, to the deterioration of grain boundaries. No δ manganese has been observed in mechanical testing—probably because it exists only over a narrow temperature interval.

Data obtained by our new method (see "iron" in this chapter) for determining the influence of temperature on the internal pressure in manganese are shown in Fig. 86 [223]. The high-temperature polymorphic transformations in manganese appear to be clearly detected by this method. The $\alpha \rightarrow \beta$ effect of the transformation on the value of the internal pressure is not noticeable.

In conclusion it may be stated that those modifications of manganese which have a simpler and a looser structure will become stabilized at elevated temperatures. These structures are typified by having the smallest number of atoms in the unit cell and the greatest distance between atoms. Such changes in the internal structure in single-type lattices lead to a weakening of the interatomic

bonding forces and facilitate their displacement. The increase in the plasticity of
manganese when it is heated is apparently
caused by these structural changes [319].

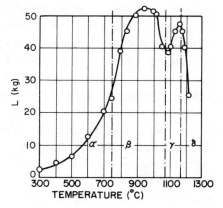

Available data suggest that changes of
internal structure caused by heat do not
apply to manganese alone, but to a number
of other polymorphic metals as well.

Alkali Earth Metals

The alkali earth metals calcium and
strontium belong to the second group of
the periodic table. Their melting temperatures (851°C for Ca and 770°C for Sr)
have not been precisely determined because
of impurities present in these metals. At

FIG. 86. Effect of temperature on the
magnitude of internal pressure in manganese.

room temperature both calcium and strontium have face-centered-cubic structures
whereas at elevated temperatures each metal exhibits two polymorphic transformations: calcium at 350 and 450°C and strontium at 248° and 614°C [320]. The
β phases of calcium and strontium have hexagonal lattices whereas the γ phases
are body centered-cubic (Table 11).

Chemically, calcium and strontium are very close to each other and both are
very active. They are often used as regenerators and getters. The metals
oxidize readily and become covered with white-colored oxides. They should be
kept in inert atmospheres (of argon or helium) or in dehydrated oil.

Calcium and strontium are readily machined or shaped. There are no
published data on the mechanical properties of calcium and strontium at various
temperatures. Such data would be of great interest, however, since the alkali
earth metals are beginning to be widely used in present-day engineering either
as alloys or in pure form. Jointly with Terekhova we have investigated the
hardness and mechanical properties of calcium and of strontium in the temperature range 20 to 800°C (up to 700°C for Sr) at 50°C intervals [247]. Distilled
calcium and cast strontium were used in the tests. The chemical compositions
of the tested metals were:

Analysis of Calcium (percent)		Analysis of Strontium (percent)	
Ca	99.08	Sr	99.93
Fe	4.0×10^{-3}	Fe	1×10^{-2}
Mn	2.2×10^{-3}	Ca	1×10^{-4}
Cu	1.4×10^{-3}	Cu	1×10^{-4}
B	1.3×10^{-5}	Si	5×10^{-3}
W	5.7×10^{-5}	Pd	none found
Cl	2.0×10^{-1}	Zn	5×10^{-2}
Si	6.2×10^{-3}		

Calcium. Samples for testing the hardness of distilled calcium were prepared as follows. They were first extruded at 300°C in a 10-mm steel container under a pressure of 60 to 70 kg/mm^2; the extruded calcium was then further extruded through a 6-mm die. The degree of reduction was 64 percent and the flow stress varied between 30 and 50 kg/mm^2 (depending on the length of the sample). To prevent oxidation argon was pumped into the extrusion chamber. The initial hardness of the material was 13.2 kg/mm^2 whereas the hardness of the deformed material was 17 to 20 kg/mm^2. After extrusion, the samples, sealed in quartz capsules, were annealed at 550°C for 1 hour. The hardness of calcium was evaluated in the universal machine in argon atmosphere by means of a pobedit cone, under a 30-kg load. At high temperatures (500°C and over) the hardness was evaluated by a special device for measuring hardness under light loads (2 to 4 kg). Data on the hardness of calcium in relation to temperature are shown in Table 15.

TABLE 15

HARDNESS OF CALCIUM AT VARIOUS TEMPERATURES

Temperature (°C)	Hardness H_c (kg/mm²)	Temperature (°C)	Hardness H_c (kg/mm²)
20	12.5	400	5.6
50	12.0	450	4.9
100	11.7	500	1.7
150	11.8	550	1.2
200	10.6	600	0.6
250	10.2	650	0.5
300	9.2	700	0.3
350	7.7	800	0.2

The hardness of calcium drops rapidly as a function of temperature. An especially abrupt softening process is observed at temperatures above 500°C.

In the graph illustrating the effect of temperature on the hardness of calcium (Fig. 87a), three straight-line sections, which correspond to the three polymorphic modifications of calcium with various temperature coefficients of hardness, are clearly evident.

Stress–strain experiments were conducted on the fracturing machine with an ultimate load of 100 kg. Special clamps and an electric furnace were devised to conduct the tests for tensile-strength experiments with 3-mm-diameter Gagarin samples. The samples were machined on a jeweler's lathe to a diameter of 3 ± 0.02 mm and a gage length of 15 mm. Argon was used to prevent oxidation of the samples tested. At least 4 or 5 samples were used for each temperature because of variations in the resulting data.

Data obtained are presented in Fig. 87b. The ultimate tensile strength of calcium at room temperature was found to be 5.4 kg/mm^2. The tensile strength increased somewhat (up to 7 kg/mm²) with an increase in temperature up to 100°C and then decreased rapidly as a function of temperature, reaching 0.5 kg/mm² at 500°C. At higher temperatures the tensile strength of calcium remained low with little effect from changes in temperature. An extruded calcium sample did not fracture in a bend test. The lack of ductility in tensile tests of sublimated calcium at 20°C is possibly related to the state of the grain boundaries and requires further study. Nevertheless, α calcium of good quality, with a cubic structure favorable to plastic deformation, should exhibit high ductility. At temperatures up to 300°C, the ductility is increased by approximately 30 percent. In the temperature range 300 to 450°C, the ductility first

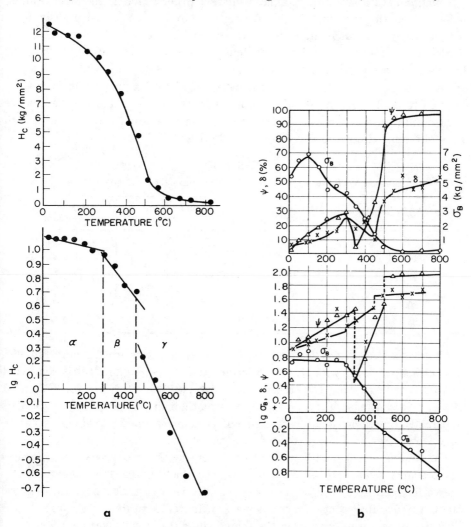

Fig. 87. Influence of temperature on the mechanical properties of calcium.
    a. Hardness.   b. Tensile properties of sublimated calcium.

decreases, then increases again. At 550°C the reduction in area of the specimens is significantly increased, attaining a magnitude of close to 100 percent. The pronounced increase in the ductility of calcium at temperatures above 450°C is explained by the presence of body-centered-cubic γ calcium. The change in shape of the curves of the mechanical properties and ductility of calcium with temperature, as expressed in semilogarithmic coordinates, confirms the presence of two polymorphic transformations in calcium in the 350 to 450°C range (Fig. 87b). An abrupt decrease in the ductility of calcium in the 350 to 450°C range confirms the existence of a more brittle hexagonal phase in this range.

Strontium. Cast-strontium samples were used to determine the metal's hardness, tensile strength, and ductility at fracture. Hardness and tension tests were conducted by the same methods as those used for calcium. Changes in the hardness of strontium in relation to temperature are given in Table 16. The hardness of cast strontium at room temperature is 19 kg/mm²; when the temperature is increased to 250°C, the hardness drops to 6 kg/mm². It is further reduced to 0.2 kg/mm² at 700°C. A logarithmic analysis of the hardness curve of strontium shows three sections, corresponding to its three modifications, with three different temperature coefficients (Fig. 88a).

TABLE 16

EFFECT OF TEMPERATURE ON THE HARDNESS OF CAST STRONTIUM

Temperature (°C)	Hardness H_c (kg/mm²)	Temperature (°C)	Hardness H_c (kg/mm²)
20	19	400	4.80
100	18	450	3.80
200	9	500	4.30
250	6.6	550	0.30
300	6	600	0.25
350	5.0	700	0.20

The mechanical properties of strontium in tension tests are shown in Fig. 88b. The ultimate tensile strength of strontium at 20°C is 5 kg/mm²; it is somewhat increased at 100°C, but the trend is then reversed and it reaches 0.1 kg/mm² at 700°C. The increase in the strength of strontium in the range 100 to 150°C is apparently caused by the superposition of phenomena similar to aging or stabilization processes in alloys and needs further study.

The low values of ductility observed for strontium at ordinary temperatures are probably related to sample defects. The ductility increases up to 450°C; thereafter, and up to 500°C, it is significantly decreased; at temperatures above 500°C the ductility continues to increase with temperature. The drop in the ductility of strontium occurs in the range where the metal takes on a hexagonal structure.

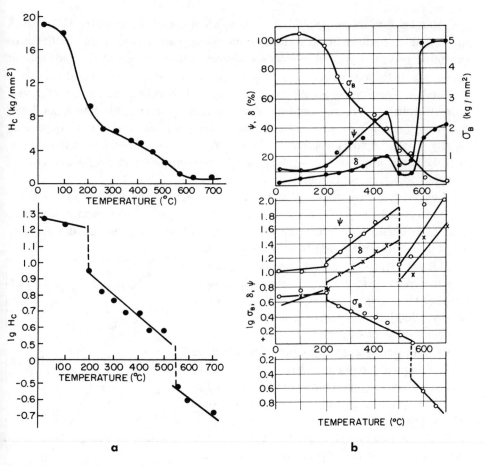

FIG. 88. Effect of temperature on the mechanical properties of cast strontium.
a. Hardness.   b. Tensile properties.

The properties–temperature curves, as expressed in semilogarithmic coordinates, confirm the existence of three modifications in strontium with different temperature coefficients of the mechanical properties (Fig. 88b).

It should be noted that for tension tests of the metals reviewed, reduction of area is a better measure of ductility than elongation.

Thus, changes in mechanical properties caused by high temperature confirm the existence of two polymorphic transformations in calcium and strontium: for calcium 350°C (transformation $\alpha \rightleftarrows \beta$) and 450°C (transformation $\beta \rightleftarrows \gamma$) and for strontium 250°C (transformation $\alpha \rightleftarrows \beta$) and 610°C (transformation $\beta \rightleftarrows \gamma$). In both calcium and strontium an abrupt drop in ductility is observed during the process of transformation into the hexagonal β phase. The high-temperature cubic-γ phases in these metals are very ductile.

Cobalt

Cobalt belongs to the group of metals widely used in industry [321]. It is utilized as a component in solid-solution alloys, cast alloys of the stellite type (up to 60 percent Co), and powder-metallurgy alloys of the "BK" and pobedit types (up to 15 percent Co), as well as in certain heat-resistant alloys [230]. Cobalt has two phases—a close-packed-hexagonal (α cobalt) and a face-centered-cubic (β cobalt). The temperature of the polymorphic transformation, as determined by a number of scientists, varies between 360 and 490°C depending mostly on the impurity content of the samples. Some authors are of the opinion that the transformation temperature also depends on the grain size; a fine-grained sample transforms at higher temperatures.

X-ray studies have shown that the α phase remains unchanged up to 500°C on heating and the β phase down to 300°C on cooling. Under certain conditions it is even possible to detect the presence of both α and β phases at room temperature [289], [322]. Addition of indium [233, p. 115] and of iron stabilizes the cubic phase of cobalt, which is found as a structural constituent down to room temperature.* Because of its high ductility, cobalt is not readily machined at ordinary temperatures.

No quantitative data have been published on the mechanical properties (hardness, strength, and ductility in compression, tension, and impact strength) of cobalt in the temperature range 20 to 1200°C (the melting point of cobalt is 1490°C). For hardness tests, the samples were prepared by remelting cobalt ingots of K2 grade in a high-frequency furnace and by vacuum suction of the molten metal into porcelain containers ($d = 11$ to 12 mm). The rods were then cut into cylinders with parallel ends. Experimental data on hardness are given in Fig. 89 and in Table 17.

It can be seen from Fig. 89 that the hardness of cobalt diminishes rapidly with increasing temperature (from 187 kg/mm^2 at 20°C down to 15 kg/mm^2 at 1100°C). An especially abrupt drop is observed in the temperature range 300 to 450°C; however, a plot of the temperature–hardness data on semilogarithmic coordinates

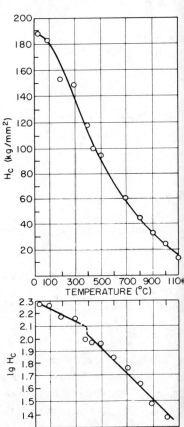

FIG. 89. Effect of temperature on the hardness of cobalt.

---

* See [323] for further information on the influence of alloying on cobalt polymorphism.

TABLE 17
HARDNESS OF COBALT AT VARIOUS TEMPERATURES

Temperature (°C)	Hardness H_c (kg/mm²)	Temperature (°C)	Hardness H_c (kg/mm²)
20	187	700	62
100	182	750	52
200	152	800	47
300	148	850	43
400	117	900	35
450	100	1000	27
500	94	1100	15.2
600	74		

TABLE 18
ULTIMATE STRENGTH AND RELATIVE CONTRACTION OF CAST COBALT IN COMPRESSION AT VARIOUS TEMPERATURES

Temperature (°C)	Ultimate Strength in Compression σ_{compr} (kg/mm²)	Relative Contraction ε_{st} (%)	Type of Fracture
20	70	25	Brittle
200	55	23	Brittle
300	46	26	Brittle
400	57	32	Brittle
450	68	24	Ductile
500	..	48	Ductile
600	68	34	Ductile
700	..	47 ⎫	Samples did
800	..	44 ⎪	not frac-
900	..	67 ⎩	ture under a
1000	..	81 ⎭	6-ton load

TABLE 19
MECHANICAL PROPERTIES OF CAST COBALT IN TENSION AT VARIOUS TEMPERATURES

Temperature (°C)	Ultimate Strength σ_B (kg/mm²)	Relative Elongation δ_5 (%)	Reduction in Area ψ (%)
20	13.0	2.5	2.0
300	8.0	2.5	2.1
400	10.0	4.6	6.5
500	9.1	3.4	4.2
600	4.5	4.0	4.0
700	3.6	2.7	4.0
800	1.4	5.3	1.3

TABLE 20
IMPACT STRENGTH OF COBALT AT VARIOUS TEMPERATURES

Temperature (°C)	Impact Strength a_k (kg m/cm²)	Temperature (°C)	Impact Strength a_k (kg m/cm²)
20	0.9	450	2.6
200	0.9	500	3.2
300	4.6	700	1.1
350	6.2	900	0.75
400	1.8		

shows a discontinuity that corresponds to the $\alpha \to \beta$ transformation of cobalt. The temperature coefficient of hardness in the range 20 to 300°C is -3.6×10^{-4}, whereas that observed in the range 400 to 1000°C is -1.6×10^{-4}.

Compression experiments were performed with samples measuring 10 mm in diameter and 11 mm in length and machined out of cast cobalt. The samples were compressed on a 35-ton hydraulic press; the tests were terminated at the sign of the first crack (Table 18).

The tests showed that with an increase in temperature the ultimate strength of cobalt diminishes at first, then begins to rise after reaching the β-phase region. At 450°C the brittle type of fracture changes to a ductile one. In spite of their high ductility at 1000°C (80-percent reduction in length) the samples deformed the steel platen, indicating their high strength. Under compression impact (work capacity of 15 kg m) the samples fractured in a brittle manner below 400°C and in a ductile manner above 400°C.

The Gagarin press was used for testing cobalt samples of 3-mm diameter, 15-mm gage length. Testing was done with the aid of a reverser placed in a tubular furnace. No experiments were conducted at temperatures over 800°C because heat above that level caused deformation in the reverser itself. Data obtained are shown in Table 19 and Fig. 90.

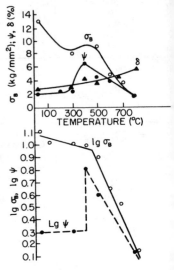

FIG. 90. Effect of temperature on the mechanical properties of cast cobalt.

In the entire temperature range, low absolute values of the mechanical properties were observed in the tension tests. At 400°C the mechanical-properties–temperature curve of cobalt shows an inflection which is related to the polymorphic transformation of the metal.

Experimental results on tests for impact strength of 10-mm cylindrical notched samples (2-mm circular notch) are presented in Table 20, in which two maxima are observed in the impact-strength–temperature relationship of cast cobalt, one at 350°C and the other at 500°C. The minimum at 400°C is apparently related to the allotropic transformation.

A comparison of the experimental data obtained at various temperatures on cast cobalt points to the fact that the properties undergo an abrupt change in the temperature range 350 to 400°C. This change in the mechanical properties is related to the polymorphic transformation of cobalt occurring in the same temperature range. Cobalt, with a stable hexagonal phase up to 350°C, has a brittle type of fracture. The ductile behavior of cobalt corresponds to the cubic phase of the metal. We were unable to ascertain the exact temperature of the polymorphic transformation because the $\alpha \to \beta$ transition occurs in the temperature range 350 to 450°C in which these two phases may exist simultaneously.

Lanthanum

Lanthanum, which belongs to the rare-metals group, is used as an alloying element in various alloys—aluminum, magnesium, copper, and others. It may exist in two allotropic forms: a close-packed-hexagonal α phase and a face-centered-cubic β phase. The transformation $\alpha \rightleftarrows \beta$ occurs in the temperature range 600 to 700°C and its melting point is above 800°C [231]. The exact melting temperature and the exact allotropic-transformation temperature for lanthanum have not been determined because of impurities present in the metal tested.

Nothing has been published on the physicomechanical properties of lanthanum at elevated temperatures. Since lanthanum will easily oxidize in air, even at ordinary temperatures, experiments with the metal should be conducted in protective atmospheres. We used microsamples for testing the mechanical properties. Hardness and the mechanical properties were evaluated in the temperature range 20 to 800°C by means of static and impact compression, by extrusion, and by tests for strength and ductility in tension. The purity of the metal used in the first experiments was about 99.0 percent. The impurities found were: 0.1 percent Fe, 0.01 percent Mg, 0.01 percent Pb, 0.1 percent Si, and 0.08 percent Al. A microstructural analysis indicated the presence of blue-gray impurities on the basic background of polyhedral grains. Unfortunately the original supply of the metal had a considerable amount of impurities, mainly cerium.

Testing was performed with the universal device in an argon atmosphere (see Fig. 46). The evaluation of hardness was done with a pobedit cone under an 80-kg load in the temperature range 20 to 800°C at 50° intervals. Hardness tests were conducted with samples immersed in heated oil up to 200°C. The samples were made from sections of cast coupons.

In order to perform experiments in compression, samples were first tested for hardness, then remelted for specimen preparation. The original specimens were 4.5 mm in height and 3 mm in diameter. Remelting was accomplished under a layer of calcium chloride. The dynamic-compression test was conducted on a vertical-impact testing machine with a work capacity of 1.5 kgm. The samples were heated in an argon stream in an electric muffle furnace. No experiments were attempted at temperatures above 600°C as the samples oxidized badly. Sample sizes were $h = 6$ mm and $d = 5$ mm.

Experiments were conducted on extruding lanthanum. Cold extrusion of lanthanum was attempted at a flow stress of 90 kg/mm² but the sample crumbled upon leaving the die. Extrusion was also performed at 700°C, which proved to be the most favorable temperature. The samples were extruded from 7-mm to 3-mm diameter (80 percent reduction) under a load of 250 to 300 kg, at which point the yield stress was approximately 10 kg/mm². The samples came out with a clean and even surface. Extrusion tests of lanthanum samples from 2- to 1-mm diameter were also performed at 500, 600, and 700°C. Samples (wires) obtained were 15 to 20-mm long and of a satisfactory quality. Microfracture specimens were machined on a lathe with paraffin continuously spread on the

TABLE 21

MECHANICAL PROPERTIES OF LANTHANUM AT VARIOUS TEMPERATURES

Temperature (°C)	Hardness H_c (kg/mm²)	Relative Contraction		Ultimate Compression Strength σ_{compr} (kg/mm²)	Flow Stress (at 75% deformation) (kg/mm²)	Ultimate Tensile Strength σ_B (kg/mm²)	Elongation δ (%)	Reduction in Area ψ (%)
		ε_{st} (%)	ε_{dyn} (%)					
20	38.0	10.0	37.5	29.0^a	....	7.1	2.0	4.0
50	36.0	....	....	....	....	....	....	....
100	34.5	13.5	....	....	....	....	....	....
150	33.5	....	....	....	....	....	....	....
200	33.0	12.6	37.0	22.2^a	....	9.0	3.0	6.3
250	28.0	....	....	....	....	....	....	....
300	28.0	13.3	41.0	....	....	11.7	2.0	5.0
350	24.0	....	....	15.5^a	....	8.4	3.0	4.3
400	24.6	17.7	63.0	....	....	12.4	3.0	4.4
450	22.9	....	....	....	....	10.8	3.0	5.8
500	22.6	38.2	64.0	....	13.2	10.0	3.0	6.0
550	16.3	....	....	....	....	9.6	4.0	5.1
600	10.0	44.5	90.0	....	19.1	11.2	4.0	8.1
650	8.9	....	....	....	....	3.8	10.5	32.0
700	6.9	75.5	....	....	22.1	3.2	12.3	40.0
800	3.6	82.0	....	....	....	2.8	8.0	20.0

^{a} For samples measuring $d = h = 1$ mm cut from extruded wire.

surface of the specimen; the samples measured 2 mm in diameter with a gage length of 10 mm.

Experimental data on the mechanical properties of lanthanum are presented in Table 21 and in Fig. 91a. The hardness of lanthanum decreases from 38 kg/mm² at room temperature to 3.6 kg/mm² with temperatures at 800°C. A rapid decrease in hardness and in the ultimate tensile strength is observed at temperatures above 600°C. At temperatures up to 400°C, the ultimate tensile strength of lanthanum tends to increase (see Table 21) probably because of the presence of impurities and possibly because of an aging phenomenon.

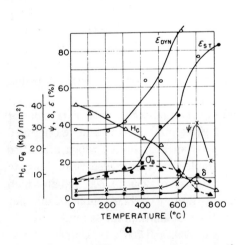

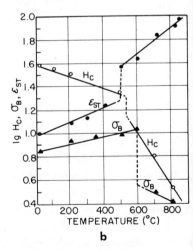

FIG. 91. Effect of temperature on the mechanical properties of lanthanum.

To determine the ultimate strength in static compression, the purer samples of lanthanum (1 × 1 mm) were deformed to fracture. The maximum deformation did not exceed 40 percent in the temperature interval 20 to 350°. All lanthanum samples deformed by static and dynamic compression in the α range fractured in a brittle manner. At temperatures above 500°C they did not fracture.

Data on the ductility of less-pure lanthanum at a constant load (140 kg) or at a constant power capacity in compression (i.e., where the samples were not tested to the fracturing point) are given in Table 21 and in Fig. 91a.

A comparatively slight increase in the ductility of lanthanum is observed at temperatures up to 500°C. An abrupt increase in this property is noticed in the 500 to 600°C interval. Maximum ductility is reached in the 700°C region, which corresponds to results obtained in compression tests for the metal. This condition corresponds to β lanthanum. Ductility decreases in tension tests at temperatures above 750°C; this result is probably related to grain-boundary weakening caused by premelting phenomena.

A summary of the data on the effect of temperature on the mechanical properties of lanthanum suggests that the hexagonal modification of lanthanum possesses limited ductility that increases with temperature; however, in this state the samples fracture by cleavage at a 45 deg angle. Because of impurities, the allotropic transformation occurs over a range of temperature and is accompanied by an abrupt increase in ductility.

A logarithmic analysis enables one to observe abrupt changes in the temperature–mechanical-properties curves in the 500 to 600°C range (Fig. 91b) and confirms that in this range the polymorphic transformation of lanthanum occurs. The temperature coefficients of the mechanical properties of lanthanum are given in Table 22. The conclusions derived from the mechanical experiments are confirmed by data obtained in a thermal analysis (Fig. 92).

The high-temperature cubic modification of lanthanum is extremely plastic.

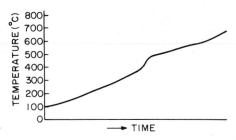

FIG. 92. Heating curve for lanthanum.

TABLE 22

TEMPERATURE COEFFICIENTS OF THE MECHANICAL PROPERTIES OF LANTHANUM

Property	Temperature Coefficient	
	20 to 500°C	600 to 800°C
Hardness	-4.47×10^{-3}	-2.22×10^{-2}
Ultimate tensile strength	-3.4×10^{-2}	-5.8×10^{-3}
Relative contraction in static compression	6.5×10^{-3}	1.11×10^{-2}

In this state, lanthanum may be subjected to any deformation, provided, of course, that adequate protection from oxidation is maintained.

It would be expedient to determine what elements could stabilize the cubic β phase at ordinary temperatures. Studies of the effects of very low temperatures on the polymorphism of lanthanum would also be desirable. Lanthanum is analogous to cerium, which, in tests at extremely low temperatures, exhibits a new crystalline structure.

Cerium

Cerium is used as an alloying element in magnesium and copper alloys to increase their heat resistance [324]. Cerium may also be used as a modifying agent for cast irons and steels and for chromium- and titanium-base alloys.

Because pure cerium is difficult to produce, its melting point varies widely (830, 815, 800, 775, 650, 630, and 600°C). The higher the purity the higher the melting point [325], [326]. All experiments should be conducted in protective atmospheres because cerium oxidizes readily.

Cerium is temperature allotropic—at about 450°C, it changes from a hexagonal to a face-centered-cubic phase [236]. Because of impurities in the metal, the exact temperature of transformation is still unknown.

According to Bridgman et al. [327–329], the volume of cerium decreases abruptly by 16.5 percent under hydrostatic compression at 15,000 atmospheres this effect does not occur if the cerium contains approximately 0.2 percent iron. It is known that cerium also shows an abrupt decrease in volume (about 10 percent at low temperatures (about −183°C) [330], [331]. Both instances of volume decrease occur with the appearance of the face-centered-cubic structure. This modification, however, is not carried out to completion and the new cubic phase exists simultaneously with the usual hexagonal phase of cerium. Under pressure both modifications show a decrease in their lattice parameters.

Keeping in mind the structural analogy of electronic shells, we believe it is reasonable to assume that similar changes in the crystalline structure will typically be caused by pressure or by low temperature, in some of the other rare-earth elements.

Data on the mechanical properties of cerium at elevated temperatures have not been published until now. We ran tests on the mechanical properties of cerium microsamples (hardness, ductility, and deformation resistance in slow compression and tension) at temperatures in the 20 to 600°C range. Testing was conducted with a universal microdevice in an argon atmosphere (see Fig. 46). The device was loaded on the Gagarin press and the results were recorded on a chart. The hardness was measured with a pobedit cone at 60-kg load. Cylindrical samples 5 mm in both length and diameter were used in static-compression tests. Microfracture specimens were of 2-mm diameter and 10-mm gage length. The experimental data (Table 23, Fig. 93a) reveal a retardation of the softening process in the range 100 to 300°C; the ultimate compression strength remains almost constant up to 350°C, while the ultimate tensile strength

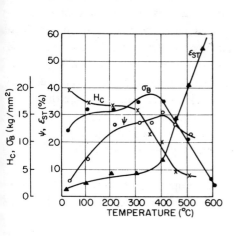 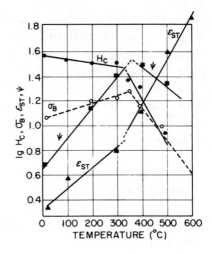

FIG. 93.   Effect of temperature on the mechanical properties of cerium.

shows a slight increase in the 20 to 350°C range.   The latter was probably caused
by an aging phenomenon, as the purity of the cerium samples was not high (97.1
percent cerium with impurities consisting mainly of other rare-earth elements).
In compression tests up to 350°C the ductility of the metal exhibits only slight
changes; it increases rapidly above 400°C and the samples remain unfractured
at 600°C with a relative contraction of 75 percent.   A 5-percent reduction in
area is observed in tensile fracture at 20°C; it is 32 percent at 400°C.   At higher
temperature the ductility decreases slightly, probably as a result of weakening
of the grain boundaries.

The brittle type of fracture, occurring in the range 20 to 350°C, is common
to the hexagonal-type metals to which α cerium belongs.   At temperatures

TABLE 23

MECHANICAL PROPERTIES OF CERIUM AT VARIOUS TEMPERATURES

Temperature (°C)	Hardness H_c (kg/mm²)	Compression			Tension		
		Ultimate Strength σ_{compr} (kg/mm²)	Relative Contraction ε_{st} (%)	Type of Fracture	Ultimate Strength σ_B (kg/mm²)	Reduction in Area (%)	Type of Fracture
20	38.0	29.5	33	Cleavage at 45° angle	12.0	5.0	Cleavage at 45° angle
100	35.0	30.6	31	Same	16.5	14.0	Same
200	34.5	30.6	31	Same	16.0	27.5	Same
300	34.0	33.0	40	Same	17.5	27.5	Same
350	24.0	....	50	Same	19.2	27.5	Ductile
400	22.0	29.0	38	Same	15.3	32.0	Same
450	9.5	40.0	60	Plastic deformation	14.6	28.0	Same
500	9.5	....	..	Same	11.4	23.5	Same
600	....	....	75	Same	4.8	....	Same

above 350°C it fractures in a ductile fashion, as do most metals of cubic symmetry. Because of the inhibiting action of impurities, the polymorphic transformation occurs over a temperature range. Changes observed in the mechanical-properties–temperature curve and in the type of fracture indicate that the polymorphic transformation in cerium occurs in the range 350 to 400°C. This observation is verified by the data presented in Fig. 93*b*, in which the mechanical-properties–temperature curve for cerium is plotted on semilogarithmic coordinates. In the 350 to 400°C temperature range an abrupt break is observed in the curves showing the change in the properties of cerium [332].

The temperature coefficients of the mechanical properties of α and β cerium are shown in Table 24.

Further study is required on the mechanical properties of cerium at low temperatures. It would be of interest to find elements which could stabilize the more ductile β cerium.

TABLE 24

TEMPERATURE COEFFICIENTS OF THE MECHANICAL PROPERTIES OF CERIUM

Properties	Temperature Coefficient	
	20–350°C	400–660°C
Hardness	-1.78×10^{-4}	-1.75×10^{-2}
Ultimate strength in compression	$-3 \quad \times 10^{-4}$	....
Ultimate tensile strength	-6.37×10^{-3}	-2.5×10^{-2}
Relative contraction	5.46×10^{-3}	....
Reduction in area in tension	2.24×10^{-2}	1.3×10^{-2}

Praseodymium

Praseodymium, like the other rare-earth metals of the cerium subgroup, is dimorphic. The polymorphic transformation (G12 $\rightleftarrows$ K12) occurs at 600°C (see Table 11). No data on the mechanical properties of praseodymium at various temperatures have previously been published.

Jointly with Terekhova, we conducted tests on the hardness, ultimate strength, and ductility in compression of praseodymium in the range 20 to 800°C. The tested metal had a considerable content of lanthanum and cerium (the praseodymium content was 90 percent). Experimental data are summarized in Table 25.

The hardness of praseodymium drops rapidly above 300°C. The ultimate strength in compression undergoes similar changes starting at 400°C. The ductility of praseodymium in compression increases rapidly at temperatures above 600°C, at which face-centered-cubic β phase is formed. In the 700 to 800°C interval, ε_{st} constitutes 80 to 90 percent of the decrease in the height of the specimen in a single stage. The nature of the fracture of praseodymium varies; α samples (with a hexagonal lattice) fracture by cleavage at a 45 deg angle, whereas β samples fracture in a ductile fashion by cracking along the edges in the process of compressing the disks.

TABLE 25

MECHANICAL PROPERTIES OF PRASEODYMIUM AT VARIOUS TEMPERATURES

Temperature (°C)	Hardness H_c (kg/mm²)	Compression Characteristics	
		Ultimate Strength σ_{compr} (kg/mm²)	Relative Contraction ε_{st} (%)
20	39.0	33	18
100	38.5	35	..
200	35.0	32	29
300	34.0	23	36
400	23.0	23	36
500	14.0	16	..
600	12.0	6	47
700	7.0	2	82
800	....	..	89

Titanium

According to recent data, the melting temperature of titanium, determined by the approximate conditions of an absolute black body, is found to be 1660 ± 10°C [333]. Titanium is dimorphic; at 885°C, the hexagonal close-packed phase is transformed into a body-centered-cubic one. This change substantially alters the properties of the metal. The density of α titanium = 4.5 g/cm³ and that of β titanium = 4.3 g/cm³ [231]. A coexistence of α and β phases is observed in impure titanium after quenching. In pure titanium the $\beta \rightarrow \alpha$ transformation temperature decreases as the rate of cooling is increased. The α titanium stabilizing elements dissolve in pure titanium more readily than in β titanium. To this group belong all elements with a small atomic radius—namely O, N, C, B, and among the metals (which are exceptions) Al and Ce. A large majority of metals—including Cr, Mn, Fe, Ni, and Mo—as well as H stabilize the β phase of titanium; in other words they dissolve in it with greater ease than in α titanium [334]. The solubility of chemical elements in titanium was studied in great detail by Kornilov [335–337] and by other authors.

Because of it is light weight, high melting point, and corrosion-resisting properties, titanium is widely used in shipbuilding and in aviation. A great future is seen for heat-resistant and structural titanium alloys in the aircraft industry. Metallic titanium is produced now by reduction of tetrachlorous titanium, by the process of molten magnesium, or by the calcium-hydride method; it may also be produced by thermal dissociation of tetraiodide titanium in vacuum and by condensing the metallic titanium on a red-hot wire. Titanium produced by the last-named method is called iodide titanium and is the purest available.

A characteristic feature of titanium is its affinity for oxygen and its ability to interact actively with nitrogen, hydrogen, carbon, and carbon-containing gases [338].

It has been found by X-ray analysis that the mechanism of plastic deformation at room temperature for α titanium differs from that for other metals with hexagonal close-packed structures (Cd, Zn, and Mg). In addition to slip along the basal plane of α titanium, slip along two other planes is observed: on the $(10\bar{1}0)$ prism plane and on the $(10\bar{1}1)$ pyramidal plane. Twinning occurs not only along the (1012) pyramidal plane but also along the (1121) and (1122) planes. The slip direction is the same as in other hexagonal metals, along the diagonal [1120] axis [339], [340]. This deviation in the behavior of titanium is explained by the smaller value of the c/a ratio in the unit cell in contrast to the ideal value of 1.633. Thus the distance between basal planes in titanium is not a maximum one. The presence of nine possible slip systems and 18 possible twinning planes insures high ductility for highly pure titanium at ordinary temperatures. Additives (oxygen, nitrogen, and others) inhibit some of the slip planes and increase the critical shear stress [341]. With an increase in temperature the amount of twinning in titanium diminishes and slip disappears along the basal plane but increases on the pyramidal plane. The recrystallization temperature for titanium is in the 500 to 700°C range, depending on the method and on the degree of cold working [231]. Ageyev and Babareko reveal that the recrystallization of titanium deformed by 86 and 88 percent does not result in a change or a disappearance of the rolling texture [342].

The properties of titanium are closely related to its purity, to the method of extraction, and to the mechanical and thermal processing techniques. The

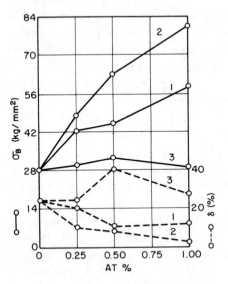

FIG. 94. Effect of impurity content— oxygen (1), nitrogen (2), and hydrogen (3) —on the mechanical properties of titanium.

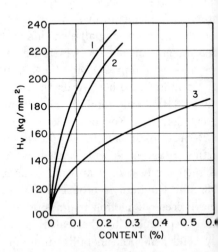

FIG. 95. Effect of nitrogen (1), oxygen (2), and carbon (3) on the hardness of cast titanium.

TABLE 26

MECHANICAL PROPERTIES OF TITANIUM AT ROOM TEMPERATURE

Properties	Iodide-Annealed Titanium (99.9%)	Industrial-Annealed Titanium (99.5%)
Brinell hardness (kg/mm²)	100.0	200-220
Vickers hardness (kg/mm²)	80-90	....
Ultimate tensile strength (kg/mm²)	32.2	56.0
Yield point (kg/mm²)	15.0	51.0
Proportional limit (kg/mm²)	7.0	26.0
Elongation (%)	50.0	25.0
Modulus of elasticity (kg/mm²)	9800-10,800	11,500.0
Contraction (%)	75.0	....

mechanical properties of the metal are extremely sensitive to the above variables (Figs. 94 and 95 of [231], [335] and [343], Table 26). It was found in 1954 that even a negligible content of hydrogen produces a sharp decrease in the ductility of titanium at the expense of formation of titanium hydride layers, in the shape of sheets, which develop between the grains of titanium [344].

Titanium is twice as strong as pure iron and nearly six times as strong as pure aluminum [231]. Yet the modulus of elasticity of titanium is only 30 percent greater than that of pure aluminum and nearly half the elastic modulus of iron. The elastic modulus may be increased by alloying titanium with other elements. Figure 96 shows the ratio of hardness to the ultimate tensile strength of titanium obtained by various methods [231]. In 1954, data were published in Russia regarding the influence of temperature on the mechanical properties of industrial titanium with varying carbon content [345]. Data on titanium with a 0.46 to 0.66 percent content are shown in Fig. 97. Industrial titanium exhibits low ductility at low temperatures; furthermore, the ductilities of different samples were found to be dissimilar, probably because of variations in the impurity content. At temperatures above 700°C, regardless of its carbon content

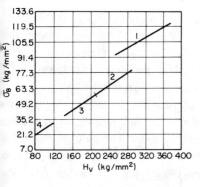

FIG. 96. Correlation between hardness and strength of titanium under various test methods.
1-forged and air cooled; 2-melted in an induction furnace after rolling and annealing; 3-melted in an arc furnace, hot-rolled, and annealed; 4-iodide titanium.

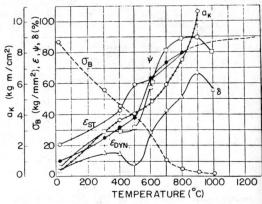

FIG. 97. Effect of temperature on the ductility of titanium melted in a resistance furnace (Sokolov, Eliutin, Zalessky).

within the 0.46 to 0.88 percent range, titanium is highly ductile under various rates of deformation.

We are citing here the experimental results (obtained in cooperation with Tylkina) on the effect of temperature on ductility and resistance to deformation observed by us in two types of titanium—the carbon-free type prepared by powder-metallurgy methods and the carbonized, remelted type. Briquets of 20 by 20 by 100 mm of the first type, with an impurity content of 0.2 percent Si, 0.11 percent Fe, 0.1 percent Ca, and 0.1 percent Mg were extruded at 900°C through a die causing 64 percent deformation. Samples for mechanical testing were cut out of the deformed rods and were subjected to diffusion annealing in evacuated quartz capsules at 850°C for three hours. The flow stress of titanium, 82 kg/mm² at 620°C, dropped to 29.3 kg/mm² at 900°C and reached 8 kg/mm² at 1050°C (Fig. 98). These data define the temperature of the polymorphic transformation of titanium as 880°C. The temperature coefficient of the flow stress in the β phase of titanium is -3.8×10^{-3} and is greater than the corresponding temperature coefficient of α titanium, which is -16×10^{-3}. This difference indicates the tendency of β titanium to soften. That β titanium is extremely plastic (as indicated by its crystalline structure) is confirmed by data obtained from tension experiments (Fig. 99).

The properties of cast titanium contaminated by carbon (0.5 to 0.8 percent during the process of melting in graphite crucibles were studied on annealed samples made of forged rods. Impurities of titanium carbide were observed in the microstructure. As shown in Fig. 100, carbon increases the hardness of titanium, especially at relatively low temperatures. The effect of alloying with carbon disappears above 700°C; the hardness of titanium at 1000°C is less than 10 kg/mm². Cylindrical samples of 10-mm diameter and length were studied in compression tests run with a 35-ton hydraulic press. The rate of motion of the press was 100 mm per minute. The carbon content caused an increase of ultimate strength in compression at 20°C from 159 kg/mm² for carbon-free tita

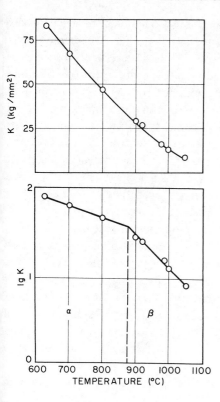

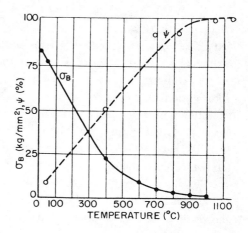

FIG. 98.   Effect of temperature on the flow stress for carbon-free titanium.

FIG. 99.   Effect of temperature on the mechanical properties of carbon-free titanium in tension.

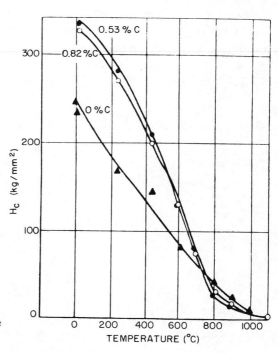

FIG. 100.   Effect of temperature on the hardness of titanium.

nium, to 242 to 254 kg/mm^2 for titanium containing 0.53 to 0.82 percent carbon. The maximum deformation at 20°C for carbon-free titanium is 30 percent, whereas for titanium with 0.53 to 0.82 percent carbon it is 15 percent. True-stress curves in compression under isothermal conditions for both types of titanium are presented in Fig. 101. These data were obtained by methods described in Chapter 2 of this book. In compression tests of titanium at temperatures below 600°C, it was observed that approximately twice the stress is required for achieving a certain degree of deformation of titanium with a 0.5 to 0.8 percent carbon content than for carbon-free titanium. For example, at 50 percent deformation the required stresses were 61 and 132.5 kg/mm^2 for carbon-free titanium and titanium containing 0.82 percent C, respectively. Above 700°C, both types of titanium are easily deformed at low and roughly equal loads apparently because of recrystallization during the deformation process. At higher temperatures, because of the formation of the β phase, titanium becomes very ductile and its resistance to deformation becomes very low [346]. We plotted a diagram demonstrating the recrystallization of iodide titanium (Fig. 102); it shows that, in cold-deformed and annealed titanium, the line for initiation of recrystallization shifts toward the lower annealing temperatures in proportion to the decrease in deformation. At 700°C, recrystallization is first observed when the sample reaches 2.5 percent deformation; at 600°C, it is observed at 5 percent. At 500°C, the samples are completely recrystallized on reaching 50 percent deformation [347]. These data on recrystallization of industrial titanium have been published by us [348–350].

In conclusion, we submit here our recent experimental data on the mechanical properties of iodide titanium at various temperatures (Table 27). The external appearance of iodide titanium samples after undergoing mechanical testing is shown in Fig. 103 [351]. An outstanding feature of iodide titanium is its high ductility at ordinary and low temperatures.

TABLE 27

MECHANICAL PROPERTIES OF IODIDE TITANIUM AT VARIOUS TEMPERATURES

Temperature (°C)	Hardness H_c (kg/mm^2)	Yield Point $\sigma_{0.2}$ (kg/mm^2)	Ultimate Tensile Strength σ_B (kg/mm^2)	Elongation δ (%)	Reduction in Area ψ (%)
−196	200	43.9	63.0	11.6	28.0
+ 20	132	15.4	25.0	50.0	78.0
100	131	....	....	....	....
200	121	10.4	13.8	38.3	66.0
300	99	....	....	....	....
400	79	11.8	13.2	26.7	55.4
500	78	....	....	....	....
600	61	3.9	7.3	35.0	72.5
700	31	....	....	....	....
800	18	....	1.5	61.6	88.7
900	13	....	....	....	....
1000	8	....	0.4	73.0	95.0

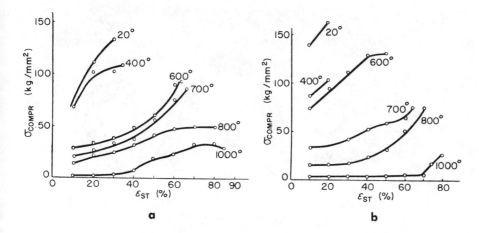

FIG. 101   True-stress compression curves for titanium at various temperatures.
a. Carbon free.   b. With 0.82 percent carbon.

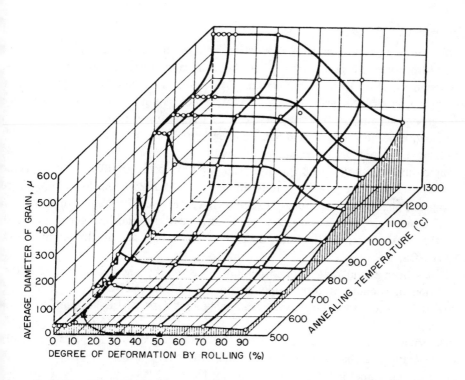

FIG. 102.   Recrystallization diagram for iodide titanium after cold rolling and
annealing (Savitsky, Tylkina, Turanskaya).

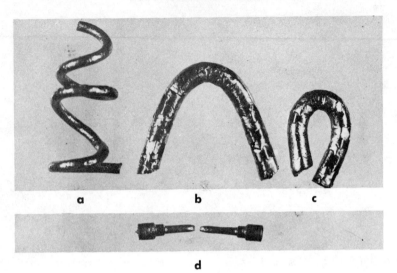

FIG. 103. Iodide titanium samples after undergoing mechanical testing (full scale).
a. Spiral bending of a 3.5-mm-diameter wire at 20°C. *b*. Sample subjected to impact
bending at −196°C. *c*. Sample bent in a vise at 20°C. *d*. Sample after a tensile
test at 20°C.

Zirconium

Zirconium is a rare metal. Production of pure zirconium is impeded not only
by its high melting point but also by its chemical activity at high temperatures,
its tendency to form stable compounds with a number of metals, and its tendency
to absorb gases. Nevertheless this metal, which has high corrosion resistance
and good mechanical properties at elevated temperature, is increasingly used in
industry, especially in the field of atomic energy [352]. Yet zirconium (especially
its alloys) has not been adequately studied.

Zirconium is similar to titanium. Its melting point is 1857°C; its specific
gravity is 6.5. Like titanium, it is dimorphic. At 862°C, the low-temperature
hexagonal phase is transformed into the body-centered-cubic phase. In the $\alpha \to \beta$
transformation, the transformation planes are (0001) for the hexagonal and (110)
for the cubic lattice [353]. The most common impurities in zirconium are O,
N, Hf, Ca, Fe, and Ti.

It has been found that pure zirconium obtained by the iodide method (dissociation in vacuum of tetraiodide zirconium and deposition of pure zirconium
on a red-hot tungsten wire) possesses technological properties similar to those
of copper [266].

Deformation and annealing textures of iodide zirconium are symmetrically
oriented and are characterized by the disposition of the basal planes at a ±40°
angle to the plane and direction of rolling [353].

The hardness of zirconium is directly related to its oxygen content [231], as shown below. The hardness test method could be recommended, therefore, for estimating the oxygen content of zirconium.

Oxygen Content (%)	0.0	0.1	0.2	0.3
Hardness H_B (kg/mm²)	100	200	250	300

Published data indicate that zirconium purified by the iodide method, after being forged and annealed at 790°C, possesses the following mechanical properties in tension [231]: $\sigma_B = 25.3$ kg/mm²; $\sigma_{0\,2} = 11.3$ kg/mm²; $\delta = 26$ percent; $\psi = 32$ percent; normal elastic modulus $E = 8000$ kg/mm²; and $H_B = 67$ kg/mm². Published data on the physicomechanical properties of zirconium as a function of temperature are very limited. Table 28 shows published data on the mechanical properties of industrial zirconium (99.7 percent Zr) at 20°C [354]. The experimental data we obtained on the effect of temperature on the mechanical properties of iodide zirconium are given in Table 29 [355].

TABLE 28

MECHANICAL PROPERTIES OF TECHNICAL ZIRCONIUM AT ROOM TEMPERATURE

Form of Zirconium	Ultimate Strength σ_B (kg/mm²)	Yield Point $\sigma_{0.2}$ (kg/mm²)	Proportional Limit (kg/mm²)	Elongation δ (%)	Elastic Modulus (kg/mm²)	Rockwell Hardness R_B
Rolled	~58.6	~49.0	22.6	18	10,250	87.4
Cast	25.0	11.1	6.0	31	7,650	30.3

TABLE 29

EFFECT OF TEMPERATURE ON THE MECHANICAL PROPERTIES OF IODIDE ZIRCONIUM

Temperature (°C)	Hardness H_c (kg/mm²)	Yield Point $\sigma_{0.2}$ (kg/mm²)	Ultimate Strength σ_B (kg/mm²)	Reduction of Area ψ (%)	Remarks
20	88.0	12.0	28.0	43	
100	70.0	11.0	22.0	50	
200	60.0	9.0	20.0	63	
300	48.0	7.0	19.0	67	Data on elongation were obtained from samples with notched heads. Sample diameter, 5 mm; gage length, 25 mm. The samples were annealed at 800°C for 1 hour.
400	37.5	5.5	16.0	80	
500	36.5	4.5	15.0	87	
600	30.0	4.5	12.0	92	
700	15.0	...	8.0	95	
800	10.5	...	3.0	93	
850	9.0	...	2.5	92	
900	4.0	...	3.0	92	
1000	2.0	...	1.0	96	

It is noteworthy that, in impact bend tests, even notched samples of iodide zirconium ($\phi = 10$ mm) at 20 and at $-196°C$ (as in the case of iodide titanium) did not fracture but displayed plastic bending.

The plasticity characteristics under tension vary irregularly. At 20°C, the reduction in area is 43 percent and increases abruptly with a rise in temperature; however, again at 20°C the elongation does not exceed 15 percent and at 900°C reaches only 40 percent.

With a rise in temperature the ultimate strength of iodide zirconium is noticeably lowered—at 1000°C it is only 1 kg/mm^2.

The curve of mechanical property versus temperature, described in semilogarithmic coordinates, clearly defines a break in continuity in the 800 to 850°C range. This break is related to the transformation of α zirconium into β zirconium. It seems possible that this transformation occurs in a temperature range because of the presence of oxygen.

As shown in Table 29, stable, cubic β zirconium is more ductile than hexagonal α zirconium above 850°C. Deformation twins, common to hexagonal metals, are sometimes observed in cold-deformed specimens of zirconium; cracking is heard during the process of deformation.

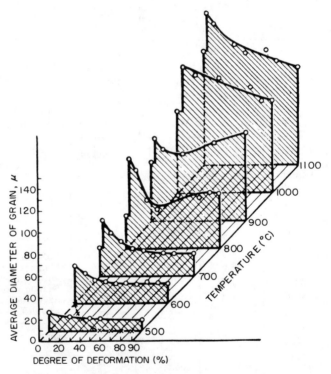

FIG. 104. Recrystallization diagram of iodide zirconium after cold rolling and annealing (Savitsky and Terekhova).

In cooperation with Terekhova we studied the process of recrystallization which takes place in annealing cold-worked iodide zirconium. X-ray analysis showed that recrystallization (in samples of iodide zirconium deformed to between 50 and 90 percent) begins at 500°C; it begins at 550°C in samples deformed to 7.5 percent and it begins at 600°C in samples with any degree of deformation.

A recrystallization diagram of iodide zirconium after cold rolling is presented in Fig. 104 [356].

Data have been published on the influence of small additions of alloying elements on the hardness and strength of zirconium cast in an induction furnace [357]. Molybdenum and possibly niobium are elements that, at temperatures below 500°C, strengthen zirconium to a considerable degree; above 600°C, aluminum, tantalum, and vanadium are more effective for this purpose. In the 300 to 700°C range, titanium apparently is the most effective alloy for increasing the hardness of zirconium.

General Conclusions on Polymorphic Metals

As previously mentioned, ductility and strength are related to the spatial disposition of atoms and to their interaction—that is, to the nature and structure of matter. A change in the crystalline structure of a polymorphic metal has considerable bearing on its property changes, including plasticity.

The most ductile metals are those which crystallize in cubic (especially face-centered) and closely related structures which have the greatest number of slip planes and the highest cohesion. For this reason such metals as Al, Pt, Cu, Ag, Au, and Pb are very ductile, even at room temperature, whereas hexagonal magnesium or rhombohedral bismuth are brittle under ordinary conditions. The high ductility of the low-temperature phases observed in certain highly pure polymorphic metals (α Tl, α Ti, and α Zr) is probably related to the presence of additional active slip planes other than the basal plane; it is likewise related to the occurrence of twinning caused by deformation.

A review of published data on the crystalline structure of various temperature modifications of allotropic metals indicates that, as a rule, the higher-temperature phases of polymorphic metals have the cubic structure, which is most conducive to plastic deformation, and, in an overwhelming majority of instances, they are face-centered lattices (see Table 11).* The metals complying with this pattern are Ca, Sr, Sc, La, Ce, Pr, Nd, Sm, Fe, Mn, Ti, Zr, Hf, U, Np, Pu, Co, Rh, and Tl. Of the 20 metals with temperature allotropy, shown in Table 11, 19 conform to this pattern. The exception is tin (ordinary white tin), which, although possessing a ductile high-temperature phase, has a tetragonal lattice.

Heating of a polymorphic metal with any complex lattice leads to a change in its solid-state crystal structure ending in the development of a new modifica-

---

* *Editor's Note*: Actually, in the majority of cases cited, the higher-temperature modification is body-centered-cubic rather than face-centered-cubic.

tion with a crystalline cubic-type structure, usually with the highest coordination number.

It may be concluded that, generally speaking, *the highest-temperature modification of a polymorphic metal should be the most ductile* [193].

Our own experimental data as well as data found in the literature on Ca, Sr, La, Ce, Pr, Ti, Zr, Co, Fe, Mn, Th, and Sn have been presented earlier in this chapter. Ample evidence exists in support of the assumption that analogous structural changes are inherent not to metals alone, but also to alloys and to other inorganic as well as organic materials [358–360], probably because, in all phase changes, the simpler and the more symmetrical lattices are more thermodynamically stable, as they have a lower energy and a higher entropy.

Several important scientific and practical premises can be based on this conclusion.

1. It indicates the method to be followed to obtain ductile alloys from normally brittle polymorphic metals such as manganese. The polymorphic metal should be alloyed with metals that contribute to the stability of the high-temperature ductile phase at ordinary temperature. As long ago as 1906, Zhemchuzhny obtained so-called "ductile" manganese by adding 3 percent copper; it is now clear that copper stabilizes the ductile γ phase of manganese under ordinary conditions. Addition of copper enlarges the ductility range of the solid solution and retards the rate of its transformation into the brittle α phase to such an extent that, after quenching and even after slow cooling, the alloy retains the high-temperature phase and hence remains ductile. Additions of certain other metals (Fe, Ni, Cr, Zn, and others) have a similar influence on manganese. Another well known example is that of austenitic steel, in which the required additions (nickel, manganese, chromium, and others) stabilize the γ phase; the stabilization of the austenitic structure may be viewed as one of the most important methods for combating the low-temperature brittleness of α iron. The number of such examples is considerable.

2. Any polymorphic metal, brittle at room temperature, will become ductile upon transforming into the high-temperature phase when heated. The most favorable temperature range for hot working of polymorphic metals can be determined from this conclusion. Other conditions being equal, it is probably best to work the metals at temperatures at which they are most ductile—i.e., at temperatures in the range of the highest-temperature modification. For this reason, the high-temperature phase of pure metals apparently cannot be heat-resistant.

3. The crystal structure of the highest-temperature phase of polymorphic metals can be predicted when it has not yet been determined. It is known that high-temperature phases should be of either a higher degree of symmetry or a higher coordination number than low-temperature phases [35]. We shall now proceed one step further to say that, since the high-

temperature phase is ductile, as a rule it should have a crystalline cubic-type lattice, preferably face-centered, which is conducive to deformation. This rule was first published in 1950 [193], at which time the crystalline structure of neptunium was still unknown. Data obtained from studies of neptunium by Zachariasen were published in 1952 [281]. It was found that the high-temperature phase of neptunium does have a cubic structure, whereas at room temperature the metal has a complex rhombic lattice. A similar situation exists with plutonium and samarium; a paper on the crystalline structure of these metals was published in 1954 (see Table 11). It is justifiable to assume that the rule will be upheld for other synthesized metals which follow plutonium if the metals are polymorphic.

The high ductility of the high-temperature phase of allotropic metals is, of course, not solely explained by the type of crystal structure; a number of other factors also come into play. As pointed out previously, the increase in the ductility of manganese caused by an increase in temperature may be explained by a decrease in the number of atoms in the unit cell and also by an increase in the interatomic spacing [319]. This last factor is of great importance for monotypic lattices.

Furthermore, ductility is not related to interatomic spacing alone, but also to the forces of interaction—i.e., to the nature of chemical cohesion between atoms. The metallic type of cohesion, which is characterized by a uniform distribution of electron density, is most conducive to ductility. Ionic (salt, for example) and homopolar (diamond, for example) crystals are brittle at room temperature. Apparently all high-temperature-phase polymorphic metals have the metallic type of interatomic cohesion, whereas in a number of low-temperature-phase metals the cohesion may be of a mixed nature (α manganese and α tin). It should also be noted that an increase in the amplitude of thermal atomic vibrations is one of the important factors which contribute to the increase in ductility of all solids when heated. Excessive atomic mobility increases the thermal contribution to ductility and creates favorable conditions which facilitate the deformation of polymorphic metals.

The most important problem requiring further study is the nature of polymorphism of metals; a complete list of all polymorphic metals should be made and the crystalline structure of their high-temperature phases should be determined. It is necessary to find out whether or not the following metals are endowed with temperature polymorphism: Cr, Be, Ge, Ru, Os, Th, Po, Gd, Sm, and certain other new metals. On the basis of a survey of the published literature we assume that the nature of the phase transformations of the metals mentioned above has not been elucidated.

If the known data on polonium are confirmed, the metal appears to be unique in that it has a simple cubic lattice [38].

New, as yet undiscovered, phases of all polymorphic metals under conditions of extreme cold as well as under high pressure should be searched out. Intensive investigations should be conducted to find alloys that will stabilize the high-temperature phases under ordinary conditions and also to formulate laws governing the effect of alloys on polymorphism. It is also imperative to continue studies on the physicomechanical and physicochemical properties of metals at various temperatures. The experimental material presented in this chapter could serve as a starting point for new investigations. It is essential that the studies be made with metals of high purity, preferably spectroscopically pure materials.

Finally, studies should be undertaken on the effect of temperature on the physicomechanical properties of those metals which have been neglected till now (scandium, technitium, hafnium, a number of rare-earth metals, transuranium elements, and certain noble metals) and on the properties of alloys based on polymorphic metals.

It is indisputable that, by changing the equilibrium factors of the system (concentration, temperature, pressure, or the intensity of the electrical and other fields), the resulting accumulated data will furnish us with the means to regulate with confidence the extremely important and as yet unexplained phenomenon of polymorphism of elements.

5

Metallic Compounds

The three known basic classes of chemical compounds are the ionic, the homopolar, and the metallic.

Metallic compounds and the phases based thereon are formed in many metallic systems. These compounds have individual crystal structures, usually complex, and are radically different from pure metals as well as from solid solutions. Ionic compounds differ, however, from metallic compounds in that the latter have a predominance of metallic cohesion between unlike atoms and exhibit metallic properties (metallic luster, electrical and thermal conductivity, and, under certain conditions, adaptability to mechanical working). Metallic compounds are formed by components that have radically different chemical properties (i.e., are far from each other in the periodic table of elements) and have distinctly different atomic volumes and different crystal structures.

The number of known intermetallic phases exhibiting metallic properties is now more than 4000; of these 300 are ternary. The crystal structure of 800 binary compounds has been rather thoroughly investigated [361], [362].

The term "metallic compounds" was first introduced by Kurnakov in 1899 in his studies on the properties of metals and compounds [363], [364]. We concur with the opinion expressed by Ageyev that neither the term "intermetallic compounds" used by Neville in 1900 nor such designations as "intermetallic phases," "intermediate phases," "ordered phases," and "superstructures" (the last two were applied to solid-solution compounds), are as concise and descriptive as the term "metallic compounds" [365]. Hence, to eliminate the various designations which became accepted by our science as a result of translations of foreign terminologies, we deem it proper to adhere to the term "metallic compounds" given by Kurnakov [365], [366]. It is probably adequate to describe phases formed by metallic consolidation as intermetallic or metallic phases.

Metallic compounds are known to be of a constant as well as of variable composition. A specific chemical compound (daltonide, as defined by Kurnakov) possesses its own type of space lattice, an ordered arrangement of atoms, a simple stoichiometric composition, and singular points on the composition-property diagram. Metallic compounds of variable composition (bertholides) have a partially ordered arrangement of atoms; their degree of order changes with changes in composition and temperature. They have their own crystal structure but are devoid of singular points on the composition-property diagram. Ageyev suggested that bertholides be viewed as solid solutions based on "imaginary" chemical compounds which have no independent existence and are observed only in a solid solution (for example, the β phase in the lead-sodium system).

In 1914 Kurnakov, Zhemchuzhny, and Zasedatelev discovered a new type of formation of metallic compounds (for example, in the gold-copper system) arising from the decomposition of solid solutions [367]. Further studies indicated that the formation of such compounds in the transformation processes of solid solutions is common to systems exhibiting a continuous range of solid solution. Credit due Kurnakov for this finding, however, is ignored in many foreign monographs and even in some of our own. This author agrees with Ageyev and Kornilov that discoveries of metallic compounds of this type should in all justice be called Kurnakov compounds; this recognition would enhance the prestige of our national science [365], [368].

Intermetallic phases exhibit the greatest variety of properties. They have a high melting point, a high hardness characteristic, and high electrical resistivity. These characteristic properties are tens of times greater in intermetallic phases than in pure metals. It is reasonable to assume that, for this category of substances (intermetallic phases), the melting temperature and hardness may be used as a measure of their interatomic cohesion. As a rule, the higher the melting point of a compound, the higher its hardness. The crystal structure of intermetallic phases is complex and characteristic—β phases have a cesium-chloride type of structure; γ phases have a complex cubic structure with 52 atoms in the unit cell; ε phases have a hexagonal structure. The ionic cohesion in daltonides is more pronounced than in bertholides [29].

The mechanical properties of alloys change abruptly when compounds are formed. Because of the complexity of the crystal structure and the variety of types of chemical bonding (of the γ phase), practically all metallic compounds are brittle at room temperature or lower; β phases, however, possess a certain, but small, degree of ductility. For this reason, it is difficult to prepare samples of such alloys. Because of their extreme brittleness, metallic compounds are used only for alloying in industry; here their brittleness becomes an asset—it facilitates grinding of the alloy and contributes to a regulation of the proportion needed in preparation of the charge. The extreme hardness of metallic compounds is widely utilized in industry, in which these compounds are used as additives to thermally processed alloys and bearing alloys. It is to the existence of certain metallic compounds (such as Mg_2Si, $MgZn_2$, $CuAl_2$, Al_2MgCu, and $Al_2Mg_3Zn_2$) that the light alloys owe their qualities of high strength after quenching and aging.

It should also be noted that solid solutions (about 90 percent of them) consist basically of chemical compounds—i.e., tungsten, cobalt, and titanium carbides. A considerable number of carbides are likewise present in tool, special, and common steels. Fe_3C is present in common steels; in addition to cementite, other components such as carbides of B, Cr, Mn, V, W, Mo, and other metals are present in special tool steels.

Heat-resistant alloys based on solid solutions containing carbides (stellites) are also utilized. The carbides of high-melting-point metals are characterized by their extreme hardness—the microhardnesses of tungsten carbide (WC), titanium carbide (TiC), and boron carbide (B_4C) are respectively 1730, 2850, and 5000 kg/mm^2 [369], [370]. These values are directly related to the high interatomic cohesion. It is considered that "penetration phases," to which metallic carbides belong, are formed by a slight distortion of the lattice in the original metal and retain the metallic character of bonding (such as metallic electrical conductivity) if the ratio of the nonmetal atomic radius to the metal atomic radius does not exceed 0.59 [369].

Effect of Temperature on Physicomechanical Properties

The physicomechanical properties of metallic alloys used in industry have been fairly well investigated, but these properties of metallic compounds have hardly been touched. Furthermore, the prevailing view is that, because of their brittleness, metallic compounds have no practical value. Yet in this vast array of materials many have special physical properties. For this reason, a detailed study on the properties of intermetallic phases in relation to equilibrium factors is an urgent problem. In addition to searching for materials with specific properties and perfecting our knowledge of existing industrial alloys, studies on the physicomechanical properties of metallic compounds will contribute to an understanding of the chemical interactions of the components of the alloy.

When our studies were first started (in 1943), practically no scientific papers had yet been published on attempts to deform pure metallic compounds or to test their mechanical properties; the only exception was a study by Tammann and Dahl, who had conducted qualitative experiments on the hardness and compressibility of a considerable number of individual compounds at various temperatures [371].

In our studies of the effect of temperature on the mechanical properties of metallic compounds [183], [184], [372], [373] and also in studies on the influence of preliminary deformation of cast samples in relation to the phase diagram of the Mg-Al and Mg-Zn systems [374], [375], [376] we were the first to achieve deformation of samples (rods) made of pure metallic compounds and of phases based on them.

In order to deform at room temperature samples prepared from brittle metallic compounds, we made use of the three basic postulates discussed below.

1. The capability of materials to soften as a function of increasing temperature is inherent to practically all materials. A detailed study proved that

metallic compounds are particularly affected by temperature. For example, the compound $MgZn_5$ has a Brinnell hardness of 146 kg/mm^2 at room temperature, but only 6 kg/mm^2 at 350°C. The hardness of compound $CuAl_2$ at 500°C is one tenth that at room temperature; β brass at 500°C is 1/100 as hard as at room temperature. Fig. 105 illustrates the softening process which results from heating the β and γ phases of the Al-Mg system. At specific temperatures all metallic compounds, particularly those with variable compositions, behave as ductile materials—β phases exhibit rather sharp increases in ductility as a function of temperature; γ phases are somewhat more heat resistant. A summary of these data leads to the conclusion that deformation of metallic compounds should be conducted at elevated temperatures.

2. A stress state, consisting of non-uniform hydrostatic compression to retain the material's ductility in the process of deformation, develops during extrusion, i.e., in the process of forcing the sample through the cylindrical opening of the die or in biaxial deformation.

3. Low-rate deformation will contribute to a material's ductility, whereas high-rate deformation may cause it to fracture in a brittle fashion. It follows that metallic compounds should be deformed by static action rather than by impact. Thus, low-

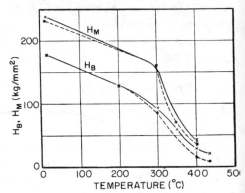

FIG. 105. Hardness and microhardness of intermetallic phases in the Al-Mg system.
$\times$———$\times$, γ phase; $\cdot$---$\cdot$, β phase.

rate, high-temperature extrusion will contribute the most to ductility.

Rods obtained by extruding metallic-compound samples and samples of alloys with a high metallic-compound content were prepared with the device shown in Fig. 27. The method followed and the testing equipment used were similar to those used in industry for hot extrusion of rods. The device was assembled on the lower transverse beam of a 35-ton hydraulic press and was surrounded by a furnace (1). The test bar (3), the punch tip (4), and the punch (5) were inserted into the container. The assembled device was then heated to the required temperature. Extrusion was carried out after one hour of soaking. Pressure from the press was applied by means of the punch and the punch tip. When the required magnitude of pressure was attained, the metal was extruded through the die (7).

To forestall the frequent loss of metal between the die and the container, tightening bolts (12) were used to fasten them to the base (11) and to the top (10) of the device. (In a variation of the device the die was fastened to the container by means of a screw.) The support (9) was introduced because no outlet for the rod was available in the press crossbeam (6).

The press was operated at the velocity of 20 mm/min. Graphite lubrication was used to facilitate extrusion.   The magnitude of the load required for extrusion was recorded by the press load gage and by means of a recording chart; this information was used to determine the flow stress.   The device was equipped with interchangeable dies of different diameters.   It is possible to perform experiments in two stages, if necessary.

Tentative tests confirmed that, given favorable conditions (temperature and

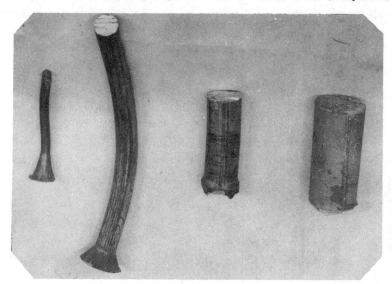

FIG. 106.   Samples made of the metallic compound MgZn$_2$—left, cast samples; right, extruded rods.

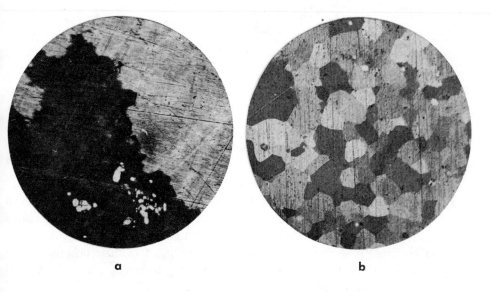

FIG. 107.   Microstructure of a γ-phase sample in the Al-Mg system ($\times 150$)—left, cast sample; right, hot-extruded sample.

rate of deformation) and adequate lubrication, every metallic compound and every alloy with a large metallic-compound content covered by our studies may be successfully processed into rods of good quality. With the aid of equipment described above we obtained rods of the metallic compounds MgZn, MgZn$_2$, MgZn$_5$, and CuAl$_2$ as well as intermetallic β and γ phases of the Al-Mg system. These compounds and phases did not fracture at 80 to 90 percent deformation in a single stage. The magnitude of flow stress varied within the limits of 30 and 50 kg/mm^2, depending on the alloy. Numerous experiments revealed that the most favorable extrusion temperatures are approximately 400°C for alloys of the Al-Mg system, and 15 to 20°C below the melting point for alloys of Mg-Zn.

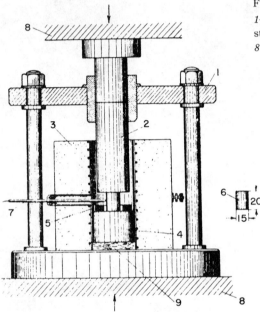

FIG. 108. Device for compressing samples. *1*–frame; *2*–punch; *3*–furnace; *4*–base; *5*–stopping ring; *6*–sample; *7*–thermocouple; *8*–press blocks; *9*–asbestos lining.

FIG. 109. γ-phase samples in the Al-Mg system —left, original sample; right, sample compressed into a disc.

Figure 106 shows MgZn$_2$ rods processed at 400°C. Rods made of the compound CuAl$_2$ in the temperature range of 440 to 460°C were prepared by the same process. The flow stress for extrusion was 40 kg/mm^2.

After cooling, these metallic-compound rods returned to their original brittle condition. In contrast to the cast state, extruded specimens are characterized by a finer grain size (Fig. 107) and a greater hardness.

We also measured the hardness and flow stress of samples obtained from the

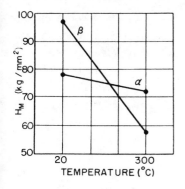

FIG. 110. Effect of temperature on
the microhardness of α and β brass.

extruded rods at various temperatures. It was
found that high-temperature extrusion of cast
material increases its ductility for subsequent
hot working. Thus, in repeated extrusions of
metallic-compound rods, deformation of greater
than 90 percent magnitude may be withstood.
Figure 108 shows a device used for compression
testing and Fig. 109 is a photograph of the
deformed γ phase of the Al-Mg alloy. The
method for compression testing has already been
described [147].

Hardness tests of α and β brass at various
temperatures were conducted; β brass softens
more rapidly as a function of temperature than its neighbor, the α solid solution (Fig. 110). Evidently a number of other β phases, in other alloy systems,
will behave analogously.

Zakharov performed experiments of long duration on a number of cast copper-
based alloys to determine their heat resistance [377], [378]. He showed that the
effect of temperature is to soften these intermetallic phases. Lowry (U.S.A.)
conducted tension experiments with nine cast metallic compounds (based on
copper, aluminum, and nickel); he confirmed that at sufficiently elevated temperatures these samples will withstand plastic deformation of considerable magnitude [379].

The above experimental data indicate that metallic compounds, in spite of
their brittleness under ordinary temperatures, will behave as fully plastic bodies
capable of withstanding considerable deformation without fracturing at fairly
high temperatures (0.7 to 0.9 T_M).

It may therefore be considered indisputable that (1) the plasticity of metallic
compounds, and of phases based thereon, increases in proportion to an increase in temperature and (2) they may be deformed. This fact has already
been demonstrated for another type of compound. A recent paper by Klassen-
Nekliudova and her associates revealed that even synthetic corundum (Al_2O_3) will
become ductile near its melting point [380]. As pointed out earlier, ionic crystals
of the NaCl type are brittle at room temperature and ductile at high temperatures.

Once a systematic study is successfully completed on the room-temperature
deformation of samples made of brittle alloys, it becomes feasible to investigate
the properties of any deformed alloy in the whole range of concentration. Such
an investigation is imperative for those systems in which the diffusion process
is slow and no equilibrium is achieved in the cast condition.

A system should be classified as completely investigated only when all of its
properties have been fully appraised in the whole range of concentrations. The
number of such systems (including binaries) is relatively small and most of them

are plastic at room temperature at all concentrations. Studies of compounds in conjunction with alloys near them in composition will result in more reliable data on their properties. Examples of such studies will be given later.

Analysis of intensive softening in metallic compounds as a function of temperature furnishes important data on the properties and structural changes of industrial alloys and will contribute to better processing and utilization of the end product. Heating of a heterogeneous industrial alloy containing an intermetallic phase results in changes in the relative hardness and strength of its individual structural components because of different reactions of the various components to a rise in temperature. The hardest component at room temperature may become the softest at a high temperature, thus affecting the properties of the alloy. This factor must be considered when appraising the properties of an alloy for high-temperature applications.

Experimental data on the crystal structure of metallic compounds is scarce; therefore, it is difficult to form any conclusions on the effect of temperature on the ductility of the compounds. One may only generalize that a rise in temperature apparently induces new structural forms favorable to plasticity. Such a structure is found in the simple cubic structure with a minimum number of atoms in the unit cell, the greatest interatomic spacing, and a predominantly metallic type of cohesion.

An analogy with highly ductile phases observed in polymorphic metals seems to be appropriate here; in addition, some metallic compounds do have polymorphic transformations [381]. The role of crystal structure in the ductility of compounds is a problem for future study. A number of intermetallic phases are known to have a crystal structure similar to that of certain specific polymorphic modifications of transition metals (γ manganese, β uranium, and others) [44].

Heat-induced dissociation of compounds, hastened by stress resulting in atom displacement, is of considerable importance. It is plainly evident, for instance, that the basic cause of abrupt softening in β brass at high temperature is the structural change in the lattice from an ordered to a disordered state.

The high atomic mobility associated with dissociation evidently contributes to the ease of plastic deformation of samples, but this feature alone does not suffice to explain why certain compounds become softer than their individual components when heated. A change in the character of cohesion may be expected in some compounds as a result of heating, but this matter has not been experimentally investigated. The possibility that metallic compounds at high temperatures are deformed by a special mechanism (e.g., by atomic-group displacement in relation to each other) activated by an oriented diffusion under stress should not be excluded. Data of a more precise character will no doubt be obtained from studies on single crystals. The softening process (recovery and recrystallization) in metallic compounds has not been fully explored, but it is certain that these phenomena have a considerable bearing on the behavior of metallic compounds in hot deformation. Increase in atomic mobility as a result of heat is a highly significant factor.

Effect of Temperature on Mechanical Strength

In the course of studies on the mechanical properties of metallic compounds, another important and interesting phenomenon—that of an increase in hardness with increase in temperature—was discovered [382]. In Chapter 1 we listed papers by Soviet scientists who have demonstrated that, in metals and alloys which exhibit no phase transformations in the temperature range of the test, resistance to plastic deformation decreases exponentially with temperature. Brittle metallic materials were not included in these studies. We have found that with an increase in temperature metallic compounds (silicon, germanium) that are brittle under ordinary conditions behave differently from ductile metals and alloys (Fig. 111). The strength of brittle materials first increases with an increase in temperature and then decreases with increasing temperature, following an exponential law (Tables 30 and 31).

The brittleness of such materials as silicon and germanium and of all metallic compounds at low temperatures is related to their complex crystal structure, to the presence of covalent and ionic bonds, to the low cohesion of the grain boundary, and to their extreme sensitivity to stress concentrations. Under these temperature conditions, these materials will deform elastically with no observable plastic deformation.

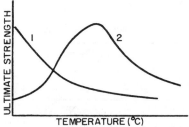

FIG. 111. Effect of temperature on the strength of ductile (*1*) and brittle (*2*) metallic materials.

Since for maximum strength a material requires a certain amount of ductility, the strength of brittle bodies will tend to rise as the heat-induced ability to deform plastically increases with temperature. Plastic deformation apparently relieves the stress concentration, thereby promoting the full strength properties of the material. Above the temperature of maximum strength, the strength of the compounds decreases with increase in temperature, as in the case of all ductile metals.

Table 30 shows that the strength of copper decreases steadily with temperature whereas the strength of the compound Ni_2Si increases 20 times between 20 and 650°C. The relative elongation for this compound is zero at room temperature and 1 percent at 650°C. A similar change in the ultimate tensile strength with temperature was observed in cast alloys, which corresponded to Ni_3Si and Ni_5Si_2 in their composition; this pattern is also followed for a mixture of both alloys [379].

Brittle alloys that consist of crystals of a compound together with small amounts of eutectic behave analogously when heated (alloys of 20 percent by weight of silicon with 80 percent nickel, and of 12 percent silicon with 88 percent copper).

The temperature of maximum strength for brittle alloys is related to their

TABLE 30

TENSILE STRENGTHS OF CAST COMPOUNDS AND COPPER AT VARIOUS TEMPERATURES

Metal or Alloy	Ultimate Tensile Strength σ_B (kg/mm²)								Melting Temperature (°C)
	20°C	300°C	400°C	500°C	600°C	650°C	750°C	800°C	
Copper (Cu)	22.0	18.0	15.0	13.0	11.5	8.0	...	2.0	1083
19.29% Si, remainder Ni (Ni₂Si)	0.6	...	....	....	11.2	14.2	5.9	...	1290
20% Si, remainder Ni	5.8	...	....	12.1	13.2	...	10.3	5.6	1240
32% Si, remainder Ni (NiSi)	0.6	...	....	0.8	2.0ᵃ	1.1	0.53	...	1000
12% Si, remainder Cu	8.2	9.0	19.3	7.0	...	...	....	...	840
13% Si, remainder Cu (Cu₃Si)	2.2	8.7	21.2	8.1	...	...	....	...	859

ᵃ For 550°C.

TABLE 31

COMPRESSION STRENGTHS OF METALLIC COMPOUNDS AT VARIOUS TEMPERATURES

Metallic Compound	Ultimate Compression Strength σ_{comp} (kg/mm²)					Melting Temperature (°C)
	20°C	300°C	500°C	600°C	750°C	
19.29% Si, remainder Ni (Ni₂Si)	31.6	....	57.9	76.0	62.5	1290
20% Si, remainder Ni	31.6	....	75.8	51.6	....	1240
32% Si, remainder Ni (NiSi)	15.8	....	46.7	50.7	32.0	1000
12% Si, remainder Cu	28.2	44.4	34.2	....	....	840
13% Si, remainder Cu (Cu₃Si)	28.2	40.5	35.7	....	....	859
32.25% Si, remainder Co (CoSi)	3.8	....	6.3	....	34.0	1460
48.77% Si, remainder Co (CoSi₂)	10.0	....	15.2	....	60.0	1300
45% Si, remainder Mg	0.3	....	....	12.0	....	....

TABLE 32

HARDNESS OF METALLIC COMPOUNDS OF COPPER AND SILICON AT VARIOUS TEMPERATURES

Metal or Alloy	Hardness H_c (kg/mm²)			
	20°C	500°C	750°C	1000°C
19.29% Si, remainder Ni (Ni₂Si)	440	320.0	120.0	...
20% Si, remainder Ni	374	300.0	....	...
32% Si, remainder Ni (NiSi)	400	256.0	....	...
12% Si, remainder Cu	321	84.5	....	...
13% Si, remainder Cu (Cu₃Si)	396	86.0	21.0	...
32.25% Si, remainder Co (CoSi)	1000	300.0	....	115
48.77% Si, remainder Co (CoSi₂)	552	322.0	....	77
Silicon (Si)	1000	500.0	....	128
Copper (Cu)	48	17.5	<8.0	...
Mg₂Si	457	180.0ᵃ	....	...

ᵃ For 600°C.

melting point; for tension tests, it is usually 0.5 to 0.8 T_M. A similar condition also prevails in fracture tests under compression of brittle materials (see Table 31) the only difference being that the ultimate strength in compression (because of the contact friction to which the faces of the sample are subjected) is several times greater than the ultimate tensile strength at the same temperature. There is a two- or three-fold increase in the compression strength with temperature for the compounds Ni_2Si, $NiSi$, and Cu_3Si, and a sixfold increase for the compound $CoSi_2$. The strength of silicon and of germanium, as already mentioned, increases ten times for silicon with an increase from room temperature to 1000°C and three times for germanium heated to 940°C.

In compression tests the temperature of maximum strength corresponds to 0.5 to 0.7 T_M. Variations in the temperature of maximum strength in tension and in compression tests for the same material may be explained by differences in the type of stress state. In the case of alloys we are also concerned with the state of the grain boundaries.

As illustrated in Table 32, the hardness of metallic compounds decreases monotonically with an increase in temperature, just as in the case of ductile metals and alloys. The difference between the effect of temperature on tensile strength and compression strength in brittle metallic materials on one hand and on hardness on the other can probably be explained by the different stress states in each of the experimental methods. Furthermore, in hardness indentation tests the material is not fractured, and hence the hardness is quite insensitive to the state of grain boundaries. When the strength of a material is tested, either in tension or compression, the material is invariably taken to fracture. Both methods of testing mechanical properties, especially the tension test, are extremely sensitive to the state of grain boundaries and to other physicochemical factors which determine the strength and ductility of materials.

Several brittle and semi-brittle metallic materials, with distinctly different degrees of hardness at room temperature, were tested under various temperatures. These materials were found to have about the same hardness at high temperatures; the materials that were more ductile and stronger at room temperature became weaker than a brittle and weaker alloy with an increase in temperature (e.g., Cu_3Si at 400°C—see Table 30). The increased strength in brittle metals and metallic compounds when heated should be considered in selecting heat-resistant alloys.

Alloys Based on Metallic Compounds

Alloys rich in metallic compounds may be examined from two basic points of view: as alloys with specific physical properties (electrical, optical, and other) and as light alloys of high hardness. Some of these materials may prove to be highly resistant to electrical conductivity, to have directed electrical conductivity, to have thermoemissive and magnetic properties, and so on. Projects to discover high-reflectivity alloys and, perhaps, transparent alloys, could present a challenge

[383]. Considerable effort is now given to research on metallic compounds with the properties of semiconductors [384]. The ability of metallic compounds to deform at elevated temperatures will be advantageous in shaping these materials into the required form.

At this writing, the light, high-strength materials are the commonly used aluminum solid-solution alloys containing other elements (magnesium, zinc, copper, and others). The strength of such alloys is considerably increased by heat treatment (quenching and aging). The strength ceiling for this group of alloys, however, has been practically reached, having approached the hardness of mild steel (50 to 60 kg/mm^2).

Some metallic compounds possess a very high degree of hardness, in the order of 1000 to 2000 kg/mm^2. Assuming that the magnitude of strength is about one-third that of hardness, one should expect to find an ultimate strength of a magnitude of 100 and even 200 kg/mm^2 for alloys based on such compounds. Such alloys, by virtue of their light weight and high melting point, could have the same mechanical properties as the strongest steel. But metallic compounds are brittle at room temperature. The problem is to combine the hardness of metallic compounds with the ductility of plastic metals or alloys into a new alloy. Such an accomplishment would be a huge step toward creating alloys with predetermined properties. The solution of this problem is difficult but not hopeless.

There are certain indications of how this may be achieved—powder metallurgy, substitution of alloy compounds [385], and so on.

The creation of heat-resisting alloys formed by extremely high-melting compounds (silicides, borides, carbides, and oxides) presents a fruitful area for research.

6

Alloys

As demonstrated in the preceding chapter, the classification of pure metals by lattice type in relation to temperature and their mechanical properties was useful and contributed to the formulation of certain general rules governing the mechanical properties of single-component systems. Generally speaking, these rules apply to both binary and more complex systems. Thus, a homogeneous solid solution will undergo changes in properties caused by variations in temperature in conformity with its crystal structure. Properties of monomorphic metallic solutions will change gradually with temperature, whereas those of polymorphic alloys will show abrupt changes with temperature changes. Metallic solid solutions of the cubic type will be considerably more ductile than metallic solid solutions of the hexagonal type; pronounced twinning and anisotropy of properties in deformed samples of the latter material are observed.

With alloys as with pure metals, one should bear in mind the possible interaction with the surrounding medium, especially gaseous. This interaction may bring about a change in the property–temperature curve of the metal as a result of some physicochemical process occurring along the crystal boundaries, i.e., the formation of brittle zones and the presence of impurities and of micro and macro nonuniformities. These factors are of greater importance in alloys than in pure metals.

The emergence of another equilibrium factor, concentration, is observed in the process of transformation from a single-component to the binary and more complex systems.

A change in the components of a system, as is well known, may cause an emergence of phases with different physicochemical and physicomechanical properties. A phase diagram describes the results of interaction of physicochemical components at various temperatures in the liquid as well as in the solid states. Consequently, in studies of alloys the changes in properties should be correlated with the changes in composition and with the type of equilibrium diagram.

The solid phases formed as a result of metallic interaction are characterized

169

by their crystal structure as well as by the type of chemical interaction between atoms. In "ideal" mechanical mixtures under ordinary conditions, however, such interaction apparently does not occur. The current view recognizes the formation of molecular structures in solid solutions [153], [386], [387]. The forces of chemical interaction between heterogeneous atoms in intermetallic phases and metallic compounds are most clearly manifested. It is not expedient for us here to go into a detailed discussion of conditions resulting in the formation of various metallic-phase types. The main factors are the position of the reacting elements in the periodic table and the resulting difference or similarity in their chemical properties, the type of crystal structure, and the atomic size [365]–[367].

Our review of experimental data on the effect of temperature on the mechanical properties of typical binary metallic systems was carried out in the order of increasing chemical interaction, as follows: eutectic systems, systems with solid-solution alloys, and, finally, systems with metallic compounds. Systems containing metallic compounds are reviewed in the following order: compounds of fixed composition, compounds of variable composition, and Kurnakov compounds.

Eutectic Systems

Eutectic-phase mixtures may consist of pure metals, compounds of pure metals, or solid solutions.

According to Kurnakov, properties of a system formed by a mechanical mixture of components are described by a linear relation in the system [9]. He probably assumed that the alloys were stabilized—i.e., they either had been cooled slowly from the liquid state or had been annealed after solidifying. It might be concluded, therefore, that the strength or hardness of any alloy could then readily be computed from the equation of the additive curve. The only requirement would be to know the hardness (or the strength) of each of the basic phases and the composition of the alloy. However, with the accumulation of experimental data, it became clear that the linear relation of properties to composition is true only in the limit, especially at high temperatures. Evidently this relation will apply quantitatively only when the components making up the mixture vary little in their mechanical properties. In real alloys consisting of eutectic or eutectoid structures the various physicochemical processes created by recrystallization, heat, or deformation (mechanical properties are always measured by deformation) bring about deviations from the additive rule. Generally speaking, the greater the deviation, the greater the departure of the alloy mixture from the ideal.

Experiments conducted by Roberts-Austen, Glazunov, Kurnakov, Akhnazarov, Ageyev, and Pogodin have shown that the eutectic alloy, when rapidly cooled, develops specific properties (i.e., a pronounced increase in hardness) which make it stand out from the neighboring intermediate alloys. This anomaly in the behavior of a eutectic alloy has been explained as the result of a joint, rapid crystallization of the two phases present during solidification of the eutectic. This phenomenon has been named thermal cold hardening and could be called crystallization cold hardening. Thermal cold hardening may be completely eliminated in certain instances by subsequent annealing of the alloy in the solid state [18]. The electrical properties are less sensitive to this structural change than are the mechanical.

Ageyev indicates that eutectic alloys have superior properties in contrast to neighboring alloys in the following systems: Pb-Sn, Cu-Ag, Zn-Cd, Au-Cd, and Au-Zn. It is possible to achieve a linear change in properties with composition for a large number of alloys by slow cooling or by annealing. For certain alloys (Pb-Sn, Pb-Cd) this can be done with ease, but in others (such as Cd-Zn) only with considerable difficulty. In the Pb-Na and Pb-Ca systems a linear change in property with composition is not achieved even by annealing [18].

Saldau suggested that the specific properties of eutectics might be ascribed to their fine grain structure as compared with that of neighboring alloys [388]. Deviations in the properties of stabilized eutectic alloys may be due to the same cause.

Silumins or Al-Si alloys illustrate the practical benefits derived by industry in utilizing the abnormal properties of eutectics. The production of "modified" silumins is based on the ability of the eutectic Al-Si system to supply a fine structure possessing mechanical properties of a high order; for this purpose, sodium or salts containing sodium are added to the system. Experiments by Hargreaves proved that after cold deformation the hardness of a eutectic composition is somewhat less than the hardness of any of its components [187].

The hardness of a considerable number of light alloys at different temperatures was studied by Shishokin and his associates [14]. In a number of cases the isothermal curves in the region of mixtures were found to be skewed in the direction of the composition axis. This skewness is acceptable if we bear in mind that different phases have different temperature coefficients of hardness and, therefore, at different temperatures, they may exhibit a different hardness correlation that determines the total macrohardness of alloys. A eutectic alloy has the highest temperature coefficient of hardness [14], [374].

Shishokin and Telitsin studied the influence of the rate of deformation on hardness as a function of composition in eutectic-type alloys. They found that the deviation from linear is greater in impact-hardness tests than in static-load tests for eutectic alloys [389].

In experiments with alloys of Ag-Zn-Cd and Sn-Sb, Korolkov demonstrated that phases formed by the peritectic reaction result in an intensive softening of the alloy as a function of temperature and time [390].

As stated earlier, the hardness of mechanical mixtures of solid solutions based on compounds MgZn, $MgZn_2$, and $MgZn_5$ varies linearly at all temperatures. It will be recalled that heating can lead to both a pronounced softening and a simultaneous increase in the hardness of metallic compounds. These factors greatly influence the linearity of the mechanical properties of alloys containing metallic compounds.

Experimenting with an 80-weight-percent-Zn and 20-weight-percent-Al alloy (eutectic composition) consisting of a mixture of two types of solid solutions, Bochvar and Sviderskaya found that their hardness and ductility values differed considerably from the linear values [267].

As viewed by Bochvar, a mixture of crystals in real alloys does not meet the two basic conditions required for a linear dependence of properties. These conditions are first, structural consistency of the components making up the mixture and second, absence of interaction between components during determination of a property value. Strictly speaking, an interacting mixture is no longer a mechanical mixture, especially in the case of mixtures of solid solutions.

Bochvar also stated that an increase in temperature may change the mutual solubility of the elements in a mixture; the microfractures which occur during deformation may be "healed" and the ductility may thus be recovered. The greater the range of solubility, the greater will be the effect [187].

Diffusion processes are not equilibrium processes. Consequently, the linearity of properties in mixtures can be maintained only at low temperatures, when diffusion is slow and when the basic deformation mechanism is slip.

Pashkov determined the ultimate flow stress in coarse-grained, two-phase alloys consisting of hard and soft grains in a ferro-martensitic steel [391].

Experimenting with ternary magnesium alloys, Bochvar, Drits, and Kadaner have demonstrated that long-duration hardness is a better indicator of heat resistance of alloys than long-duration strength [392].

It should be noted that the presence of the second phase may render the alloy stronger at low temperatures, whereas it may contribute to a lowering of resistance to deformation at high temperatures. Furthermore, attention should be paid to micro nonhomogeneities, to the mosaic structure of grains of the same phase, and to the effect of soluble or insoluble impurities and additions. The presence of microheterogeneities apparently brings microhardness closer to linear values. As shown later, in addition to these factors the arrangement of structural components as well as the degree of dispersion has a considerable influence on the composite hardness of the mixture [393]. As in steel, the properties are determined not only by the type of components but also by the alloy's microstructure [394].

The presently existing mass of experimental data in the realm of physicochemical analysis and metallography has been instrumental in determining the general outline of characteristics of alloy structures endowed with high mechanical strength, but the possibilities for improving alloys have not yet been exhausted and a follow-up of additional factors will contribute to the solution of the problem.

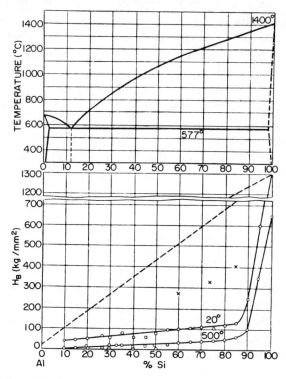

FIG. 112. Phase diagram and hardness of Al-Si alloys.
x—hardness of powder-metallurgy specimens.
----—additive curve of hardness.

Unfortunately we still lack knowledge of the optimum microstructure to obtain alloys of certain predetermined mechanical properties; it is not always possible to regulate the microstructure.

However, a great deal is understood. It seems definitely proven that (1) a granular structure induces ductility, and a needle or slaty structure produces brittleness; (2) a reduction in grain size increases hardness characteristics; and (3) the presence of low-melting impurities along grain boundaries results in hot-shortness and in cold-brittleness when the impurities are brittle.

One of the important problems of metallography is the regulation of the physicomechanical properties of alloys and alloy mixtures. Solution of this problem would help to promote better understanding of the ways to select alloys with predetermined properties. We have attempted to correlate the mechanical properties of mechanical mixtures with their structure. To this end we have carried out experiments on (1) the determination of the micro-structure, (2) the measurement of the hardness and compression characteristics at various temperatures of cast and powder-metallurgy samples in the systems Al-Si, Mg-Si, Cu-Si, Mg-Ge, Ni-Si, Co-Si, and Al-Cu, and (3) the fabrication of samples. We also obtained alloys by substitution with a low-melting component. These systems, excluding Al-Cu, are characterized by the presence of eutectic mixtures composed of low-melting metals and high-melting metallic compounds or pure silicon. The difference in the melting temperatures of the structural components determines the solidification range in the alloys studied. This interval is especially great in systems with silicon; thus, in the Al-Si system it is 830°C and in the Mg-Si system, 555°C. However, in the Cu-Al system, the difference between the melting temperature of the compound $CuAl_2$ and the eutectic temperature (to the left of the compound) is only 42°C. Special attention was directed to the relation of the composite hardness of the mixture to the arrangement of the structural components and to the degree of their dispersion.

Al-Si System

The group of Al-Si compounds is often referred to as an example in which the linear hardness-of-the-mixture rule does not apply, because the components are so radically different in hardness (1300 kg/mm² for silicon and only 25 to 28 kg/mm² for aluminum). The debatable point on the proper method of composition designation does not apply to this group (gravimetric, atomic, volumetric percentages) since the components have approximately the same atomic and specific weights. The phase diagram of this group is of the eutectic type (Fig 112). The melting temperature of the eutectic is 577°C.

TABLE 33

HARDNESS OF CAST ALLOYS IN THE AL-SI SYSTEM

Silicon Content (wt. %)	Hardness H_c (kg/mm²)		Remarks
	20°C	500°C	
0.0(100% Al)	25.0	2.0	
10.0	43.1	3.0	
11.7	52.8	2.7	
15.0	56.6	3.9	
20.0	49.4	3.9	
25.0	66.8	4.3	
30.0	59.5	5.0	
35.0	75.7	6.3	$\varepsilon_{st} = 37\%$; $\sigma_{comp} = 31$ kg/mm²
40.0	70.7	9.2	
45.0	66.8	7.8	
50.0	74.5	8.7	After being cast into water (to refine grain size), sample registered $H_c = 100$ kg/mm² and $\sigma_{comp} = 22.8$ kg/mm²
55.0	93.5	15.4	
60.0	101.0	18.0	
65.0	108.0	22.0	
70.0	108.0	24.7	
75.0	108.0	38.7	
80.0	120.0	50.0	
85.0	128.0	66.8	
90.0	264.0	112.0	
95.0	923.0	346.0	
100.0	1300.0	560.0	

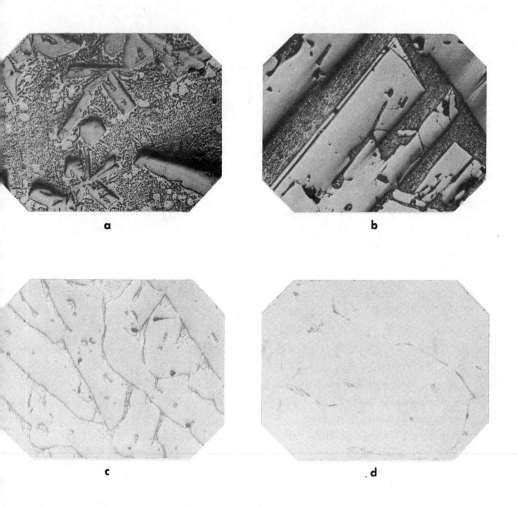

FIG. 113. Microstructure of cast Al-Si alloys ($\times 150$).
a. 25 weight percent of Si ($H_c = 67$ kg/mm²).
b. 75 weight percent of Si ($H_c = 108$ kg/mm²).
c. 90 weight percent of Si ($H_c = 264$ kg/mm²).
d. 95 weight percent of Si ($H_c = 923$ kg/mm²).

Because of the high melting temperature of silicon (1400°C) the majority of silicon alloys were melted in a high-frequency furnace. The modifying treatment was not used. Alloys containing up to 11.7 weight percent of silicon consisted of crystals of α solid solution of aluminum and eutectic $\alpha + \beta$ (hypoeutectic alloys); alloys with a large silicon content consisted of eutectic and a solid solution of aluminum in silicon (hypereutectic alloys). In cast alloys the eutectic was distributed along grain boundaries of silicon. Hardness was measured by means of a pobedit cone having a 90° apex angle under a 125-kg load. High-

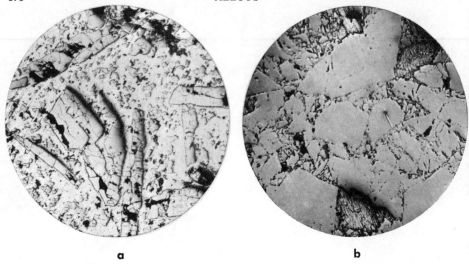

a   b

FIG. 114. Microstructure of Al-Si alloys.
a. 55 weight percent of Si, extruded at 400°C ($\times$150).
b. 85 weight percent of Si, produced by the powder-metallurgy method ($H_c = 400$ kg/mm^2)
($\times$210).

silicon-content alloys were tested under a 30-kg load. The results are shown in Table 33 and in Fig. 112.

It should have been reasonable to expect that, with increased silicon content, the hardness of eutectic alloys of this system would exhibit a uniform increase approaching the hardness of silicon. This rule of linearity, however, does not apply to cast alloys as illustrated by the data presented, or to alloys annealed at 500°C for 24 hours.

The hardness of cast alloys containing less than 90 weight percent of silicon rises slowly with an increase in silicon content; at room temperature, the hardness of an alloy containing 85 weight percent of silicon reaches 128 kg/mm^2. The hardness of an alloy containing more than 90 weight percent of silicon increases abruptly and, at room temperature and 95 weight percent of silicon, rises to 923 kg/mm^2. The hardness of the cast alloys at 500°C undergoes similar changes. This abrupt rise in hardness occurs when the hard silicon crystals interlock and form a continuous network which contains eutectic inclusions (Fig. 113). The hardness of alloys prior to this stage is determined basically by the hardness of the eutectic located along the grain boundaries; in this case, the eutectic is a comparatively soft component (microhardness of 80 kg/mm^2).

Consequently, the presence of a considerable amount of soft component (such as a eutectic along the grain boundaries of the hard component, silicon) in the absence of a strong intercohesion, results in an abrupt decrease in the hardness of the alloys. The magnitude of hardness in such cases is determined by the mutual arrangement of hard and soft components in the alloy as well as by the size of the component crystals.

To achieve an additive change in hardness with a change in composition, a uniform distribution of the soft and hard components and a general break-up of the structure are required.

It is very difficult to break up the silicon crystals in alloys with a high silicon content. Needle and slaty inclusions of brittle silicon contribute to a considerable lowering of the ductility properties of silumins. Only alloys approaching the eutectic composition respond to the modifying effect induced by sodium.

Attempts to obtain Al-Si alloys with a different arrangement of structural components by changing the conditions of casting, by prolonging annealing, or by deforming have not produced any positive results. The hardness of a hot-

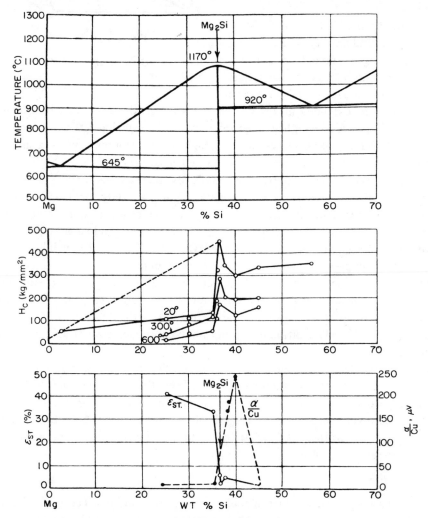

FIG. 115. Phase diagram, mechanical properties, and thermal emf. (α/Cu) of Mg-Si alloys.

--------additive straight line for strength.

extruded alloy containing 55 weight percent of silicon showed no material change
in comparison with that of a cast alloy
(90 kg/mm^2); the distribution of the
structural components also showed no
change (Fig. 114a). The established fact
that plastic deformation of Al-Si alloys
with 55 weight percent of silicon is
possible, however, presents an interesting problem for metallography and for
technology.

It might be noted that the resistance
to electrical conductivity in Al-Si alloys
(up to 25 weight percent of silicon) is
similarly not an additive property [395].

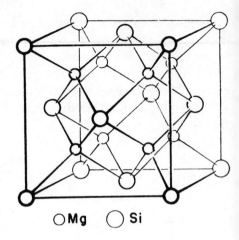

○Mg ◯ Si

FIG. 116. Crystal lattice of the compound
Mg$_2$Si [236].

Wire rods made of 25-weight-percent-
Si alloy may be extruded at 400°C; thin ribbons of the alloy can be obtained
by cold rolling. A 55-weight-percent-Si alloy can be rolled at 500°C. It becomes
evident, therefore, that alloys with a high silicon content may be used to
fabricate various semi-finished products when necessary.

It was decided to use the powder-metallurgy method to achieve a uniform
distribution of the structural components. After a study of methods to be
followed for extruding the powders, of extrusion conditions, of temperature
ranges (500°C), of pressure (8 to 9 t/cm^2), of lubrication, and so on, high-quality
powder-metallurgy samples were obtained with 60, 75, and 85 weight percent
of silicon. Samples of adequate density were obtained with a good-quality,
shiny surface. The hardness of these samples was several times greater than
that of cast alloys. Thus the hardness of an 85-weight-percent-Si–15-weight-
percent-Al sample was 400 kg/mm^2 as compared with 128 kg/mm^2 for a cast
sample (Fig. 112). The ultimate strength in compression rose from 22.8 to 25.6
kg/mm^2.

Research on the microstructure and microhardness of the powder-metallurgy
samples revealed that the microhardness of both the hard and the soft structural components coincides with their microhardness in cast samples. The
eutectic, however, does not surround all of the boundaries of the silicon crystals
in these samples; rather, it is distributed in the form of clusters within the
silicon grains (Fig. 114b).

Mg-Si System

Alloys based on the Mg$_2$Si compound are of great interest because of its high
hardness, high melting point, and low density. Alloys that, by their composition, are located between Mg$_2$Si and Mg start melting at 645°C and those between
Mg$_2$Si and Si, at 920°C (Fig. 115). Magnesium silicide has a complex face-

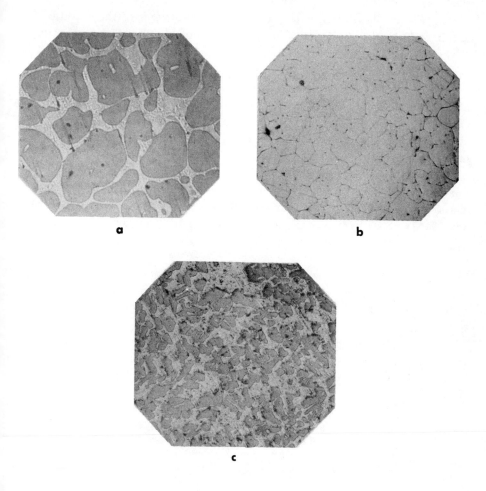

FIG. 117.   Microstructure of Mg-Si alloys ($\times 150$).

a. 30 weight percent of Si, cast ($H_c = 120\ \text{kg/mm}^2$).

b. 36.9 weight percent of Si, cast crystals of Mg$_2$Si ($H_c = 457\ \text{kg/mm}^2$).

c. 30 weight percent of Si, hot deformed.

centered-cubic lattice of the fluorspar type (Fig. 116).   Ageyev and Guseva have classified Mg$_2$Si as a coordination compound on the basis of electron density [396].

Practically no research on the properties of the Mg$_2$Si compound had been conducted prior to our studies.   Our samples were produced by casting and powder-metallurgy methods.   The compound was melted in a high-frequency furnace in a graphite crucible under a carnallite flux.   The cast samples obtained were very porous.   To increase their density they were compressed in a 22-mm-diameter steel cylinder at 620 to 630°C under a 20-t weight.   Tests showed the microhardness of Mg$_2$Si to be only 450 kg/mm^2, whereas, considering the relatively high melting point of this compound (about 1200°C), a much greater hardness would have been expected. The microhardness of the eutectic Mg + Mg₂Si is 75 kg/mm², whereas that of the eutectic Si + Mg₂Si is approximately 190 kg/mm². The microstructure of a typical cast alloy composed of Mg₂Si crystals and eutectic is illustrated in Fig. 117a.

For testing ductility in compression, the eutectic alloys were reduced under a 2-t load at "relative" temperatures (563 and 800°C) representing 90 percent of the respective melting temperatures on the absolute temperature scale. An argon atmosphere was used in the tests because the alloys become highly oxidized under standard atmosphere at elevated temperatures.

After the samples were reduced in a container, the thermal emf was determined in cast alloys paired with copper by means of a device built by Abrikosov. The temperature differential between cold and hot junctions varied between 20 and 390°C. The thermal emf was computed by the equation

$$\alpha = \frac{\Delta E_{\mathrm{Cu}-x}}{\Delta t},$$

where Δt is the difference between the cold and hot junctions, $\Delta E_{\mathrm{Cu}-x}$ is the thermal emf of the sample paired with copper, and α is the thermal emf in microvolts per degree.

The experimental data are given in Table 34 and Fig. 115. It appears that the conclusions reached for Al-Si alloys with regard to the effect of crystal boundaries on hardness are also applicable to Mg-Si alloys. The linear rule is

TABLE 34

HARDNESS, DUCTILITY, AND THERMAL ELECTROMOTIVE FORCE
OF CAST ALLOYS BASED ON MG₂SI

Si Content (wt. %)	Hardness H_c at Various Temperatures (kg/mm²)			Relative Contraction in Compression $\varepsilon_{st} = 90\% \ T_m$	Thermal emf When Paired with Cu $(\mu v/°)$	Microstructure of Alloys
	20°C	300°C	600°C			
3.0	46	. . .	. . .	. . .	. . .	
15.0	70	. . .	. . .	. . .	. . .	Mg₂Si crystals and the eutectic Mg + Mg₂Si
25.0	113	30	14	43.4	4	
30.0	120	86	32	. . .	. . .	
35.0	133	128	40	38.2	6	
36.5	332	187	108	5.0	. . .	
36.9	457	320	180	2.2	180	Mg₂Si crystals
37.0	350	200	. . .	4.4	. . .	Mg₂Si crystals and the eutectic Mg₂Si + Si
40.0	308	204	117	2.0	240	
45.0	346	200	169	1.6	126	
57.0	365	. . .	. . .	. . .	. . .	
100.0	1100	. . .	. . .	. . .	150	Si crystals

not observed on either side of the compound. Thus, the hardness of the 35-weight-percent-Si alloy (with a 75-percent-volume content of Mg_2Si) is only 130 kg/mm² at 20°C instead of the expected 400 kg/mm².

Alloys having less than 35 weight percent of silicon are characterized by a relatively low degree of hardness (less than 133 kg/mm²) at any temperature. The microstructure of these alloys reveals that the comparatively soft Mg_2Si eutectic is distributed along the grain boundaries of the compound. Alloys in which free silicon is present in the eutectic are noted for their high hardness.

The comparatively high value of hardness in alloys adjacent to the compound may probably be explained by the fact that the eutectic does not entirely fill the crystal boundaries of the compound. The hardness of a 36.5-weight-percent Si alloy is close to the additive one (332 kg/mm²).

The compound Mg_2Si exhibits a relatively greater decrease in hardness at high temperatures than the alloys, yet its hardness value at 600°C is still quite high (180 kg/mm²). Alloys with a high silicon content (40 and 45 weight percent) also retain their high hardness value at 300 and 600°C. Alloys based on Mg_2Si exhibit a low degree of ductility in compression (on the order of 2 percent). Alloys with a considerable amount of relatively soft magnesium eutectic (up to 35 weight percent of silicon) are considerably more ductile at higher temperatures (up to 40 percent at 600°C). Thus we see that the ductility of cast alloys changes inversely with hardness.

In agreement with findings discussed earlier, the compression strength increases with an increase in temperature; thus, in alloys with a 45 weight-percent-Si content, the compression strength is 12 kg/mm² at 600°C and 0.3 kg/mm² at 20°C. Consequently samples appear to become more metallic as a function of increasing temperature.

Alloys based on Mg_2Si have a high value of thermal emf on the order of 200 $\mu v/$°C. In a 40-weight-percent-Si alloy composed of Mg_2Si crystals and the eutectic $Mg_2Si + Si$, the value of the thermal emf is about 50 times that of alloys with a 35-weight-percent-Si content (see Fig. 115). The thermal emf of alloys of the given system changes with composition the same way the hardness changes. The thermal emf is a very structure-sensitive property and should be used more often in physicochemical studies of alloys.

It has been proved that properties of cast Mg-Si alloys are to a great extent determined by the distribution of their structural components. The location of the eutectic along grain boundaries results in a violation of the law of linearity in the change of properties as affected by composition. Attempts to change the distribution of the components by compressing the samples in a heated container produced no significant changes (Fig. 117c). As with the Al-Si alloys, the reason for failure in this instance was apparently the enormous difference in the hardnesses and the melting points of the individual components.

It might be in order to assume that, were it possible to distribute the eutectic uniformly within the grains of the compound, the hardness of an alloy would be controlled mainly by the hardness of the crystals of the compound. It was

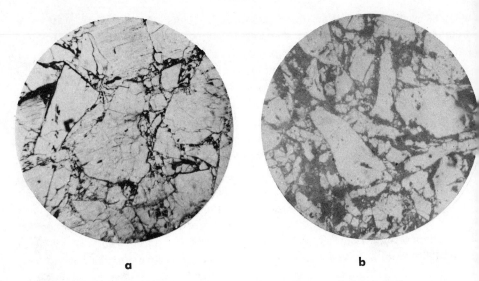

FIG. 118.   Microstructure of powder-metallurgy samples (×150).
a. Mg₂Si + 5 weight percent of Al.
b. Mg₂Si + 30 weight percent of Cu.

also considered of great interest to observe the changes in an alloy's hardness, which would occur if some plastic metals, such as aluminum or copper, instead of the eutectic mixture were deposited along the boundaries of the hard compound. To this end we decided to use powder-metallurgy techniques.

Powder-metallurgy samples of Mg₂Si with various aluminum contents (up to 20 weight percent) were prepared. Similarly prepared samples of the same compound containing 30 weight percent of copper were also obtained. To make these samples, a pulverized alloy (corresponding to Mg₂Si in composition) was blended with a corresponding quantity of either aluminum or copper powder. Both powders were first sifted through a 0.25-mm-diameter sieve. The powders were mixed in a special eccentrically rotated drum. Oleic acid was added to the powders (1 mg/g of the mixture) to provide surface-active lubrication which contributed to the formation of a solid adsorptive film on the surface of the

TABLE 35

HARDNESS OF POWDER-METALLURGY ALLOYS BASED ON MG₂SI

Temperature (°C)	Hardness H_c (kg/mm²)				
	Addition of Aluminum (wt. %)				Addition of 30 wt. % of Cu
	0ᵃ	5	10	20	
20	457	400	250	180	220
300	320	197	122	117	197
600	180	96	92	54	100

ᵃ Cast alloy Mg₂Si.

powder particles. The blended powders were cold-formed in a press. They were next compressed at 500 to 530°C under a 3- to 10-t/cm² load.

Figure 118 illustrates the microstructures of the powder-metallurgy samples obtained. The hardness testing procedure was the same as that used for cast alloys. The resulting data are given in Table 35.

Apparently here too the presence of soft components along the grain boundaries of a hard compound produces a sharp decrease in the hardness of samples, but the values of hardness are closer to those predicted by the law of linearity. This result is true for all temperatures; however, at considerably higher temperatures the increase in the volume of the soft component brings about a

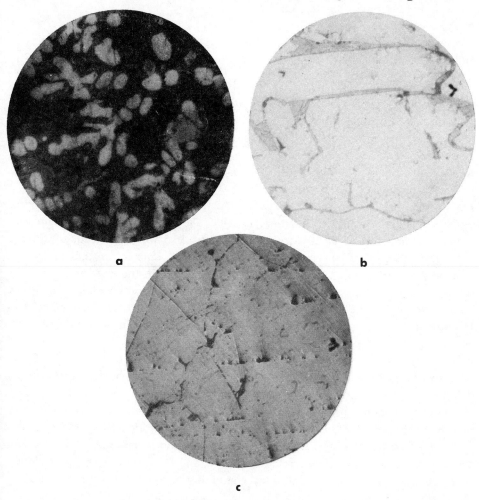

a

b

c

FIG. 119.   Microstructure of cast annealed Cu-Si alloys (×210).
a. 40 weight percent of Si.
b. 80 weight percent of Si.
c. 95 weight percent of Si.

relatively smaller decrease in the macrohardness of samples. The substitution of a somewhat harder copper, even with a 30-weight-percent content for plastic aluminum, produced an increased hardness in samples.

The relatively high values of hardness of powder-metallurgy samples at any temperature are likewise noteworthy. These samples, however, were found to have low compression strength at 20°C, and they fractured in a brittle manner.

Cu-Si System

A specific feature of this system is that the melting points of the components are reasonably close to each other.

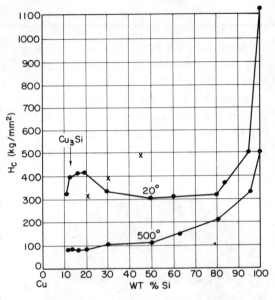

FIG. 120. Isothermal curves for hardness of Cu-Si alloys.

x–hardness of powder-metallurgy samples.

The hypereutectic Cu-Si alloys (20 to 100 weight percent of silicon), which consist of silicon and eutectic, exhibit considerable differences in properties. The microhardness of the eutectic, which is composed of a mixture of Cu_3Si and 16.5 weight percent of silicon, averages 380 kg/mm²; whereas the microhardness of silicon, in this particular instance, is 1000 kg/mm². The melting temperature of the eutectic is 802°C. The lower-melting eutectic, while being cooled, is distributed along the grain boundaries of the high-melting silicon. Annealing at 600°C does not affect the microstructure of the alloys (Fig. 119). The hardness of an 80-weight-percent-Si Cu-Si alloy at 20°C is close to the hardness of the eutectic and, as in previous cases, is considerably below the "additive" hardness (Fig. 120). The hardness of alloys at 500°C rises at a relatively slow rate with increase of silicon up to 80 weight percent and rapidly beyond that.

The compression strength of alloys with 80 weight percent of silicon is considerably greater at 20° and 500°C than that of silicon alone (Fig. 121). In the isothermal curves of Fig. 121, the eutectic composition stands out by its specific characteristic of maximum strength at 20°C and minimum strength at 500°C. The compression strength of an alloy containing 80 weight percent of silicon is three times greater at 500°C (32.5 kg/mm²) than that of pure silicon (11 kg/mm²). Therefore, changes in the crushing strength of alloys with high silicon contents occur inversely with changes in hardness.

To forestall any formation of complex intermetallic phases inherent to Cu-Si alloys, it was found expedient to have the samples prepared by the powder-metallurgy method. Samples with 20, 30, and 50 weight percent of silicon were obtained by the hot-extrusion method from a mixture of copper and silicon powders.

The hardness of the powder-metallurgy samples exhibited a uniform increase with increased silicon content. Thus, the hardness of a sample containing 50 weight percent of silicon was 500 kg/mm² (300 kg/mm² for a cast alloy); in alloys with 30 and 20 weight percent of silicon it was 380 and 300 kg/mm², respectively. However, all these alloys exhibited very little ductility.

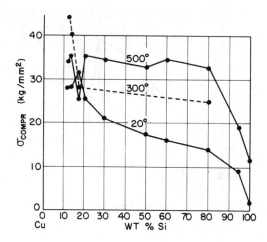

FIG. 121. Isothermal curves for compression strength of Cu-Si alloys.

Mg-Ge System

Similar data were obtained in hardness tests of Mg-Ge alloys. A phase diagram of this system is similar to that of the Mg-Si system. The structure of the Mg_2Ge compound is analogous to the Mg_2Si structure (see Fig. 116).

Magnesium-germanium alloys are unstable in air; consequently, an argon atmosphere was used in their preparation and hardness testing at high temperatures.

The hardness properties of alloys composed of the eutectic $Mg + Mg_2Ge$ and of the compound Mg_2Ge remain comparatively low; however, with higher percentages of germanium (above 60 weight percent of Ge) the hardness increases rapidly (Table 36, Fig. 122). A radical difference in the microhardness of com-

TABLE 36

HARDNESS OF MG-GE ALLOYS AT VARIOUS TEMPERATURES

Germanium Content (wt. %)	Hardness H_c (kg/mm²)	
	20°C	600°C
0 (100% Mg)	32	3.7
34	67	17.0
40	70	19.0
42	87	22.0
44	99	31.5
50	107	27.0
58	110	38.0
61	180	46.0
65	190	73.2
100	400-500	240.0

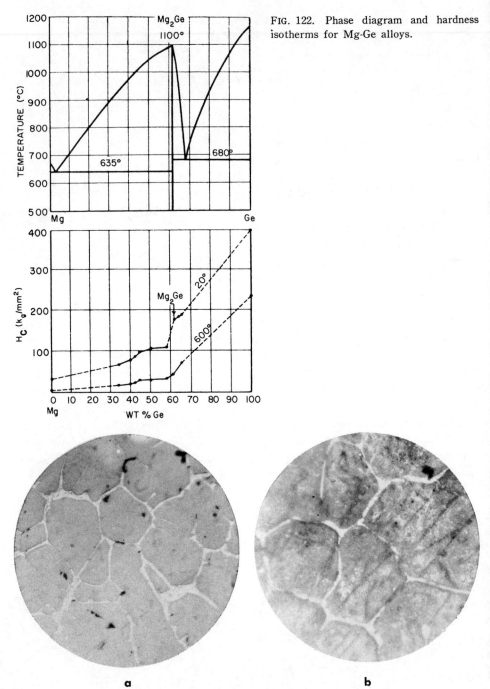

FIG. 122. Phase diagram and hardness isotherms for Mg-Ge alloys.

FIG. 123.   Microstructure of cast Mg-Ge alloys ($\times 210$).

a. 50 weight percent of Ge.

b. 61 weight percent of Ge.

ponents is observed; the microhardness of the eutectic $Mg + Mg_2Ge$ is low, averaging $66.0 \, kg/mm^2$, whereas that of Mg_2Ge is between 330 and $350 \, kg/mm^2$. The microstructure of Mg-Ge alloys is given in Fig. 123.

Ni-Si and Co-Si Systems

Figures 124 and 125 illustrate the experimental data we obtained on the hardness of Ni-Si and Co-Si alloys.

TABLE 37

MECHANICAL PROPERTIES OF CO-SI ALLOYS IN COMPRESSION
AT VARIOUS TEMPERATURES

Silicon Content (wt. %)	Ultimate Crushing Strength σ_{compr} (kg/mm²)		Relative Contraction at 1000°C
	20°C	500°C	
0 (100% Co)	91.8	89.2	71.0
5.0	14.2	99.3	66.8
52.0	16.8	30.0	61.0
54.5	16.1	46.0	55.0
58.82	13.5	72.0	52.0
62.0	4.8	41.0	56.0
70.0	4.9	36.0	55.0
95.0	5.3	25.0	55.0
100.0	70.0	48.0	81.0

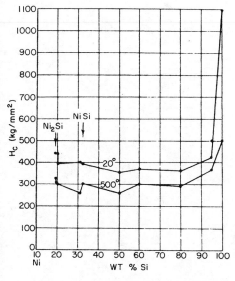 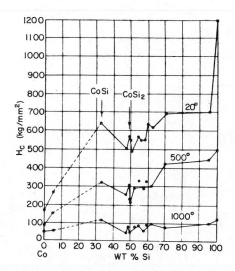

FIG. 124. Isothermal curves for hardness of Ni-Si alloys.

Fig. 125. Isothermal curves for hardness of Co-Si alloys.

The hardness of two-phase Ni-Si alloys within the range 20- to 95-weight-per-cent-Si content changes only slightly at room or elevated temperatures. Only when the silicon content reaches 95 weight percent is the hardness of the alloy abruptly increased (see Fig. 124).

Several metallic compounds are formed by cobalt and silicon. Our findings did not confirm the existence of the compound $CoSi_3$, but the presence of the compound $CoSi_2$ appears indisputable. Alloys of this system are very stable in air. The room-temperature hardness of Co-Si alloys with a 30- to 95-weight-percent-Si content is radically different from that of alloys containing over 95 weight percent of silicon (see Fig. 125).

It is of interest to note the high hardness values of Ni-Si and Co-Si alloys at

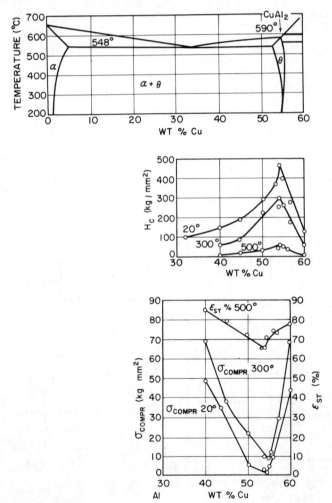

FIG. 126. Phase diagram and mechanical properties of Cu-Al alloys.

500°C. Alloys of the Co-Si system exhibit a considerable increase in hardness in the 500 to 700°C temperature range, and a considerable degree of relative contraction in compression is observed in these alloys at 1000°C (Table 37).

It follows, therefore, that the linear relationship of mechanical properties with composition, either at room or at elevated temperatures, is absent in all the examined alloys of Al-Si, Mg-Si, Mg-Ge, Cu-Si, Ni-Si, and Co-Si.

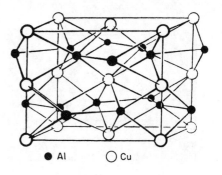

● Al   ○ Cu

FIG. 127.   Structure of CuAl₂.

Cu-Al System

The phase diagram of this system of alloys is given in Fig. 126. The solidification range of alloys near the compound $CuAl_2$ is considerably less than that of similar alloys described in the earlier systems, because the difference between the melting points of the compound and that of the eutectic is negligible. This compound has a comparatively low melting temperature (approximately 600°C), which simplifies methods of preparation. The eutectic melts at 548°C. The compound $CuAl_2$ (θ phase) contains 54.1 weight percent of copper and has a tetragonal body-centered lattice with 12 atoms in the unit cell (Fig. 127) [38]. The microhardness of $CuAl_2$ is approximately 450 kg/mm². Special consideration was given to alloys of this compound. Experiments with alloys having 40 to 70 weight percent of copper were conducted in cast and in hot-extruded conditions.

The metal was melted in an electric crucible furnace and poured into a 21-mm-diameter steel casting mold. Rods 10 mm in diameter were extruded with an 80 percent reduction at 520 to 530°C. The microstructure of the alloys was investigated; their micro- and macrohardness and their strength and ductility in compression were determined. Samples were deformed on the universal device without the aid of a protective medium; the cylindrical-sample dimensions were $l = d = 10$ mm. The appearance of the first crack was signalled by a drop of the indicator dial.

The data on the hardness of alloys is given in Table 38 and in Fig. 126. Hot deformation caused an increase in the hardness of samples at the expense of a uniform distribution of components (Fig. 128). Alloys with a copper content up to 45 weight percent have a relatively low hardness, as the eutectic content is quite large (the microhardness of the eutectic is 80 kg/mm²). The complete analogy observed in the hardness curves of these alloys with those of alloys in the earlier systems is due to a similarity in structure. Deviations from additivity are also seen in this case but are less pronounced at high temperatures.

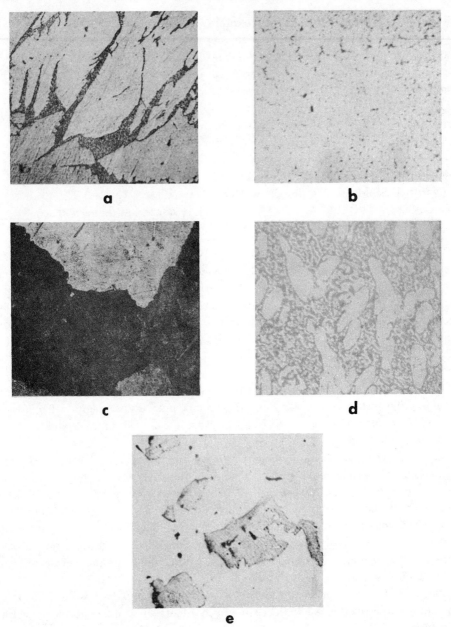

FIG. 128.   Microstructure of Cu-Al alloys ($\times$150).

a. 50 weight percent of Cu, cast ($H_c = 143 \, \text{kg/mm}^2$).

b. 50 weight percent of Cu, hot-extruded ($H_c = 300 \, \text{kg/mm}^2$).

c. 54.1 weight percent of Cu, hot-extruded, crystals of compound CuAl$_2$ ($H_c = 460 \text{kg/mm}^2$).

d. 60 weight percent of Cu, hot-extruded ($H_c = 130 \, \text{kg/mm}^2$).

e. 95 weight percent of CuAl$_2$–5 weight percent Al, powder-metallurgy sample ($H_c = 280 \, \text{kg/mm}^2$).

TABLE 38

HARDNESS OF CAST AND EXTRUDED AL-CU ALLOYS CONTAINING CUAL₂
AT VARIOUS TEMPERATURES

| Copper Content (wt. %) | Hardness H_c (kg/mm²) | | | | Microstructure of Alloys |
| | Cast Alloys | Hot-Extruded Alloys | | | |
	20°C	20°C	300°C	500°C	
40.0	125	140	60	11	CuAl₂ compound and the
45.0	138	180	90	19	eutectic CuAl₂ + solid
50.0	143	300	220	27	solution of Al
54.0	280	370	233	39	
54.1	370	460	300	51	CuAl₂ compound
54.5	221	400	260	42	CuAl₂ compound and the
56.0	200	280	208	33	eutectic CuAl₂ + η
60.0	129	130	64	10	

Alloys with 50- to 60-weight-percent-Cu content remain hard at 300°C but become very soft at 500°C (see Tables 38 and 39 and Fig. 126).

The compound CuAl₂ and the alloys adjacent to it by composition are brittle in the 20 to 300°C range. An increase in the eutectic content along the crystal boundaries presents certain possibilities for plastic deformation and for increased strength in compression. Thus, the strength of a 40-weight-percent-Cu alloy at 300°C is about 70 kg/mm² and that of the compound is approximately 10 kg/mm². At 500°C, all of the tested alloys were ductile to such a degree that they were able to withstand over 80-percent reduction in height without fracturing and, as mentioned before, could be extruded.

The possibilities of successful hot deformation of such alloys depends on the

TABLE 39

COMPRESSION STRENGTH AND DUCTILITY OF HOT-EXTRUDED ALLOYS BASED
ON THE COMPOUND CUAL₂

| Copper Content (wt. %) | Ultimate Compression Strength σ_{comp} (kg/mm²) | | Ductility in Compression at 500°C ε_{st} (%) |
	20°C	300°C	
40.0	48.0	68.5	84.5
45.0	36.0	37.1	79.0
50.0	8.0	23.0	73.4
54.0	5.5	11.0	70.5
54.1	3.0	10.2	67.5
54.6	7.0	12.5	75.2
56.0	11.4	30.0	73.0
60.0	45.3	68.5	77.2

relatively small differences in the melting temperatures of the structural components—of the compound $CuAl_2$ and of the eutectic ($CuAl_2$ plus a solid solution of aluminum). Our inability to fracture samples at 500°C prevented us from determining their ultimate strength; the relative contraction of samples was determined under a constant load of 6000 kg. Alloys based on the compound exhibited a somewhat smaller reduction than did the other alloys at this load (Table 39) and hence can be assumed to be somewhat stronger.

Data presented in Fig. 126 show that, because of a specific arrangement of the soft and the hard structural components, the linear rule for mechanical properties of these alloys does not apply at 20 and 300°C; however, it may approximately apply at 500°C.

Powdered-metal samples based on the compound $CuAl_2$ with 3- to 15-weight-percent-Al content (Fig. 128e) were prepared. The method used was similar to that followed for samples of Mg_2Si and Al. As compared with cast samples, these were found to be harder and somewhat more ductile. The hardness of a sample with 5-weight-percent-Al was 280 kg/mm^2. With an increase in temperature to 300°C, the powdered-metal samples softened rapidly.

On the whole it may be concluded that, where the difference in the melting points of the alloy components is not significant, the powdered-metal method of preparing samples (which redistributes the arrangement of phases) does not present any advantages in comparison with deformation (hot extrusion, for example) of cast samples.

On the strength of studies made on eutectic-type alloys, a conclusion may be drawn that the deviation from the rule of linearity is greater as the difference in the hardness of the components and in the degree of their dispersion is greater. Also uniformity in crystal size and in the arrangement of phases in the cast state is greater as the solidification range is greater.

Alloys of Predetermined Structure

We suggested a method for obtaining alloys with a predetermined structure by replacing the low-melting component with another metal or alloy [385]. The purpose of this study was to determine the feasibility of decreasing the brittleness of metallic-compound alloys having an equilibrium composition by surrounding their crystals with soft-alloy films. Theoretically, such an achievement is possible. It is well known from phase diagrams that compounds of a specific composition which crystallize from the melt associate with relatively low-melting eutectics. For this reason alloys based on such compounds, as a rule, possess a wide solidification range describing the condition in which the compound has already solidified but the eutectic is still in the liquid state. The concept of the method consists of removing the liquid eutectic and replacing it with a liquid alloy or metal through hydrostatic or external pressure or suction; the eutectic connecting the dendrites of the compound would thus be replaced.

The assumption was that the infiltration of a ductile component into the dendrite branches would increase the plasticity of the alloy without lowering its hardness. For additional changes in the structure such an alloy could be further processed by pressure and by hot working if necessary.

A schematic arrangement for obtaining alloys by substituting the low-melting component is illustrated in Fig. 129. Alloys obtained with a crystallizer in the form of a cone (3) were found to be of a greater density.

Attempts to replace the eutectic (in the Mg-Si system) with aluminum were successful where the silicon content was approximately 20 weight percent (silicon content of the compound was 36.9 weight percent). The alloy hardness prior to adding aluminum was about 80 kg/mm^2 and 65 kg/mm^2 thereafter. The alloy was then extruded and, because of a structural alignment which took place, its hardness rose to 100 kg/mm^2. Rods of good quality were obtained.

An experiment was conducted to substitute the eutectic in an alloy consisting of 40 weight percent of silicon and 60 weight percent of aluminum with an alloy containing 87 weight percent of tin and 13 weight percent of aluminum. The cast alloys and the substituted ones were found to be of equal compression strength (31 kg/mm^2); the maximum contraction of a cast sample was 37 percent and that of a substituted one, 47 percent. Hardness of the substituted alloy

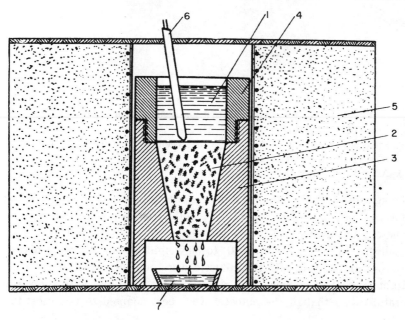

FIG. 129. Sketch of a device to produce alloys by the substitution of the light-melting component.

1-incoming alloy; 2-basic alloy in the solid-liquid state; 3-conical mold (recrystallizer); 4-headpiece; 5-electric furnace; 6-thermocouple; 7-eutectic receptacle.

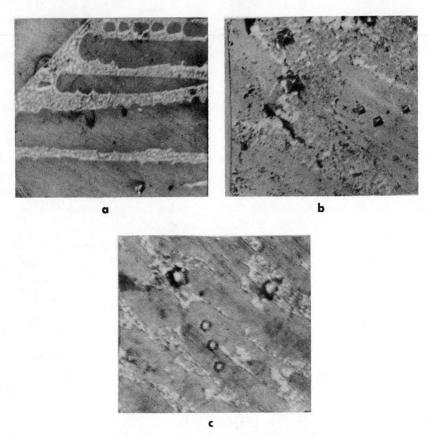

a   b

c

FIG. 130. Microstructure of cast and "substituted" alloys (×150).
a. 47 weight percent of Cu, balance Al, cast.
b. Same as a, except that the eutectic has been replaced by an 87-weight-per-
cent-Sn and 13-weight-percent-Al alloy.
c. Alloy b, after hot deformation.

was 32 kg/mm^2, only half as hard as the cast alloy (70 kg/mm^2). It has been found impossible thus far to expel the eutectic from a high-silicon-content alloy.

In these pouring-off experiments the main interest was centered around the CuAl$_2$ alloys. Alloys containing 40- to 50-weight-percent Cu were tested. The best results in "pouring off" the eutectic were achieved with alloys containing 40 weight percent of copper. It was found that the alloys with a lower melting temperature than that of the eutectic were best adapted to the substitution of the latter.

Pouring in of tin was first tried. The hardness of a cast alloy with 47 weight percent of copper was 200 kg/mm^2 before substitution; it decreased to 120 kg/mm^2 after substitution. The microhardness of the components (50-kg load) was 460 kg/mm^2 for CuAl$_2$, 26 kg/mm^2 for tin and 135 kg/mm^2 for the eutectic ($v + \alpha$). Thus we see that substitution of the eutectic with soft tin decreased the macrohardness of the alloy to approximately half its original value. The subject alloy separated after being extruded at 220°C, probably because of overheating of the tin. It was not deemed expedient to extrude at lower temperatures since the compound $CuAl_2$ would not be soft enough. Consequently an alloy of 87 weight percent of tin and 13 weight percent of aluminum was used instead. In the solid state, this alloy is characterized by a mixture of crystals in these metals and its hardness is 100 kg/mm² (liquidus temperature 530°C). The substitution made it possible to extrude at a higher temperature, 440°C. The hardness of the 47-weight-percent-Cu alloy dropped to 140 kg/mm² after substitution of the eutectic by the above alloy. Eleven-mm-diameter rods of this alloy were obtained by 77-percent extrusion. The flow stress during extrusion was 50 kg/mm². After extrusion the hardness of the alloy rose to 245 kg/mm². The hardness was not affected by annealing at 400°C. In static deformation at room temperature, the substituted-alloy specimen exhibited a higher degree of strength and ductility; its ultimate strength in compression was 52.6 kg/mm² (40 kg/mm² in the cast alloy). The relative contractions were 11 and 6 percent respectively.

The resultant changes in alloy structure are shown in Fig. 130. The microstructure of a cast alloy consists of large crystals of the compound $CuAl_2$ with the eutectic ($\alpha + CuAl_2$) along its boundaries. Such an alloy is brittle. The role of the substituted eutectic is taken over by a mixture of tin and aluminum crystals and the hardness of the alloy is consequently decreased. The process of extrusion breaks up the structure but the grains of the compound still retain their large size. The hardness of the alloy is increased because of a high degree of structural uniformity and an elimination of pores. One of the causes of the alloy's inadequate impact ductility appears to be the coarse structure. Oxidation of the alloy occurring in the process of the pouring off of the eutectic could likewise have been a major factor. Consequently, experiments where a low-melting compound is substituted are now being conducted in a helium atmosphere or in vacuum [397].

An experiment was also performed on the pouring in of a compound closely related in composition to $CuAl_2$; this alloy, consisting of 80 weight percent of zinc and 20 weight percent of aluminum, is superductile according to Bochvar. After being annealed at 200°C, the macrohardness of the sample was 150 kg/mm², or less than half that of a cast alloy without substitution.

On the strength of experimental data obtained on alloy-component substitution, the following preliminary conclusions may be made:

1. The method for replacement was mastered for cases where a low and medium content of the high-melting component (Si, Mg_2Si, $CuAl_2$) was present.

2. In this case, as well as in experiments with cast and powder-metallurgy samples, the composite hardness of an alloy is primarily dictated by the hardness of the soft component at the boundary.

3. "Substituted" alloys are more ductile than cast alloys.

4. Substituted alloys yield to hot working, which results in a more uniform structure and increases the density and the hardness of samples.

5. The method of alloy-component substitution opens a wide field of possibilities in controlling alloy structure and provides the means to obtain samples with completely new phases.

6. Thermal and mechanical processing creates additional opportunities for controlling the structure of substituted alloys.

7. Another factor of importance is the ability to reduce the crystal grains of the hard-alloy component and to resolve the mechanical properties of alloys which, by their structure, consist of soft-component crystals surrounded by films of a hard component (analogous to the structure of hypereutectoid steel) [394].

Solid-Solution Systems

Typical pure metals are ductile but their strength is relatively low. Metallic solid solutions as distinct from pure metals, on the other hand, have greater strength while retaining their high ductility. Because of this favorable combination of mechanical properties, solid solutions are most extensively used as structural materials in industry. The majority of industrial alloys are either solid solutions or alloys in which the solid solution is the primary phase.

A number of brasses, bronzes, alloys of aluminum, titanium, and magnesium, and a number of special steels are solid solutions. Such alloys are subject to changes in mutual solubility with changes in temperature; this factor leads to strengthening from the effects of hot working, quenching, and aging, which are additional valuable properties of solid solutions. This feature has contributed in a major way to the high level of excellence achieved in contemporary endeavors, especially aviation.

Alloys of limited and unlimited solid solubility may be formed by the melted components. The ability of metals to form solid solutions is determined by 1) the closeness of the chemical properties of elements in relation to their position in the periodic table; 2) the relatively low difference in interatomic spacing—of 8 to 10 percent for continuous solid solutions and 14 to 16 percent for limited solid solutions; and 3) the isomorphism of metallic crystal lattices (for forming continuous solid solutions) [397]. This dependence is substantiated by a series of examples, for instance, in which the solvents are Cu and Ag (Hume-Rothery [398], [399]), Al (Kuznetsov [400]), Fe, Ni, and Ti (Kornilov [297], [366], [401]), and Mg [402]. Generally speaking, experimental data support this rule. The presence of deviations, in a number of cases, points to the fact that the effect of all the factors has not as yet been determined and that development and studies of the theoretical basis of the mutual solubility of metals must be carried on.

As determined by Kurnakov, the physicomechanical properties of continuous solid solutions change according to continuous concave-shaped curves; this is caused by a continuous transition of one of the components to the crystal lattice of another component. The characteristic features of resistance to deformation, such as hardness, flow stress, ultimate strength, and others, are to exhibit curves containing a maximum. According to Tammann, this may possibly be explained by the general principle that the cohesive forces are greater between hetero-geneous than between homogeneous atoms [309]. The maximum strength, as a rule, corresponds to the highest saturation of a solid solution and, consequently, to the highest degree of lattice distortion.

According to the present-day concept, the fundamental cause of strengthening in solid solutions is associated with the degree and the character (tension or compression) of distortion of the crystal lattice of the solvent formed by the presence of an alloying element. The greater the distortion of the solid solu-tion crystal lattice (and the greater the stress from these changes in volume), the more intensive will be the strengthening. Strength properties are more affected by compression than by tension in the lattice. When a solid solution is formed the relative strengthening depends on the nature of the alloying element and does not depend on the nature of the solvent metal [403]. Shisho-kin and Ageyeva state that the strength of dilute solid solutions is determined by two opposite factors—the relative sizes of the particles and the mutual polar-izing effect of the particles [404]. Ageyev pointed out that the maximum hard-ness for the majority of systems with continuous series of solid solutions is at 50 atomic percent, since, at this point, a maximum distortion of the crystal lattice's field force is observed [18]. Ductility characteristics in binary solid solutions vary along analogous curves but in a convex manner. In binary salt and metallic systems, at least at room temperature, not a single deviation from Kurnakov's rule was ever found on the variations in hardness of a solid solution. Limited solid solutions retain the crystal structure of the solvent metal; the degree of lattice change, however, is affected by the type of solid solution formed (interstitial, substitutional).

Apparently solid solutions that form with heats of formation about equal to the heat observed in the formation of metallic compounds may be considered as solutions of metallic compounds in the base metal [386]. Because of the chemical interaction when such a solid solution is formed, in which the neighbor atoms belong to two distinct elements, the shortest interatomic distances are consider-ably altered (as compared to the shortest distances between atoms of a solvent metal). Thus, in Ni-Cu alloys with 25 percent of copper, the root-mean-square value of atom displacement is 0.19A with a 0.02A difference in the atomic radii of nickel and copper. This displacement is apparently accompanied by a con-siderable distortion of the electron shells [59].

The presence of intermolecular cohesion forces may be judged by the non-additive changes in volume occurring in the process of solid-solution formation observed in a number of instances [405]. Another convincing proof is the widely spread tendency of continuous solid solutions to form into Kurnakov solutions.

Kornilov has examined several cases in which binary metallic compounds are able to form continuous solid solutions [406]. About 60 continuous solid solutions among metallic compounds are known at present.

Ageyev cites a number of instances where solid solutions were formed with compounds. However, in a number of systems—Al-Ag, Sb-Pb, Na-Pb, and others —no diluted molecular solid solutions (i.e., of dissolution of the chemical compound in a pure metal) were found [18].

It goes without saying that molecular formations do affect the mechanical properties of a solid solution. This fact was convincingly illustrated by Urazov and Shushpanova in the molecular formation of Mg_2Si in a solid solution of aluminum during studies on the ultimate strength of alloys in the system Al-Mg-Si [155]. Kuznetsov and Makarov have demonstrated by the X-ray method that, in some of these alloys, the increase in hardness which accompanies natural aging is not related to precipitation from a saturated solid solution but, apparently, to the segregation of atoms into molecular complexes in the solution [407]. Badayeva confirmed the presence of such formations by measuring the electrical resistance of annealed alloys of a given system, at various temperatures [386]. Consequently, molecular complexes are retained in a number of instances, even at high temperatures. The hypothesis advanced by Urazov on the formation of molecular complexes in solid solutions was confirmed by Mikheyeva, who detected the presence of anomalies in the melting diagrams of the aluminum solid solution in Al-Mg-Zn alloys [408]. Also Grum-Grzhimaylo discovered the presence of chemical compounds in the Fe-Cr and Cu-Ni systems [387] by measuring the electrical resistance and the galvanomagnetic capacity of cast alloys. Furthermore, metastable phases in solid solutions have been observed in a number of systems.

The present theory on liquid solutions takes into account all possible types of interaction of components in a solution, beginning with the physical, conditioned by purely molecular forces, and ending with purely chemical ones [409].

The facts enumerated above are in agreement with views expressed by Mendeleyev that solutions have a complex structure, representing an aggregation of mixtures of a solvent with dissolved matter in which the compounds are in various stages of dissociation [410], [411]. "Compounds are, to this day, a dark and a very difficult subject because of their complexity. This is the current problem for science and it will not be amiss to have new Russian efforts directed toward this section of chemistry" [410, p. 29]. These words by Mendeleyev, written with reference to solid metallic solutions, have not lost their significance to this day.

Plastic deformation contributes considerably to the breaking up of a supersaturated solid solution. Using an electron microscope, Buynov and Savinykh investigated the alloys Al-Si and Al-Mg-Si and proved that, in an Al-Si (1.2 percent) alloy, the number of particles precipitated from solid solution is from two to three times greater in deformed specimens than in nondeformed specimens [412]. Deformation of metals as a result of phase transformations (which also includes deformation observed during decomposition of solid solutions) is examined in a paper by Zakharova and Lashko [413].

Iveronova and her associates have cleared up a number of points on the influence of composition of the solid solution in relation to the kinetics of recrystallization [202], [414]. As they demonstrated, at a given degree of deformation, the internal stress of an alloy increases in proportion to the concentration of solute. Recovery in pure metals occurs basically along slip planes in a crystal at elevated temperatures. Redistribution of atoms of both components takes place on the slip planes in solid solution, especially for high-alloy materials, as a result of the phenomenon of directed diffusion first observed by Konobeyevsky [415]. In processes of this type, the chemical state becomes heterogeneous rather than uniform; a concentration of large atoms is found in expanded parts of the lattice and small atoms in the compressed parts of the lattice. As a result of this unique process of diffusion, the internal stress is relieved but the crystal lattice remains distorted. Because of these phenomena, the recrystallization curve is complex and depends on the solute content of the alloy. Figure 131 shows the curve for a typical system, Al-Mg. Other typical systems are: Cu-Sn, Cu-Al, Ag-Zn, Al-Mg, Al-Zn, and Cu-Zn. Under these conditions, the greater the difference in the atomic radii, the greater should be the directed diffusional stream and the higher the recrystallization temperature of the alloy with increased alloying. A dip in the recrystallization curve is related to the strengthening of the solid solution. An increase in the temperature of recrystallization begins in the region of maximum solubility and is caused by phase transformations occurring in solid solutions simultaneously with recrystallization [202]. The effect of magnesium on the recrystallization of aluminum is presented in Fig. 131 as an example of the phenomena described.

In their experiments with solid solutions of aluminum in magnesium, Kornilov and Priakhina found that the strongest heat-resistant alloy was displaced towards higher aluminum concentrations as a function of increasing temperature and, at 400°C, pure aluminum becomes more heat resistant than its alloys [416].

In our opinion, and on the basis of the strength of the earlier observations, the mechanical-properties–composition curves of solid solutions may take on two different shapes. When pronounced molecular formations are present in the flow curves of properties, maxima and minima may be present. Where little or no molecular interaction is

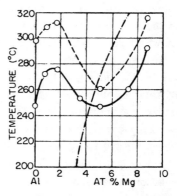

FIG. 131. Curves describing the beginning and end of recrystallization for Al-Mg alloys (Iveronova).

observed, the curves describing mechanical properties will show a uniform increase (strength) or a decrease (ductility) with an increase in concentration up to the limit of solid solubility. Our assumption, confirmed by experimental data, is that the first type of curve is observed when a chemical compound is introduced into a composition bordering with the solid solution of a multiphase mixture (Cu-Zn system and others); the second curve is observed when the mixture consists of pure

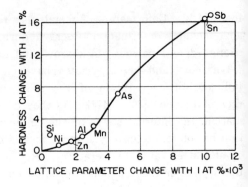

FIG. 132. Relationship between strengthening observed in copper-base alloys and changes in lattice parameter.

metals or solid solutions, as in such systems as Pb-Sb, Pb-Sn, Ag-Bi, Ag-Cu, Ag-Ge, Ag-Pb, and Ag-Si. The above assumptions, confirmed by a good number of examples, constitute further proof of the presence of solid molecular solutions.

Osipov and Stiukhov hypothesized on the basis of thermodynamic data that solid solutions approaching the limit of solid solubility may possess high resistance to plastic flow, provided the second phase is potentially able to precipitate in the process of deformation. Furthermore, this second phase should be significantly different either in composition, in crystalline structure, or in density [417]. In the process of deformation, alloys become thermodynamically unstable and will precipitate the second phase; consequently plastic deformation contributes to the decomposition of a solid solution, especially along grain boundaries, and decreases solubility in the solid state.

As will be seen later, copper alloys (brasses and bronzes) in the region of homogeneous solid solutions do not show a uniform decrease in ductility with alloying, but certain maxima are often observed. The lower ductility of copper is probably caused by insufficient deoxidation of the metal. Completely deoxidized copper is invariably more ductile than any solid solution based thereon.

Changes in properties of limited solid solutions as a function of temperature are controlled not only by the nature of the components but also by the extent of solid solubility, by the relative decrease in the melting point from alloying, and by softening processes. As the temperature is increased the mechanical property–composition curves become more uniform while the maximum hardness veers toward the pure component.

In our presentation of experimental data on the mechanical properties of solid solutions, we shall first examine the solid solutions based on monomorphic metals and then those based on polymorphic ones.

The majority of solid-solution alloys we studied are based on copper (Cu-Ni, Cu-Zn, Cu-Mn, Cu-Zn-Al). Published data [250] indicate that an addition of 0.1 atomic percent of an alloying element to copper results in a strengthening effect which is approximately proportional to the difference in atomic radii of the solvent and solute atoms. This dependence may also be expressed in the form of strengthening as a function of changes in the lattice parameter; such a dependence for copper is illustrated in Fig. 132.

Nickel, whose atomic radius is quite similar to that of copper, distorts the copper lattice slightly. For this reason nickel is completely dissolved in copper and its effect on increasing the strength of copper is less than for any other element quoted in the graph. Zinc and aluminum likewise contribute little to solid solution strengthening of copper. Antimony and tin, with radii distinctly different from those of copper, distort the copper lattice severely, possess only limited solubility (0.6 and 1 atomic percent respectively) and produce the highest strengthening effect. Magnesium and manganese contribute greatly to the strength of solid solutions based on copper. The possibility of increasing the strength properties of any of the discussed alloys by cold working is directly related to the increase of its strengthening by alloying. Composition versus long-duration-hardness curves for alloys based on copper between 400 and 800°C have been plotted by Zakharov.

Cu-Ni System

More than 35 papers have been devoted to the Cu-Ni system. Studies on the microstructure, electrical conductivity, and thermal analysis of the system undertaken by Kurnakov and Zhemchuzhny in 1906 and on hardness in 1908 have been confirmed by subsequent investigators. Our experimental data on the various mechanical properties of this system are shown in Fig. 48. It is worth noting that the maximum of hardness is related to the filling of the

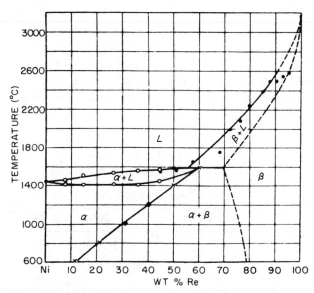

FIG. 133. Phase diagram for the Ni-Re system (Pogodin and Skriabina).

d-shell in nickel (60 atomic percent) [418]. Consequently, in the Cu-Ni system, the influence of interatomic cohesion of hardness is more effective than that of lattice distortion which would have resulted in the maximum hardness taking place at 50 atomic percent of nickel.

According to Bochvar and Korolkov, heating to 500°C is sufficient to displace the characteristic maximum of the hardness curve for Cu-Ni and to render it considerably less pronounced. Apparently the increase in resistance to slip as a result of introduction of solute atoms into the atomic lattice of the base metal decreases as the diffusion processes increase at elevated temperature [187].

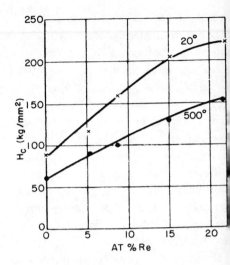

FIG. 134. Hardness of Ni-Re alloys at 20 and 500°C.

Ni-Re System

Rhenium has a high melting point, about 3200°C [242], [419]. The phase diagram for this system has been established by Pogodin and Skriabina (Fig. 133) [420]. Alloys of this system present the noteworthy situation where the components, radically unlike in their crystal structure (nickel–face-centered-cubic, rhenium–hexagonal), form large regions of solid solutions.

Pogodin and Skriabina furnished cast samples for our experiments. These samples, annealed at 1200°C, were in a hardened state; they had a polyhedral structure containing dendrites which were not eliminated by annealing. To attain the required shape, the samples were formed on a vertical-ram impact machine at 700 to 800°C. Their hardness was next measured at 20 and 500°C. The experimental data are presented in Fig. 134 and Table 40. As shown in the table, both isotherms rise smoothly with increase in rhenium content in the solid-solution region. In an alloy containing 21.6 atomic percent of rhenium

TABLE 40

HARDNESS OF NI-RE ALLOYS AT 20 AND 500°C

Rhenium Content (at. %)	Hardness H_c (kg/mm²)		Temperature Coefficient of Hardness α
	20°C	500°C	
0 (100 % Ni)	90	60.5	$-3.6 \cdot 10^{-4}$
5.17	116	90.0	$-2.3 \cdot 10^{-4}$
8.65	161	97.0	$-4.6 \cdot 10^{-4}$
14.93	208	131.0	$-4.2 \cdot 10^{-4}$
21.54	226	156.0	$-3.4 \cdot 10^{-4}$

the hardness at 20°C is 226 kg/mm², which is more than two and one half times the hardness of nickel. Yet, when the large limits of solid solubility are taken into account, it may be inferred that, in this particular case, rhenium is not an outstanding strengthening agent. All alloys exhibit a 25 to 30 percent decrease in hardness at 500°C. As seen in Fig. 132, the hardness-composition curves take on a convex nature at 20 and 500°C.

Re-Mo System

Data have recently been received on the structure and hardness of alloys of the Re-Mo system (smelted in an arc furnace) at various temperatures (Fig. 135) [421]. Apparently a large region on solid solutions is also formed in this system. An abrupt increase in hardness occurs with the formation of the compound Re_3Mo_2. Even at 1150°C, the hardness isotherm (in an argon atmosphere) appears in the form of a convex curve.

Cu-Zn System

The phase diagram for the Cu-Zn system of interest to us is shown in Fig. 136. The limit of solid solubility of the copper solid solution is 67.5 percent Cu at 902°C and 60.5 percent at 400°C. It has long been considered that the solubility of zinc in copper exhibits little change with decrease in temperature, remaining between 38.5 and 39 percent of zinc at temperatures below 400°C. Experiments by Konobeyevsky and Tarasova, who used the X-ray method and very long-duration annealing at low temperatures, demonstrated that as temperature is decreased the α-phase boundaries shift toward copper and the solubility

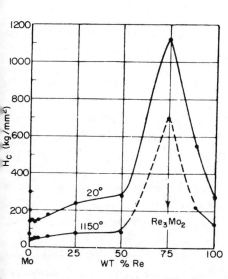

FIG. 135. Hardness of Re-Mo alloys at 20 and 500°C.

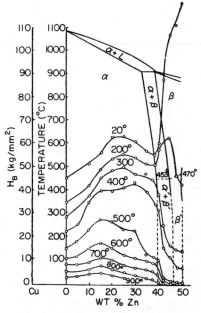

FIG. 136. Effect of temperature on the hardness of Cu-Zn alloys (Savitsky and Terekhova).

limit is 33.35 percent of Zn at 167°C [181].   In industrial alloys not in equilibrium, the boundary of the α phase shifts toward lower concentrations of copper (up to 63 percent) following a decrease in temperature [422].   The boundary $\beta -$ ($\beta + \gamma$) corresponds to 43.5 percent of copper at 834° and 50 percent of copper at 400°C.   The β phase is unstable and becomes an ordered β' phase at low temperatures (Fig. 137).   At high temperatures the probability is equal that atoms of either copper or zinc will occupy any given lattice position.   At temperatures below the transition temperature, copper atoms are more frequently located in the center of the cube whereas zinc atoms are located in the corners [28].   This transition occurs in the 450 to 470°C interval.   This mechanism has not as yet been fully explained [287], [423].   Cu-Zn alloys were selected because of their great industrial importance and because the Cu-Zn system exhibits a wide range of solid solutions.

Studies on the room-temperature mechanical properties of Cu-Zn alloys had

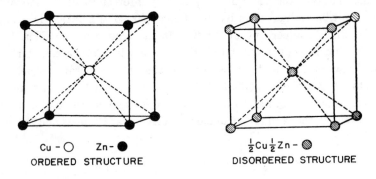

Cu – ○   Zn- ● $\frac{1}{2}$Cu$\frac{1}{2}$Zn – ◎
ORDERED STRUCTURE   DISORDERED STRUCTURE

FIG. 137.   Structure of β brass [28].

their beginning more than a century ago (in 1842).   Among early studies, the most thorough was a dissertation by Kurdiumov, a professor at the Academy of Artillery [424].   His paper, now practically forgotten, is in many respects of considerable significance even now.   According to his data, the hardness of cast alloys rises when zinc is added, attaining the maximum with a 34.58-percent-Zn content.   This alloy also has the greatest thermal-solidification effect and exhibits a maximum in its electrical-resistivity properties.   The ultimate tensile strength is observed in a 40- to 45-atomic-percent-Zn alloy, whereas the maximum in elongation is seen in a 30-percent-Zn alloy—to be more precise, in the 66- to 74.5-atomic-percent-Cu interval.   Transverse-compression data did not show a clear picture since the experiments were done with sheet specimens.   The curve describing the temporary resistance to rupturing shows a two-way curvature.

Kurdiumov was first to note the presence of molecular interaction in brasses. He considered as possible the presence of Cu_3Zn, Cu_2Zn, and $CuZn$ compounds in those alloys.

Gubkin and Zakharov [199] studied the changes of characteristics of resistance to deformation in the Cu-Zn system at various temperatures up to 750°C. They found that alloys containing 9 to 12 percent of zinc increased abruptly in hardness and in flow stress at temperatures above 450°C. They attributed the rise in hardness to an increase in the coefficient of the external friction of these alloys.

Studies by Iveronova and Zhdanov point out that the recrystallization temperature of copper rises sharply when small quantities (up to 5 percent) of zinc are added and drops again thereafter [425].

In our experiments with forged samples (reduced 50 percent) the hardness of Cu-Zn alloys (up to 50 percent of zinc) was tested in the temperature range 20 to 900°C. Cone hardnesses were determined under a 500–1000 kg load. The compositions of the alloys were checked by chemical analyses. The samples were tested in molten potassium nitrate at temperatures up to 500°C and in an electric furnace in air at temperatures above 500°C. The experimental data are shown in Table 41 and in Fig. 136 and 138.

As pointed out in Chapter 1, a β-phase alloy is characterized by high hardness at room temperature; however, it softens more rapidly than an α-phase alloy as a function of temperature. The high room-temperature hardness of β brass is apparently due to the presence of a larger number of zinc atoms (hence a more severely distorted lattice) than in α brass.

The sharp decrease in hardness of β brass at about 300°C proves that the stresses present in mechanical testing result in a considerable drop in the

TABLE 41

HARDNESS OF CU-ZN ALLOYS AT VARIOUS TEMPERATURES

Zn (wt. %)	H_c (kg/mm²)										Temperature Coefficient of Hardness α 20-800°C
	20°C	100°C	200°C	300°C	400°C	500°C	600°C	700°C	800°C	900°C	
0	48.0	51.0	36.0	28.8	22.3	17.5	10.0	8.0	7.4	3.5	$-1.12 \cdot 10^{-3}$
5	44.5	39.0	34.2	28.3	25.5	19.2	10.2	7.2	5.1	3.1	$-1.16 \cdot 10^{-3}$
10	51.5	48.0	41.2	37.4	35.2	25.0	15.3	8.7	6.8	4.9	$-1.22 \cdot 10^{-3}$
15	55.6	53.0	49.0	45.0	40.0	27.0	17.4	10.3	7.8	5.0	$-1.19 \cdot 10^{-3}$
20	63.5	58.5	53.5	49.0	39.5	26.5	16.0	10.2	5.4	4.9	$-1.37 \cdot 10^{-3}$
25	63.5	61.0	54.5	50.0	41.0	23.0	12.8	7.7	4.9	3.1	$-1.45 \cdot 10^{-3}$
30	61.0	55.5	53.5	47.0	45.0	23.0	10.3	7.4	4.3	...	$-1.47 \cdot 10^{-3}$
35	57.0	51.0	51.0	48.0	39.5	12.5	9.8	6.9	2.8	...	$-1.68 \cdot 10^{-3}$
38	55.0	47.0	50.0	45.0	34.0	11.0	7.9	5.7	2.2	...	$-1.94 \cdot 10^{-3}$
40	60.0	62.5	58.5	38.6	32.0	10.5	8.7	4.8	1.3	...	$-2.31 \cdot 10^{-3}$
42	87.0	76.5	50.0	26.0	15.5	3.1	2.2	0.95	0.60	...	$-3.10 \cdot 10^{-3}$
45	106.0	103.0	62.5	15.5	11.3	1.2	1.0	0.75	0.52	...	$-3.20 \cdot 10^{-3}$
48	110.0	95.0	45.0	14.0	7.9	1.1	0.78	0.70	0.43	...	$-3.34 \cdot 10^{-3}$
50	120.0	90.0	42.5	13.6	8.2	1.1	0.9	0.64	0.40	...	$-3.34 \cdot 10^{-3}$

disorder temperature (450 to 470°C).* Because
of the ability óf copper and zinc to diffuse
mutually, the processes of ordering and dis-
ordering take place very rapidly. The degree
of disorder in β brass explains its poor response
to working at low temperatures and its ease
of working at high temperatures.

The shape of the hardness isotherm for Cu-
Zn alloys in the α range is quite peculiar and
does not yet yield to any precise interpretation.
According to M. V. Zakharov, the long-duration-hardness isotherms of cast brasses show
a similar trend, but these tests were performed
only up to 600°C [378], [427]. In our experiments, as well as in those done by Gubkin
and P. A. Zakharov, it has been demonstrated
that maxima in the hardness isotherms are
present at all temperatures. Our data reveal,
however, that the maximum hardness at low
temperatures (to 400°C) is found in the range
of 25 percent of zinc; at higher temperatures
the maximum is reached at lower zinc concentration (up to 15 percent). According to
Gubkin and P. A. Zakharov, alloys with 9 to
12 percent of zinc exhibit maximum hardness.
The cone hardness-testing method is probably
the most sensitive. Some credit should also be given to the fact that our
samples were tested in potassium nitrate to prevent oxidation.

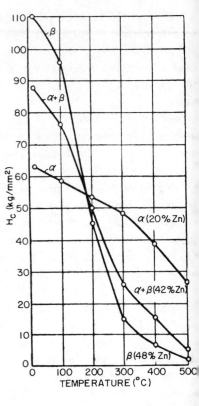

FIG. 138. Softening of brass as a
function of heating.

A shift of the maximum hardness toward the solvent metal as a function of
increasing temperature has also been observed in certain other systems such as
Cu-Sn [487]. This shift apparently occurs when the pure metal has a higher
melting point than the solid-solution alloy and, consequently, is less softened
over a given temperature range.

If only the static nature of solid solutions were examined, a uniform increase
in hardness of α brass would be expected as a function of zinc content up to
the point of saturation. The presence of maxima and minima could be attributed, we are inclined to think, to molecular interaction. In this respect we are
close to the viewpoint expressed by Kurdiumov. It is appropriate to mention
that the method for an approximate computation of the composition of compounds
by atomic volumes and by ionization potentials of component ions, points to the

* *Editor's Note*: Work by Martin, Herman, and Brown [426] seems to indicate that the
order-disorder temperature is unaffected by concurrent plastic deformation or the presence
of uniaxial stress.

possible existence of the Cu_3Zn compound [428]. The tensile properties of Cu-Zn alloys (Table 42) shows that an alloy of this composition (25 atomic percent of zinc) has a low ultimate strength comparable to that for copper (21.8 kg/mm²) and a high value of contraction in area (90 percent). Data obtained on the ductility of copper were somewhat low, suggesting the presence of insufficient deoxidation. The maximum elongation corresponds to an alloy with 33.4 percent of Zn (compound Cu_2Zn) and agrees with findings by Kurdiumov. In certain temperature ranges, this same alloy exhibits a somewhat lowered hardness in relation to neighboring alloys. The proportional limit and ultimate tensile strength increase with increasing zinc content, but minima are observed with alloys containing 25 and 33.4 percent of zinc. The ultimate tensile strength is considerably increased with the presence of some β phase.

TABLE 42

MECHANICAL PROPERTIES OF HOT-ROLLED COPPER-ZINC ALLOYS AT ROOM TEMPERATURE

Zn (at. %)	Proportional Limit σ_{prop} (kg/mm²)	Ultimate Strength σ_B (kg/mm²)	Elongation δ (%)	Reduction in Cross sectional Area ψ (%)	Hardness H_B (kg/mm²)
0 (100 % Cu)	4.6	21.0	51.0	65	46.5
3.6	5.6	13.6	54.0	81	49.0
4.8	5.8	22.6	57.5	85	50.0
5.0	6.0	23.3	56.0	87	50.0
7.2	5.3	24.2	48.0	77	49.0
9.8	5.9	24.2	48.0	75	51.0
14.4	7.5	27.0	46.0	71	57.0
15.0	5.0	25.2	64.0	84	43.0
25.0	4.8	21.8	56.0	90	46.5
30.0	9.0	30.3	65.3	78	60.0
33.4	7.6	26.5	93.0	76	50.0
40.0	10.8	34.5	48.5	63	76.0

A change in the composition of maximum hardness with increase in temperature may probably be explained by a weakening of interatomic cohesive forces caused by thermal vibration of atoms. The relative increase in hardness of α brass diminishes as the temperature is increased; at elevated temperatures, the hardness of a high-zinc brass becomes less than that of copper. This effect is due to the difference in melting points. The temperature coefficients of hardness for the Cu-Zn alloys are tabulated in Table 41.

Figure 136 shows that the hardness of the $\alpha + \beta$ alloy is close to the linear value.

The presence of order-disorder transformations in α brass has been suggested from time to time by a number of scientists. We now have facts which tend both to confirm and to refute this theory [429]. It is unfortunate that X-ray techniques cannot be used for determining the presence or absence of order; copper and zinc are neighbor elements in the periodic table and are hard to distinguish by X-ray. In such cases, except for neutron diffraction, the only reliable method is the property test [430]. Transformations occurring in brasses are not only of theoretical but also of practical interest since the so-called brittle or hot-short zones exist in certain temperature intervals. These zones are found in the 300–700°C interval and become somewhat narrower for high-zinc-content alloys. At higher temperatures (above 700°C) the ductility properties of these alloys are sharply increased. A well defined explanation of the brittle zones in brasses is still lacking. As previously stated, in improperly deoxidized copper, a brittle zone is observed in the 450–900°C interval.

TABLE 43

TEMPERATURE ZONES OF BRITTLENESS AND DUCTILITY OF BRASSES

Alloy Designation	Chemical Composition According to GOST (wt. %)			Melting Temperature (°C)	Brittle zone (°C)		Ductile Zone (°C)	
	Copper	Lead	Zinc		Beginning	End	Beginning	End
Tombac LT-90	88–91	...	Remainder	1045	300	700	750	950
Brass L-62	60.5–63.5	... ...	Remainder	910	350	650	700	850
Brass LC-59	57–60	0.8–1-9	Remainder	900	350	650	700	800

We studied the effect of temperature on the mechanical properties of three different brasses. Specimens were machined from industrial ingots. As a result of these experiments, the zones of the ductile and brittle states of the brasses mentioned (Table 43) were evaluated more precisely; it was demonstrated that the temperature intervals related to these zones coincide with the limits of homogeneity of the solid solution for cast and cold-worked samples. According to prior studies, lead does not materially affect the ductility-temperature curve; the lead is uniformly distributed inside the grains of brass [431].

The most important result of this study was the discovery that the brittle zones are detected by mechanical tests which involve tensile stresses (elongation or contraction in area in tension tests, impact toughness). The characteristics of resistance to deformation exhibit uniform decreases as a function of temperature. This fact indicates that hardness tests should not be substituted for strength tests in such studies.

The values of mechanical properties of cast tombac at various temperatures are presented in Table 44.

Considering all the tensile characteristics of ductility, only that of contraction under impact reduction ε_{dyn} is insensitive to the formation of brittle and ductile zones and increases uniformly with a rise in temperature; between 600 and 700°C,

TABLE 44

MECHANICAL PROPERTIES OF CAST TOMBAC LT-90, AT VARIOUS TEMPERATURES

Test Tempera-ture (°C)	Mechanical Properties				
	σ_B (kg/mm²)	δ_{10} (%)	ψ (%)	a_K (kg·m/cm²)	ε_{dyn} (%)
20	22.8	28.5	43.0	17.5	25.0
200	20.8	39.0	36.0	15.0	29.4
250	....	....	....	16.3	....
300	19.0	32.0	36.2	17.2	30.0
350	13.3	19.0	19.0	7.4	30.8
400	11.0	9.5	19.1	5.1	31.1
450	10.6	7.2	11.3	5.2	31.6
500	8.0	9.6	9.8	4.1	35.2
550	5.7	12.9	9.0	4.0	35.9
600	5.6	11.3	10.7	4.6	37.3
650	4.6	10.0	8.5	4.9	39.0
700	3.4	24.2	28.8	6.3	39.6
750	3.0	28.0	31.8	10.6	44.2
800	3.0	30.0	34.4	12.8	47.3
850	2.1	42.0	44.0	>15.0[a]	49.8
900	1.3	74.0	79.8	>15.0[a]	55.0
950	....	....	....	>15.0[a]	59.2

[a] Note: These specimens were bent but not broken.

however, small cracks were observed in the tested samples (work capacity-40 kg·m). A similar change in the ductility characteristics of L-62 brass is shown in Fig. 139.

In a number of ductility-temperature tests on industrial brasses, bronzes, and nickel alloys, Gubkin and associates found brittle zones when the tests involved tensile stresses [203]; the physicochemical nature of this phenomenon has not yet been explained.

Tension-stress experiments (tension and bending) are mainly tests for strength of grain boundaries. This is not true for compression stresses.

An important deduction to be made from the presently known facts on brasses is that the grain boundaries are drastically weakened in the brittle temperature range. Consequently, the task of explaining the nature of the brittle zone is confined to finding the physicochemical causes which result in brittleness along grain boundaries.

An interesting fact is that fracturing of L-68 brasses between 500 and 600°C is sometimes accompanied by audible cracking and a sawtooth type of fractured surface is produced. The most likely causes for a lowered grain-boundary cohesion could be either the presence of low-melting components such as lead or a eutectic, or the oxidation of surface grains in air tests and sublimation of zinc. We are informed that, in protective atmosphere experiments, no brittle

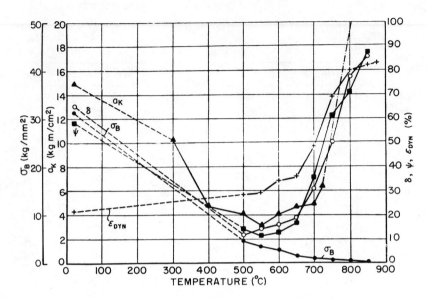

FIG. 139. Effect of temperature on the mechanical properties of L–62 brass (Savitsky and Stepanova).

zones were observed in brasses [233], [432]. A further increase in ductility beyond the brittle range may be explained by the "welding" of microcracks [432].

It would seem that a solution of the physicochemical nature of the brittle zones should likewise be sought in the state of the brass lattice at various temperatures. It is considered possible that, in the brittle range of temperatures, the phase state of brass, especially along grain boundaries, becomes susceptible to oxidation. Studies of microstructure, using standard procedures,

TABLE 45.

EFFECT OF TEMPERATURE AND PROLONGED SOAKING
ON THE HARDNESS OF CU-ZN ALLOYS

Zn (wt. %)	Quenched	Annealing Condition				
		250°C 1 hr	400°C			
			6 hr	1 wk	4 wk	6 wk
0 (100% Cu)	45.5	45.5	48.6	45.5	46.5	43.0
5.0	45.5	44.0	47.5	51.9	44.0	48.0
10.0	47.5	49.0	47.5	49.6	51.0	52.0
15.3	46.5	54.0	49.6	53.0	56.0	50.0
25.0	38.6	48.0	49.6	43.7	48.0	50.0
30.5	53.0	48.0	50.7	51.9	50.0	52.0
35.6	59.5	57.0	55.5	59.5	56.0	53.0
40.6	97.7	85.0	89.7	82.6	63.0	71.0

give no positive results. Thus Bauer and Hansen made the pessimistic deduction that it was impossible to explain the brittleness of brasses from studies of their structure [429]. To solve this problem we attempted to avail ourselves of the hardness method, which, as is well known, is a sensitive indicator of changes in the phase state of alloys. Eight alloys, rolled and variously processed, were tested for hardness (Table 45). The alloys were first quenched from 850°C.

It is worthy of note that a 25-percent-Zn alloy exhibited a hardness minimum in the quenched state after annealing at 250°C as well as after annealing for one week at 400°C. This alloy also exhibited a stable minimum in hardness measurements at 400°C (see Fig. 136). Slip lines were sometimes observed in microsections of alloys in this area of zinc concentration following prolonged annealing at 400°C.

The possibility of a tendency to form the low-stability Kurnakov compound Cu_3Zn, which dissociates at temperatures above 400°C, is not to be excluded. Compounds of a similar stoichiometric composition are observed in many systems.

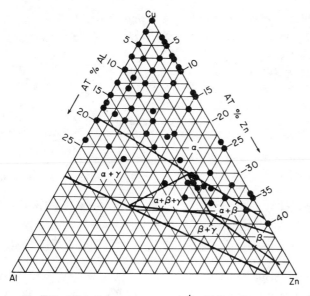

FIG. 140. Copper corner of Ću-Al-Zn alloys.

Cu-Zn-Al System

To achieve stability in an unstable alloy, the third-component method is widely used in physicochemical analysis. We tried to stabilize the α-brass structure by addition of aluminum and have investigated the mechanical properties of solid solutions of the Cu-Zn-Al system in the area of high copper concentration. Systematic and quantitative data on the changes in mechanical properties do not exist in the literature for this alloy system. It was considered important to study the mechanical properties of ternary alloys of such materials as α brass and aluminum bronzes. Finally, it became necessary to pinpoint the best thermal-processing conditions for Cu-Zn-Al alloys; this research has been contemplated in studies undertaken by Bakuniayeva, Bochvar, and Shaposhnikov [433]. We investigated about 70 alloy compositions in the hot-rolled (750 to 850°C) and annealed (at 650°C) states—99.9-percent copper, 99.9-percent zinc, and 99.7-percent aluminum were used as base metals. The highest solute content was 40 percent for zinc and 12 percent for aluminum for the alloys studied. The compositions of the alloys investigated are shown in Fig. 140.

Microscopic examination of the alloys indicated that their phase state corresponds to the phase diagram.

The special feature of this ternary system is the isomorphism of α, β, and γ solid solutions of the Cu-Zn and Cu-Al systems. The eutectoid decomposition of the β phase in the binary system of Cu-Al is the basic factor affecting the character of phase transformations in the solid state [434]. Changes occurring in the properties of alloys of the Cu-Zn system have already been discussed. The hardness of the binary system of Cu-Al alloys rises rapidly with increased aluminum content

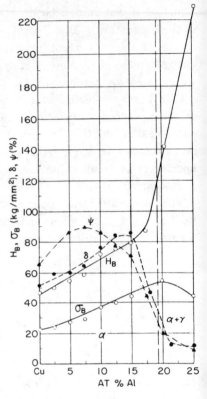

FIG. 141. Mechanical properties of Cu-Al alloys (vertical dashed line indicates the phase border).

(Fig. 141), especially during the transition into the two-phase area. Thus, the hardness of a 12-weight-percent-Al alloy (24.3 atomic percent) is 230 kg/mm². The appearance of eutectoid crystallites ($\alpha + \gamma$), containing the hard and brittle γ component, results in an abrupt change in hardness but lowers toughness and ductility. On the whole, the mechanical properties of aluminum bronze are of a considerably higher order than those of brass. It should be noted that the ductility properties show a maximum in the solid-solution region.

Pertinent experimental data on the effect of zinc on the mechanical properties of several Cu-Al alloys are presented in Fig. 142 through 144 (the phase boundaries are shown by dashed lines).

With the transition into the two-phase areas, the hardness exhibits an abrupt increase; the ultimate strength of alloys, surprisingly, also rises in this region (Fig. 142). The γ phase of this ternary system is described by the stoichiometric formula $Cu_4Zn_7Al_2$. This phase differs from the γ phase of the Cu-Al binary system, which probably explains the peculiar changes in the ultimate strength

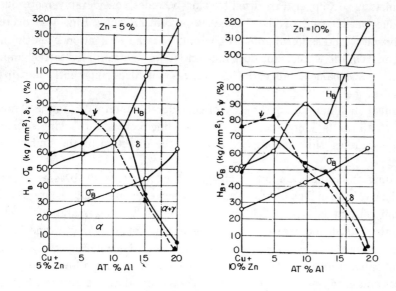

FIG. 142. Mechanical properties of Cu-Al-Zn alloys corresponding to cuts at 5 and 10 percent of zinc.

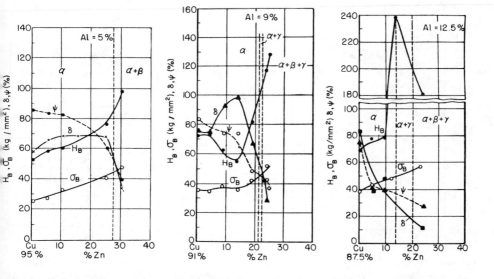

FIG. 143. Mechanical properties of Cu-Al-Zn alloys with various amounts of aluminum.

in this instance. Copper deoxidized by zinc becomes considerably more ductile. The reduction in area of the 5- and 10-percent-Zn cuts (Fig. 142) decreases smoothly with increasing aluminum content, but the elongation goes through a maximum. On the whole, zinc does not contribute substantially to the improvement of the mechanical properties of bronzes, but does apparently impair their industrial properties [234].

The effect of aluminum on brass is of considerable interest. As the aluminum content of alloys is increased, the dividing line between the single- and the two-phase brasses shifts more and more in the direction of the higher copper content.

According to Guillet, aluminum changes the structure of brasses six times more effectively than zinc [397]. This effect, however, probably occurs where the aluminum content is low. Addition of aluminum to Cu-Zn alloys contributes considerably to an increase of the flow stress, ultimate strength, and hardness without materially affecting the elongation and deformation characteristics. With the appearance of the brittle γ component in the alloys, the ductility decreases and hardness increases. Our experimental data are given in Fig. 143.

The minimum in the hardness-composition curve at about 15 percent of zinc in the Cu-Zn-9-percent-Al system (Fig. 143b) should be rechecked; this same alloy exhibits a maximum elongation. On the basis of data shown on the phase diagram and on evaluation of mechanical properties, there is no possibility of stabilizing the transformation in α brass with aluminum but this fact has been determined only for room-temperature conditions.

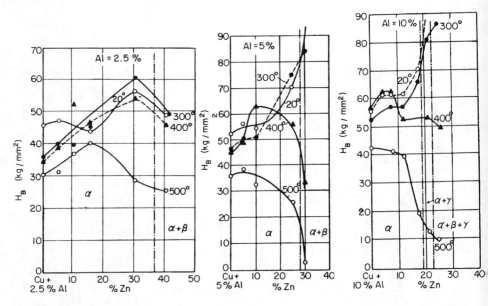

FIG. 144. Effect of temperature on the hardness of Cu-Zn-Al alloys, corresponding to cuts with various amounts of aluminum.

It should also be noted that elongation and contraction characteristics observed in specimens of alloys in the ternary-solid-solution zone exhibit changes following different laws.

The elevated-temperature hardness of ternary alloys in the solid-solution range was also evaluated in this system (Fig. 144). The experiments were performed for alloys corresponding to sections with a constant content of aluminum (2.5, 5, and 10 percent).

Here, as in Cu-Zn alloys, the hardness of a two-phase alloy decreases at a higher rate with temperature (above 400°C) than a homogeneous solid solution. It seems that alloying β brass with aluminum does not contribute materially to its heat-resistant properties. It is noteworthy that, at 2.5 and 5 percent of aluminum, alloys rich in zinc do not soften when heated; rather, they are hardened. The hardness–composition curves at 400°C show a maximum in hardness at about 10 percent of zinc for all aluminum contents. The nature of this transformation deserves special study.

The ability of these alloys to be thermally processed has also been investigated. The possibility of thermal processing is suggested by the occurrence of abrupt changes in the mutual solubility of components as a function of temperature. Thus, for instance, alloys containing from 18 to 30 weight percent of zinc and 3 to 5 weight percent of aluminum consist of α or $\alpha + \beta$ phases at 800°C and of $\alpha + \beta + \gamma$ crystals at 410°C. All of these alloys may be exposed to quenching and annealing techniques which can result in the creation of finely dispersed γ-phase precipitates.

Experimental data have confirmed these assumptions. The thermal processing

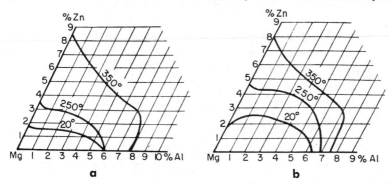

FIG. 145. Diagram of aluminum and zinc solubility in magnesium. "Industrial" diagram (Sergeyev).

a. State of equilibrium.   b. State of nonequilibrium.

was carried out as follows: annealing at 850°C for 4 hr, then quenching, followed by annealing at 250°C for 2 hr. The hardness of selected samples was evaluated prior and subsequent to thermal processing; other mechanical properties were measured by fracturing Gagarin samples. The experimental data are shown in Table 46.

TABLE 46

MECHANICAL PROPERTIES OF CU-ZN-AL ALLOYS BEFORE AND AFTER THERMAL TREATMENT

Composition of Alloys		Properties before Thermal Treatment					Properties after Thermal Treatment				
Al	Zn	H_B	$\sigma_{0.2}$	σ_B	δ_5	ψ	H_B	$\sigma_{0.2}$	σ_B	δ_5	ψ
(wt. %)		(kg/mm²)			(%)		(kg/mm²)			(%)	
5.7	5.5	78	19	43	38	42	159	42	54	16	4
5.0	25.0	76	15	40	68	60	114	28	44	16	10
7.5	25.0	125	26	50	30	18	218	54	64	6	2
5.0	30.0	98	22	47	33	38	193	40	54	16	6
0.0	40.0	76	10	34	48	63	148	33	43	20	34
10.0	0.0	140	35	53	11	18	261	..	78	6	2
4.0	25.0	117	26	52	43	42	218	..	66	8	6
3.5	25.0	104	21	47	52	50	227	..	60	6	4
3.0	28.0	107	19	46	50	50	238	..	51	4	..
4.0	26.0	129	24	49	29	36	227	..	55	4	2
4.5	23.5	125	25	42	23	35	261	..	50	..	..

As illustrated in the table, the hardness of the tested samples becomes nearly twice as great after solution heat treating and aging. In the majority of alloys, hardness increases by more than 100 kg/mm². As is usually the case, the aging process is followed by a rise in the ultimate strength of alloys, but not in the same ratio as that of hardness. The ductility of alloys is considerably impaired after such thermal treatment. The high hardness of thermally treated copper alloys containing inexpensive and readily available metals such as zinc and aluminum is of indisputable interest, especially with regard to cast alloys. For more ductility in working these alloys, some other additional component will probably be needed. The basic additives presently used in industrial alloys, in addition to aluminum, are: Ni, Fe, Sn, Pb, Si, and Mn.

Mg-Al-Zn System

Another example of a change in mechanical properties in the zone of ternary solid solutions is the Mg-Al-Zn system (high magnesium content). To date only room-temperature studies have been conducted along cuts at Al + Zn = 5 and 7 weight percent.

Data on high ductility of industrial alloys of magnesium which, by their structure, represent solid solutions of aluminum and zinc in magnesium, were given in Chapter 3 (see Fig. 66–68). Studies of the process of recrystallization in magnesium and its alloys with zinc and aluminum have already been described in research papers [217], [260]. The solubility of zinc and aluminum in magnesium was investigated by Bochvar and Kestner [435], Urazov and associates [436], Sergeyev [437], Saldau [438], and Mikheyeva [439].

Figure 145 shows the solubility of aluminum and zinc in magnesium as analyzed

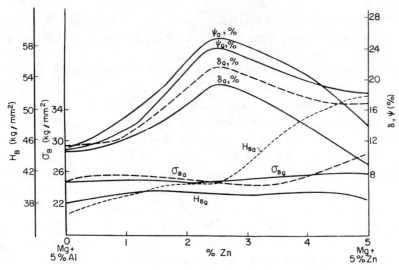

FIG. 146. Mechanical properties of Mg-Zn-Al alloys (cut Al-Zn = 5 percent) in the quenched (q) and annealed (a) states.

by Sergeyev [437]. As demonstrated by these diagrams, a large difference exists in the limits of solid solubility for nonequilibrium commercial alloys and for stable alloys.

Alloys possessing the ability to age lie between the curves of solubility of aluminum and zinc in magnesium at 20 and 350°C (eutectic temperature). The Mg-Al-Zn system is an example of a system which contains a ternary inter-metallic phase with a face-centered-cubic structure. A majority of researchers consider its composition as being close to the formula $Al_2Mg_3Zn_2$. This phase exists over a wide composition range and dissociates completely above 535°C, while the compounds $MgZn_2$ and $MgZn_5$ dissociate in the 410 to 440°C range [440].

The samples tested were cast and extruded alloys in annealed (five-day soak), quenched, and aged conditions. The samples were annealed in evacu-ated glass capsules in the temperature range 330 to 400°C; they were aged at 150°C. For the sake of brevity we shall present here only the experimental data pertaining to alloys with 95 weight percent of magnesium (Fig. 146).

As shown in Fig. 146, the observed change of properties within the solid-solubility limits is unique. The hard-ness and strength of the quenched

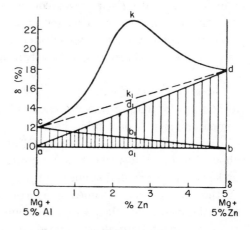

Fig. 147. Combined effect of aluminum and zinc on the elongation of magnesium.

alloys change little; these properties apparently are controlled by the coarse grains formed during prolonged heating which preceded quenching. Ductility characteristics are at a maximum.

The combined effect of aluminum and zinc on magnesium, as demonstrated by changes in the ductility of the alloys, may be tentatively analyzed as follows. In Fig. 147 the distance $o-a$ corresponds to the value of elongation of pure magnesium, the distance $o-c$ corresponds to the elongation of the Mg-Al binary alloy with 5 percent of aluminum, and the distance $s-d$ represents the elongation of the Mg-Zn binary alloy with 5 percent of zinc. Then, when we compare the Mg-Zn binary alloy with pure magnesium, it becomes evident that, with an addition of 5 percent of zinc, the elongation is increased from 10 to 18 percent. Apparently lesser addition of zinc (of 4, 3, and 2 percent) will contribute to smaller elongation increases; the points which correspond to indices of elongation for each alloy will lie along the line $a-d$. The area of the triangle abd shows the effect of zinc on the magnesium alloys of the given section. Reasoning analogously with respect to aluminum, let us assume that the acb triangle area will serve to express the quantitative effect of aluminum on the elongation of magnesium alloys for this section.

Assuming that atoms of aluminum and zinc interact separately from atoms of magnesium, thus contributing separate influences on the elongation of alloys, then, for each alloy of the given section, the composite effect of additives will be graphically expressed by a value equal to the sum total of influence of ordinates for aluminum separately from zinc. For example, the length of an alloy with 2.5 percent of zinc $a_1b_1 + a_1d_1 = a_1k_1$. By joining the points thus determined, we find the additive curve for change of elongation as a function of the amount of aluminum and zinc. Unfortunately, the experimental curve lies above the theoretical one. The considerable deviation between the theoretical and experimental curves proves convincingly the interaction of zinc and aluminum atoms not only with magnesium but with each other. The effect due to interaction of mutually dissolved atoms is apparently equal to the difference in value of the experimental and the theoretical curves of each alloy ($\Delta\delta = a_1k - a_1k_1$ for a 2.5-percent alloy).

These discussions, naturally, are of a very sketchy character, yet they seem to help in deciding on the presence or absence of atomic interaction of added components; and to determine, however approximately, the quantitative magnitude of the change occurring in properties caused by the interaction mentioned above. In order to make a better presentation, it would be more expedient to undertake experimental studies on the effect of each of the components separately on the changes in mechanical properties occurring in the basic metal; the curves thus obtained would then be used to compare the expected composite curve with the experimental curve determined in connection with joint additions of components to the basic metal. In any event, this approach to the study of mechanical properties of complex solid solutions is considered to be fruitful.

To return to magnesium alloys with 5-percent-Al + Zn content, it should be noted that, as illustrated in Fig. 146 and in line with the solubility diagram (Fig. 145), alloys with a high content of zinc exhibit a greater tendency to harden by aging.

The effect of zinc is still more pronounced in alloys with Al + Zn = 7 percent. Our explanation for this is that, as we shall show later, the metallic compounds formed in the Mg-Zn system have a daltonide (MgZn, MgZn$_2$, MgZn$_5$) character, whereas those formed in the Mg-Al system have the bertholide (β and γ phase) structure. In the process of aging, the precipitated daltonide-type (MgZn and MgZn$_2$) compounds cause a greater distortion of the crystal lattice than the bertholide-type phases (γ). The ternary intermetallic phase T (Al$_2$Mg$_3$Zn$_2$) is also of the bertholide type.

Cu-Mn System

Cu-Mn alloys are considered industrial alloys endowed with specific physical and mechanical properties (high resistance to electric conductivity, high hardness, high deformability).

A number of treatises have been published on Cu-Mn and Mn-Ni-Zn alloys, their objective being to create substitutes for alloys such as German silver, constantan, cupronickel, and others [313], [441], [442]. The fundamental deficiency of manganese alloys is their supersensitiveness to impurities (strong gas absorption) and an inadequate stability of electrical properties [443].

Furthermore, this Cu-Mn system presents an interesting problem because one of the components (manganese) is a polymorphic metal.

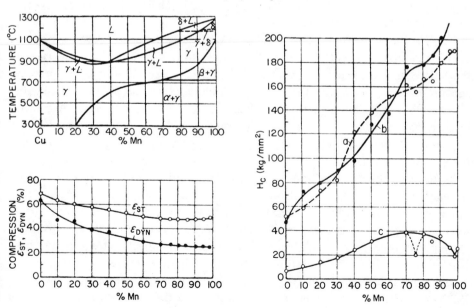

FIG. 148. Phase diagram and certain mechanical properties of Cu-Mn alloys.

The phase diagram of the Cu-Mn system has been investigated by a number of scientists. Among the first were Zhemchuzhny and Urazov [444]. The phase diagram of this system, plotted according to most recent findings [397], is shown in Fig. 148, but it may not be reliable. The minimum melting point of alloys in this system, with 34.5 percent of manganese, is 868°C. Copper and γ manganese are completely miscible. Polymorphic metals may form continuous solid solutions with monomorphic metals only through modifications, isomorphic with other components. In this case, γ manganese may be considered as the isomorphic modification with copper especially if we remember that the tetragonal structure is formed only after quenching [316]. The phase diagram and the

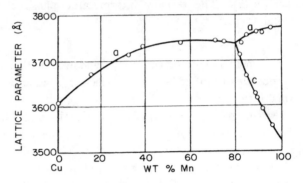

FIG. 149.   Change of the lattice parameter in Cu-Mn alloys.

property changes in relation to composition are considerably affected by this specific feature of polymorphic metals.

Fig. 149 illustrates changes occurring in the lattice parameters of γ manganese as a result of addition of copper [397]. Under the influence of dissolved copper, the lattice of γ manganese increases and, with 19 percent of copper, becomes equal to one unit; the lattice then becomes identical with the body-centered-cubic structure (the lattice parameters were studied on quenched samples). According to thermodynamic principles a two-phase zone should be observed on the phase-diagram between the cubic and the tetragonal phases; this, however, has not been shown experimentally [445].

As mentioned earlier in order to create technically desirable alloys based on manganese, the ductile γ manganese must be first stabilized by additions of other elements which should expand the γ-phase region and retard transformations, thus preserving the γ state not only by quenching but also by slow cooling. It follows that stabilizing admixtures should displace the ductile phase border toward lower temperatures. To judge by the phase diagram, copper belongs to metals which contribute to expanding the γ phase of manganese. Published data from systematic investigations on the mechanical properties of Cu-Mn alloys are not available.

We prepared 16 different alloys of electrolytic metals, melted in either a silit or a high-frequency furnace. Alloy hardness and impact strength were evaluated for cast, annealed, and quenched conditions as well as at 800°C. Alloys annealed after deformation were also studied.

Cast alloys were heated in a silit furnace to near the solidus temperature for 1 hr and then quenched in water. The quenching temperatures are indicated in Table 47. The alloys were annealed in argon atmosphere in an electric furnace. The alloys were double annealed to achieve equilibrium. The samples were first heated to 500°C and soaked for 2.5 hrs; the temperature was then raised to 700°C and the samples were soaked from 4 to 5 hr. Deformed alloys were annealed at 650°C for 4 hr in argon atmosphere. The hardness was evaluated with the aid of the pobedit cone under a 62.5-kg load (Table 47).

TABLE 47

HARDNESS OF CU-MN ALLOY SYSTEM

Mn Content (wt. %)	Hardness H_c (kg/mm²)					Temperature of Quenching (°C)
	Cast	Quenched	Annealed	Deformed	Annealed after Deformation	
0	56	51	47	76	49	850
10	68	59	73	112	71	850
20	78	74	80	125	86	850
30	92	82	90	129	112	850
40	122	122	98	156	126	850
50	142	138	129	157	130	850
60	151	152	138	156	147	850
70	158	162	178	167	194	950
75	153	156	216	187	168	950
80	149	167	178	167	180	950
85	151	165	186	186	168	1050
90	169	180	201	217	224	1050
95	176	190	267	200	256	1050
98	168	190	216	208	256	1050
99	168	186	390	181	...	1050
100	380	...	...	...	...	....

Curves describing the relationship of alloy hardness to its composition for cast (a) and quenched (b) states at 20°C, and also the hardness of cast samples at 800°C (c) are shown in Fig. 148c, and curves of ductility under slow and impact compression are presented in Fig. 148b. The data obtained show that the hardness of cast and quenched samples at 20°C increases rapidly as a function of the manganese content; it is 380 kg/mm² for pure manganese. Changes in the hardness of cast and quenched samples are similar; in the process of cooling, a partial quenching of alloys apparently takes place in the given conditions.

Alloys rich in manganese are characterized by highly scattered values of hardness and other properties. Quenching contributes to a certain decrease of hardness for the copper-base cast alloys (see Table 47). In cast alloys with 60 percent of manganese, the hardness is considerably decreased after the quenched material is annealed.

Cold deformation, resulting in work hardening, increases the hardness of alloys. Annealing of alloys after deformation lowers their hardness especially in high-copper-content alloys.

Changes in the hardness of alloys with a high manganese content are linked to their structural condition. Wherever the γ phase is present (rapidly cooled as well as quenched casting), the hardness values decrease. In annealed alloys of the same composition, the α phase is formed and the hardness increases. A break in the hardness curve can be observed in the range 75 to 80 percent of manganese, showing a certain decrease in hardness; this effect may be explained by the process of structural changes occurring in the lattices of the alloys. It thus follows that the transformation of the tetragonal lattice of γ manganese into the cubic lattice, induced by copper, is clearly detected by the hardness method.

To test the hardness of alloys at high temperatures, the samples were heated to 800°C in an electric furnace placed directly adjacent to the testing machine (30-min soak). At 800°C the hardness of all alloys is significantly reduced (see

TABLE 48

IMPACT STRENGTH OF CU-MN ALLOYS AT VARIOUS TEMPERATURES

Mn (wt. %)	20°C		800°C		1000°C	
	a_K (kg·m/cm²)	Type of Fracture	a_K (kg·m/cm²)	Type of Fracture	a_K (kg·m/cm²)	Type of Fracture
0	3.3	...	4.2	brittle	...	...
10	13.5	ductile	4.8	brittle	...	...
20	>15.0	ductile	8.8	brittle	...	...
30	13.0	ductile	9.2	brittle	...	...
40	5.5	brittle	1.0	brittle	...	...
50	3.4	brittle	3.0	brittle	...	...
60	3.1	brittle	0.6	brittle	...	...
70	3.5	brittle	0.8	brittle	...	...
75	4.3	brittle	1.8	brittle	...	...
80	2.6	brittle	1.4	brittle	0.6	brittle
85	4.4	brittle	4.8	brittle	0.6	brittle
90	1.0	brittle	3.4	brittle	0.8	brittle
95	0.8	brittle	3.2	brittle	7.0	ductile
98	0.8	brittle	4.2	brittle	8.2	ductile
99	1.0	brittle	0.6	brittle	7.2	ductile
100	0.1	brittle	0.2	brittle	5.8	ductile

Fig. 148). The 75-percent-Mn alloy shows an unusually low hardness that is probably associated with a transformation into the two-phase zone ($\beta + \gamma$).

The ductility of cast samples was studied at normal temperatures. In impact compression, the applied force was 30 kg m. The static reduction was performed on a 35-t press at a constant load of 15,000 kg. The samples were 10 mm in diameter and 12 mm in height. In conditions of constant load or constant work capacity, the ductility decreased as a function of increasing manganese content (see Fig. 148). This decrease is particularly noticeable in alloys with up to 70 percent of manganese. Generally speaking, however, the ductility is retained even in alloys which are rich in manganese. The maximum ductility was not measured since samples were not tested to fracture. Pure manganese samples were found to be brittle and crumbled in both dynamic and static compression.

The impact strength was evaluated at 20, 800, and 1000°C. Cast cylindrical samples, 10 mm in diameter with an annular groove 1 mm deep, were used. Experimental data are presented in Table 48 and in Fig. 150.

Alloys with 10- to 30-percent-Mn content are most ductile at 20°C. Samples made of these alloys are ductile to such an extent as to withstand fracturing usually; they only bend. These alloys apparently have the capability of absorbing vibrations; it would be desirable to evaluate this property quantitatively. At higher manganese concentrations the ductility diminishes. In the 75- to 85-percent-Mn range, a certain increase in impact resistance occurred, but the samples fractured in a brittle manner. Beyond this point ductility exhibits an abrupt

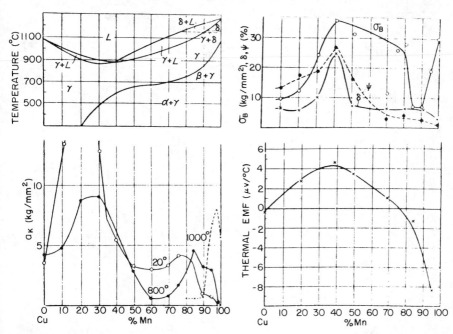

FIG. 150. Impact strength, tension characteristics, and thermal emf of Mn-Cu alloys.

decrease and is 0.1 kg·m/cm² for pure manganese. At 800°C, the maximum impact strength is observed in alloys with a 20- to 30-percent-Mn content (9 kg·m/cm²) and a second maximum occurs in the 85-percent-Mn alloy (4.8 kg·m/cm²). The impact strength of alloys with 85 percent or more of manganese is greater at 800°C than at room temperature.

Some alloys containing 80 to 99 percent of manganese were tested at 1000°C; these alloys showed considerable improvement in ductility at this temperature. A comparison of the changes in the curves for impact strength at 20, 800, and 1000°C, indicates that the ductility maximum on the manganese-rich end coincides with the transition from a single-phase to a two-phase structure and, as a result, the maximum shifts toward pure manganese as the temperature is increased (Fig. 150).

Fracture tests were performed and recorded on microsamples (2 mm in diameter and 10 mm in gage length) using the Gagarin press. Testing was conducted at room temperature with cast, annealed, and quenched samples. Quenching temperatures are indicated in Table 47 and the samples were annealed for 6 hr at 650°C. The tension data obtained with microsamples should be viewed as preliminary, especially with alloys rich in manganese, because of their extreme brittleness (Table 49, Fig. 150).

The thermal emf of alloys paired with copper was also studied. The emf value changes sign at about 75 percent of manganese (see Fig. 150).

TABLE 49

MECHANICAL PROPERTIES IN TENSION AND THERMAL EMF OF ALLOYS
OF THE CU-MN SYSTEM

Mn Content (wt. %)	Mechanical Properties					Thermal emf Paired with Cu (μv/°)
	Ultimate Strength σ_B (kg/mm²)			Ductility of Cast Alloys		
	Cast	Quenched	Annealed	ψ (%)	δ (%)	
0	....	14.3	12.7	....	....	0.0
10	9.7	19.1	13.0	13.0	6.5	...
20	12.0	15.5	....	17.5	5.5	2.5
30	24.0	38.0	....	18.5	10.0	...
40	36.2	40.0	38.0	26.8	25.3	4.1
50	31.2	14.3	8.0	15.7	6.8	3.3
60	....	10.0	11.0	....	....	...
70	11.4	....	2.5	2.3	6.2	0.7
75	26.0	1.6	....	5.0	6.2	...
80	28.0	1.6	....	4.0	6.3	...
85	7.6	...	15.9	10.0	6.3	−2.0
90	6.4	...	....	2.5	6.2	...
95	19.0	...	....	1.0	6.6	−9.0
98	....	...	....	3.0	3.2	...
99	30.0	...	....	7.0	3.1	...

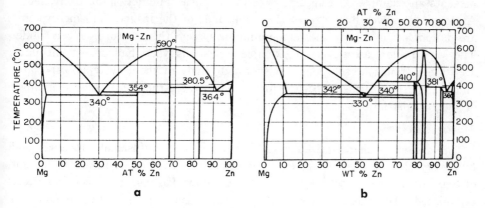

FIG. 151. Phase diagram for the Mg-Zn system.
a. After Hume-Rothery.   b. After Takei.

The strength-composition curve on the copper-rich side is typical of solid solutions, i.e., the value of the ultimate tensile strength tends towards a maximum, whereas alloys with 85 to 90 percent of manganese exhibit a break in the strength curve. This break will require further investigation. The strength and ductility of the Cu-Mn alloys in any condition increase with increased manganese content up to approximately 40 percent. The ductility of samples in which the magnesium content exceeds 70 percent is relatively low. The ductility changes with composition appear unusual and suggest that structural transformations might be taking place in alloys which exhibit low values of ductility.

In the Cu-Mn system, alloys with 30 to 50 percent of manganese are very ductile and strong. They merit a more thorough investigation.

It is indisputable that by careful elimination of impurities in the process of alloying (absorption of oxygen and nitrogen), the absolute values of mechanical properties may be greatly improved. Alloys containing over 95 percent of manganese have low ductility in tension because of a relatively large amount of the hard α phase.

We evaluated the flow stress in alloys which we considered to be of interest from the viewpoint of ductility. The samples were extruded from 20- to 10-mm diameter. Samples containing up to 75 percent of manganese were extruded at 850°C. The flow stress under these conditions varied between 20 and 40 kg/mm². In processing alloys containing more than 70 percent of manganese the temperature should be raised to 1000°C. Rolling of the Cu-Mn alloys at 1000 and 1100°C presented no difficulties.

Systems Containing Metallic Compounds

Changes of properties in alloys of three metallic systems will be examined in this section. Magnesium will be a basic component in each of them. Each presents an example of a specific type of chemical interaction of components. As definitely proven by our tests, the compounds of the magnesium-zinc systems are daltonides; in the magnesium-aluminum system their nature is bertholide. The Mg-Cd alloys are a classical example of systems where Kurnakov compounds are formed from solid solutions. A thorough study of these systems, especially of the first two, furnishes basic information on the structure of a good number of light industrial alloys.

Mg-Zn System

This system is characterized by a sluggishness of diffusional processes and by a very slow process of achieving equilibrium. In spite of the large amount of work done, the phase diagram of these alloys has not yet been definitely established. Divergencies are noted on some basic points: on the amount and composition of the various compounds and also on their ability to form solid solutions. As claimed by various authors, metallic compounds of: $MgZn$, Mg_7Zn_3, Mg_2Zn_3, $MgZn_2$, $MgZn_5$, Mg_2Zn may be formed in the Mg-Zn system [436], [439], [445]-[453]. They are in complete agreement only on the $MgZn_2$ compound, the only one to crystallize from the liquid state. Other compounds, formed in the solid state by peritectic reactions, are observed by some investigators but denied by others. Some scientists hold exactly contradictory views on the ability of compounds to form solid solutions [447], [448] (Fig 151).

The situation is still worse in regard to studies related to mechanical properties (over the full range of concentrations).

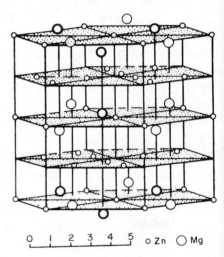

0 1 2 3 4 5   o Zn   ◯ Mg

Fig. 152.   Structure of $MgZn_2$ [44].

Data furnished by Grube and Burkhardt (on hardness) as well as by Koster and Rosenthal (on elastic modulus) refer only to room-temperature tests. Furthermore, they are contradictory and do not tie in with the phase-diagram [454], [455].

The $MgZn_2$ compound crystallizes in the C_{14} hexagonal lattice with parameters of $a = 5.15A$, $c = 8.48A$; $c/a = 1.65$. There are four atoms in the unit cell (Fig. 152). On the basis of the crystallographic data, $MgZn$ and $MgZn_2$ compounds are very similar. $MgZn$ also crystallizes with a hexagonal structure except that the lattice parameters are nearly twice as large ($a = 10.66A$, $c = 17.16A$, $c/a = 1.61$). The elementary nucleus contains 48 atoms [456]. It should be pointed out that even by microscopic examination $MgZn$ is very similar to $MgZn_2$; this explains why it has been only detected recently by means of a special etching solution (Benedict's etch). The compound $MgZn_5$ crystallizes in a simple cubic lattice, whose lattice parameter is equal to 8.53A. The number of atoms in the unit cell is approximately 32 [456].

The compound $MgZn_5$, as claimed by Laves [452], is better described by the formula Mg_2Zn_{11}. This suggestion is apparently incorrect.

No published data are available as to the chemical cohesion in the compounds mentioned.

The contradictory nature of published data related to the Mg-Zn system prompted us to attempt a resolution of these divergencies. There was another important motive for our research: all previous work on alloys rich in metallic compounds was done with cast samples. Because such alloys are brittle, no one has ever been able to obtain deformed samples at room temperature. We conducted experiments with both cast and wrought alloys. We had two primary objectives: first to determine the kinetics of achieving equilibrium with the alloys studied together with the relation of composition to mechanical properties, and, second, to establish the effect of temperature on to the mechanical properties of alloys containing metallic compounds.

Twenty-five alloys were investigated in the range 24 to 96 weight percent of zinc. Samples were made of magnesium of MG-1 grade (99.9 percent Mg) and of zinc of Z-1 grade (99.94-percent Zn). The samples were melted in an electric crucible furnace in graphite crucibles protected by dehydrated-carnallite flux. The compositions of the alloys were determined by chemical analysis. The samples were deformed by hot extrusion with the device shown in Fig. 27. The task proved to be very involved since, in order to obtain comparable data, all the alloys of the system had to be identically processed; in this respect we were handicapped by the low ductility of the more brittle alloys. Consequently, in order to determine the conditions of testing to be used for all the alloys, we were compelled to pre-test each one and to find the best conditions for plastic deformation most suitable for each alloy separately. The time spent to plan methods and comparative conditions proved to be greater than that involved in testing.

Preliminary testing proved that, under properly chosen conditions for extrusion (temperature, rate, degree of deformation, and adequate lubrication) all cast alloys may be converted into rods of good quality. It is true, however, that

TABLE 50

ANNEALING CONDITIONS FOR ALLOYS OF THE MG-ZN SYSTEM

Zn Content (wt. %)		Annealing Temperature (°C)	Duration of Annealing (days)	Conditions for Cooling
From	To			
20.00	72.89	300		
72.89	84.74	320	5, 10, and 20	Samples remain for 2 days in the cooling furnace
84.74	92.70	340		
92.70	100.00	335		

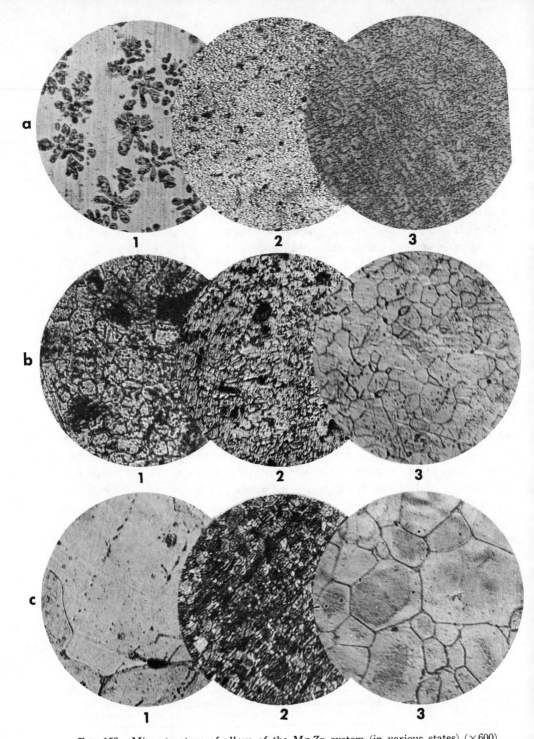

FIG. 153. Microstructure of alloys of the Mg-Zn system (in various states) ($\times 600$).

a. 45.6 weight percent of zinc: *1*–cast (α + eutectic); *2*–deformed (α + eutectic); *3*–annealed (α + eutectic).

b. 76.8 weight percent of zinc: *1*–cast (MgZn + eutectic); *2*–deformed (MgZn + eutectic); *3*–annealed (MgZn).

c. 85 weight percent of zinc: *1*–cast (MgZn$_2$ + eutectic); *2*–deformed (MgZn$_2$); *3*–annealed (MgZn$_2$).

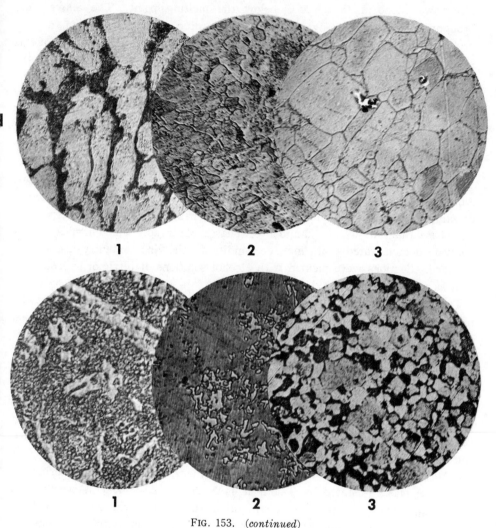

FIG. 153. *(continued)*

d. 93.1 weight percent of zinc: *1*-deformed, annealed 5 days (MgZn$_2$ + MgZn$_5$); *2*-deformed, annealed 10 days (MgZn$_5$); *3*-deformed, annealed 20 days (MgZn$_5$).

e. 1-96.6 weight percent of zinc: cast (MgZn$_5$ + eutectic); *2*-deformed (MgZn$_5$ + eutectic); *3*-annealed (MgZn$_5$ + eutectic).

some of the cast alloys did not withstand more than 50-percent reduction. For better deformation results extrusion was done in two stages. In the first pass, a 22-mm bar was extruded through a 15-mm die, thereby being reduced by approximately 50 percent. In the second pass the 15-mm rods were extruded through a 10-mm die, resulting in an additional 50 percent reduction. Graphite and machine oil were used as lubricants in the extrusion process. The samples obtained were tested for evaluation of hardness and flow stress of the wrought alloys at various temperatures. Extrusion of samples and evaluation of flow stress was done at 15 to 20°C below the melting point. The alloys were brought into equilibrium by annealing. According to published data, a very prolonged period of annealing (up to 90 days) is required for cast alloys of this system [448]. To accelerate the process of diffusion it is desirable that the alloys be annealed at exceedingly high temperatures. Considering, however, that the Mg-Zn alloys differ considerably as to their melting temperatures, they were divided into four groups, each group comprising alloys with closely related melting points. Alloys were annealed at temperatures indicated in Table 50.

The samples were annealed under a layer of powdered aluminum oxide; the gap between the alloys and the cover of the muffle furnace was sealed by clay. The degree of equilibrium achieved was evaluated by microstructural analyses. An alloy was considered as having reached equilibrium when the microstructure of samples, with further annealing, ceased to change and would correspond to the phase diagram by the number of phases observed. The chemical check analysis demonstrated that, in such conditions, the zinc content remained unchanged. Sections were pickled with alcohol solutions of nitric or hydrochloric acid as well as with methyl benzoate acid.

The hardness of alloys in the 20 to 365°C range was evaluated on a 7-t machine with a 5-mm ball, under a 125-kg load. The flow stress was determined when 80 percent deformation was reached. Examples of the microstructure of alloys in various states are presented in Fig. 153.

Apparently, we were the first to demonstrate clearly the single-phase structure of the MgZn compound (Fig. 153-b-3). Researchers who have dealt previously with cast samples always had traces of the second phase on their photomicrographs. A single-phase structure for compositions close to the compound composition is difficult to detect even after annealing. In wrought samples, this single-phase structure will form after 10 days of annealing. In the area of the MgZn compound, as stated by Hume-Rothery, the ratio of magnesium to zinc is 1:1 [448]; as stated by Takei, it is 1:1.5 (Mg_2Zn_3) [449]. According to our findings (microstructure, hardness), this ratio is 1:1.2, which corresponds to the stoichiometric formula Mg_5Zn_6. Until the composition of this compound is finally determined by the X-ray method, we shall designate it as MgZn. The basic results of our investigations are submitted below [373], [375].

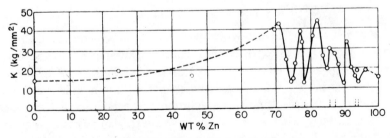

FIG. 154. Flow stress of cast Mg-Zn alloys.

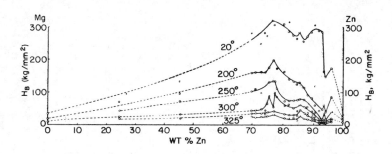

FIG. 155.   Hardness of deformed Mg-Zn alloys at various temperatures.

The structure and the properties of the Mg-Zn alloys are much more affected by the previous thermal- and mechanical-processing history than are many other alloys, because of the slow rate of diffusion, which results in a prolonged return to equilibrium.   The degree of equilibrium determines: the type of phase diagram obtained (absence or presence of solid solutions based on compounds) and the shape of the composition-property curves.   In harmony with the above stipulations, the cast state of specimens determines: the presence of rough two-phase and of nonequilibrium three-phase structures (Fig. 153), a considerable scatter of property values and the absence of characteristic points on the composition-property curves at compositions corresponding to metallic compounds (Fig. 154, Table 51).   Solid-solution zones based on compounds do not appear in cast alloys. The maxima in Fig. 154 correspond to coarse-grained materials and the minima to fine-grained materials, although this observation needs further verification. Even after 5 days' annealing, microstructural differences (presence of large or small grains) in cast alloys have a greater effect on the alloys' hardness than composition differences.

Heating accelerates the process of diffusion in cast alloys and creates favorable conditions for chemical interaction of solid-state components.   However, in order to achieve equilibrium in Mg-Zn cast alloys, prolonged annealing (of several months' duration) is required.

Continuous annealing of cast alloys for 20 days did not result in a single-phase structure in the zone of compounds (see Fig. 153).   This inability to form a single-phase structure also affected the property changes in relation to composition (Table 51).   Those who previously studied this system (Grube, Chadwick, Hume-Rothery, Takei, Laves, Köster, and others) have worked with cast, annealed alloys.   The sharp differences in their findings are undoubtedly due to the degree of equilibrium in the cast alloys tested, brought about by the different conditions of annealing selected by each individual researcher.

Hot extrusion drastically breaks up the structure (see Fig. 153), forms new intergranular bonds, and contributes to an acceleration of atomic-diffusion

TABLE 51

MECHANICAL PROPERTIES OF ALLOYS OF THE MG-ZN SYSTEM

Zn Content (wt. %)	Temperature of Test (°C)	Cast Alloys Hardness H_B (kg/mm²) Not Annealed	Cast Alloys Hardness H_B (kg/mm²) Annealed for 5 Days	Flow Stress K of Unannealed Alloys (kg/mm²)	Deformed Hardness H_B (kg/mm²) Not Annealed	Annealed 5 Days	Annealed 10 Days	Annealed 20 Days	Temperature Coefficient of Alloy Hardness, Annealed 20 Days (20–325°C)	Flow Stress K (kg/mm²) Not Annealed	Annealed 5 Days
24.2	20	128	102	20.0	118.0	90.7	…	73.2	$-0.26 \cdot 10^{-3}$	29.9	17.7
	325				15.9	18.4		12.0			
45.6	20	194	138	17.1	109.0	164.0	…	126.0	$-0.35 \cdot 10^{-3}$	23.0	21.1
	325				15.9	18.4		11.0			
69.8	20	260	303	40.7	280.0	233.0	…	138.0	$-0.2 \cdot 10^{-3}$	57.0	20.4
	325				38.1	31.2		25.0			
70.8	20	303	…	43.7	204.0	233.0	159	242.0	…	59.8	15.3
	325				25.9	28.4		18.9			
72.9	20	297	280	25.0	270.0	280.0	…	233.0	$-0.23 \cdot 10^{-3}$	45.4	20.7
	325				31.2	34.4		45.6			
74.3	20	260	225	13.1	280.0	303.0	291	233.0	$-0.25 \cdot 10^{-3}$	—	19.9
	325				31.2	31.2		31.3			
74.8	20	…	242	14.7	270.0	260.0	…	270.0	$-0.2 \cdot 10^{-3}$	40.8	23.6
	325				37.0	34.4		65.0			
75.4	20	291	373	23.1	315.0	280.0	303	280.0	$-0.27 \cdot 10^{-3}$	38.8	26.1
	325				34.4	47.5		41.6			
76.8	20	303	342	39.4	315.0	357.0	150	107.0	$-0.15 \cdot 10^{-3}$	63.7	29.3
	325				38.1	41.9		37.0			
77.0	20	233	315	33.4	303.0	303.0	303	246.0	$-0.25 \cdot 10^{-3}$	42.0	22.1
	325				34.4	38.1		43.9			
77.5	20	280	315	13.1	303.0	315.0	315	280.0	$-0.25 \cdot 10^{-3}$	35.0	23.1
	325				34.4	41.9		50.0			
80.6	20	265	260	36.8	303.0	280.0	…	260.0	$-0.21 \cdot 10^{-3}$	38.7	23.5
	325				31.2	38.1		60.4			
81.5	20	255	280	44.7	280.0	342.0	…	290.0	$-0.25 \cdot 10^{-3}$	40.1	14.5
	325				27.5	40.0		50.0			
83.1	20	197	225	26.3	270.0	315.0	…	280.0	$-0.26 \cdot 10^{-3}$	34.7	22.9
	325				27.0	38.1		45.6			
84.3	20	200	208	19.7	260.0	199.0	…	246.0	$-0.33 \cdot 10^{-3}$	31.5	18.1
	325				24.8	31.2		25.2			
85.0	20	280	170	28.9	280.0	290.0	…	255.0	$-0.24 \cdot 10^{-3}$	42.3	25.1
	325				47.5	53.1		45.6			
86.6	20	197	208	27.6	251.0	233.0	…	212.0	$-0.31 \cdot 10^{-3}$	20.6	21.1
	325				38.0	25.2		25.2			
87.9	20	237	251	22.3	265.0	303.0	…	251.0	$-0.35 \cdot 10^{-3}$	20.4	14.8
	325				25.9	26.1		22.4			
89.4	20	150	242	11.8	280.0	270.0	…	191.0	$-0.36 \cdot 10^{-3}$	24.4	15.3
	325				18.5	19.3		15.0			
90.2	20	144	260	33.7	303.0	291.0	…	242.0	$-0.4 \cdot 10^{-3}$	33.5	15.1
	325				23.8	20.1		14.5			
91.7	20	142	225	20.3	285.0	280.0	…	242.0	$-0.39 \cdot 10^{-3}$	20.4	16.3
	325				7.0	17.1		15.7			
92.6	20	233	260	15.8	280.0	303.0	…	251.0	…	14.1	22.9
	325				7.0	28.4		28.3			
92.7	20	129	242	18.4	159.0	185.0	…	218.0	$-0.43 \cdot 10^{-3}$	22.9	15.03
	325				9.1	15.9		11.0			

Annotations in the Flow Stress columns: 335°, 365°, 345°.

232

processes. Yet, because of the inherently slow diffusion process in the MgZn compound zone, deformed unannealed alloys are not in full equilibrium. In accord with this fact, the microstructure of alloys in the metallic-compound zone still retains a small amount of the second phase (see Fig. 153), whereas the composition–mechanical-property curve at 20°C reveals that only MgZn$_5$ exhibits a singular (minimum) point (Fig. 155, Table 51). The hardness and flow-stress properties of the worked alloys show a maximum corresponding to a composition near the MgZn compound both at normal and elevated temperatures (Fig. 155 and Table 51). As a result of deformation or low-temperature heating, atomic rearrangement in the lattice may be taking place in these alloys to form the MgZn compound, or, perhaps, finely dispersed precipitates form in the compound; these may produce a distortion in the structure and cause an increase in hardness to 350 kg/mm^2. A partial "coagulation" of the compound may be assumed to be taking place in the process of evaluating hardness above 300°C, because the hardness maxima tend to disappear. This assumption also applies to the compound MgZn$_2$. In this case the kinetics of the aging process should be more thoroughly studied, because MgZn and MgZn$_2$ are strengthening agents for certain thermally processed Mg-Al-Zn alloys.

Considerable time may be saved by mechanical and thermal processing of samples in bringing the alloys close to a state of equilibrium and, consequently, more accurate phase diagrams can be obtained. The hardness of alloys studied is related to the duration of annealing (Fig. 156).

Deformed alloys which were subsequently annealed for 20 days were found to be closest to equilibrium. The 5-day annealing treatment contributed no

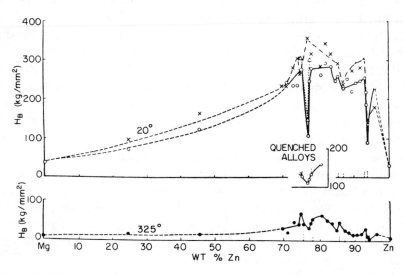

FIG. 156.   Hardness of deformed and annealed Mg-Zn alloys.
x-x-x—annealed 5 days; △---△—annealed 10 days; 0-0-0—annealed 20 days;
·-·-·—hardness of deformed and annealed (20 days) alloys at 325°C.

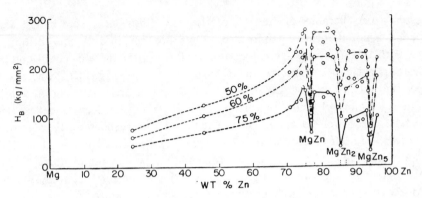

FIG. 157.   The hardness of Mg-Zn alloys at homologous temperatures (50, 60, and 75 percent of the absolute melting temperature) (Savitsky and Baron).

material changes in the hardness-composition curve in contrast to the cast state, although some alloys did exhibit an increase in hardness.   Thus, a 76.8-percent-Zn deformed alloy, corresponding to the compound MgZn, showed a hardness of 315 kg/mm^2; whereas after a 5-day anneal its hardness increased to 357 kg/mm^2. After a 10-day anneal the compound MgZn began to exhibit a pronounced minimum on the hardness isotherm.

Even a superficial examination of the 20°C isotherm of hardness, subsequent to a 20-day anneal, reveals that, in spite of certain fluctuation caused by structural heterogeneity, the hardness is determined mainly by the chemical nature of the alloy.   All three compounds are conspicuously represented by characteristic points on the hardness isotherm—MgZn and MgZn$_5$ by minimum values and MgZn$_2$, by a small maximum value.   In the zone of the MgZn and MgZn$_5$ compounds, a change in alloy composition by 1.5 to 2 percent may produce a change of hardness by 150 to 250 percent.   Thus, an alloy with 76.8 percent of zinc exhibits a hardness of 170 kg/mm^2 whereas a 75.4-percent-Zn alloy shows 280 kg/mm^2; likewise the hardness of a 95.1-percent-Zn alloy is 85 kg/mm^2 in contrast to 251 kg/mm^2 for a 92.6-percent alloy.   Figure 156 illustrates the hardness-composition curve at 325°C after a 20-day anneal as well as the hardness of alloys at 20°C after quenching from 325° in the MgZn compound region. Both curves show wider ranges of composition where the hardness increases from the minimum hardness at MgZn in contrast to the room-temperature curves; this effect indicates an increase of the solid-solution zone caused by an increase in temperature.   The hardness of an annealed alloy corresponding to the compound MgZn (Mg$_5$Zn$_6$ to be exact, 76.8 percent of zinc) is 117 kg/mm^2 whereas alloys with 74.8 percent of zinc and those with 80.6 percent of zinc exhibit, respectively, a hardness of 132 and 159 kg/mm^2.

The MgZn$_2$ compound has a considerably higher melting temperature (about 590°C in contrast to 354 and 380°C of neighbor alloys).   For this reason a minimum is not observed in the hardness isotherm.   Minima, as well as the existence of solid-solution zones, are clearly observed only when the hardness isotherms are plotted at "homologous" (same ratio of the absolute melting temperature) temperatures (Fig. 157).

Three single-phase zones in the Mg-Zn system were observed for deformed samples which were annealed for 20 days; these regions correspond to the compounds MgZn, MgZn$_2$, and MgZn$_5$ (see Fig. 153).

As demonstrated by the hardness method, these regions appear to expand somewhat with an increase in temperature.

At 20°C, the approximate boundaries of single-phase areas are as follows: for the MgZn compound, from 75.4 to 77.5 weight percent Zn; for the MgZn$_2$ compound, from 85.0 to 86.6 weight percent Zn; for the MgZn$_5$ compound, from 92.7 to 93.1 weight percent Zn.

An exact determination of the single-phase regions as a function of temperature was not included in our present work.

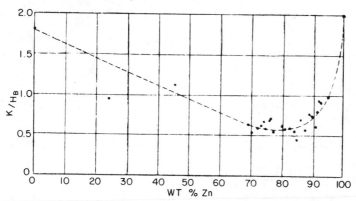

FIG. 158. Relation of the flow stress to hardness of alloys in the Mg-Zn system.

The hardness of alloys which are mixtures of solid solutions based on compounds generally follows the linearity rule, at both normal and elevated temperatures.

The three compounds mentioned above are characterized by singular minima on the hardness isotherms (see Fig. 156 and 157). These experimental data not only testify to the existence of the compounds mentioned but also confirm their daltonide character. Thus, all assertions as to the existence of compounds Mg$_7$Zn$_3$ (Köster), Mg$_2$Zn$_3$ (Takei) and Mg$_2$Zn (Laves and Werner) and claims that compounds of the Mg-Zn system do not have the ability to form solid solutions (Hume-Rothery and Rounsefell) are refuted by our findings. The previously observed presence of compounds MgZn, MgZn$_2$, and MgZn$_5$ (Urazov, Filin, Shashin, Hume-Rothery, Zakharova and Mlodzeyevsky, Mikheyev, Shamrai, and others) on annealed samples has been verified. The formation of solid solutions based on each of these compounds is likewise beyond doubt.

We studied in great detail the influence of temperature on the mechanical

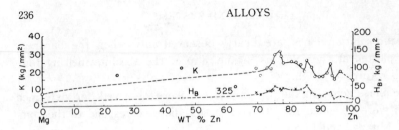

FIG. 159. Hardness and flow stress
of Mg-Zn alloys at elevated temperatures (annealed 5 days.)

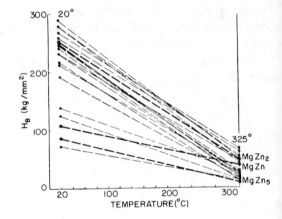

FIG. 160. Relative softening of Mg-
Zn alloys when heated (data obtained
at 20 and 325°C).

properties of alloys. It was found that the Mg-Zn alloys, in the regions rich
in compounds, are characterized by high hardness and low ductility at room
temperature (Table 51, Fig. 155–157). The hardness of these alloys is about
ten times that of magnesium or zinc. Alloys based on MgZn and MgZn$_2$ have
an average hardness of 300 kg/mm^2 at 20°C. After working, the hardness
of these alloys increases still further because of grain refinement; some of them
will scratch glass. The flow stress of these alloys is considerably higher than
the flow stress of pure metals and reaches 40 to 60 kg/mm^2 (Table 51). At this
temperature, the flow stress of magnesium is 15 kg/mm^2 and 17 kg/mm^2 for zinc.
The low value of the ratio of flow stress to hardness of alloys rich in compounds
is worthy of note (Fig. 158).

Alloys soften rapidly with an increase in temperature (see Table 51, Fig. 155
–160). For instance, their hardness at 325°C is 30–50 kg/mm^2, or in the order
of 10 percent from its value at room temperature. Based on an approximate evaluation (for hardness), the ultimate tensile strength of the MgZn$_5$ compound is less than 1 kg/mm^2 at 350°C. The greatest relative decrease in hardness
caused by temperature is observed in alloys consisting of a mixture of metallic
compounds or, especially, of their solutions (see Fig. 160). Next in line are
alloys containing large amounts of eutectic. Thus, for instance, the hardness
of a 45.6-percent-Zn alloy, which is close to the eutectic, is 109 kg/mm^2 at 20°C,
and only 16 kg/mm^2 (a sevenfold decrease) at 325°C. The hardness of an

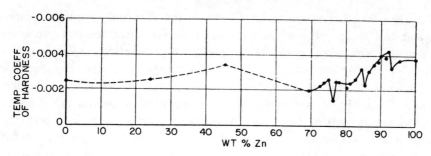

Fig. 161. Temperature coefficient of hardness for Mg-Zn alloys.

80.6-percent-Zn alloy, which is a mixture of solid compound solutions of MgZn₂ and MgZn₅, is reduced from 303 to 31 kg/mm² (one-tenth) in going from room temperature to 325°C. Similar behavior has been observed in other alloys of analogous structure. This sharp change in hardness caused by heat apparently occurs because of the radical difference in the degree of hardness of both groups of alloys at room temperature. Thus, Lowry's bewilderment regarding this behavior [379] has no basis. As proved in this system, we find that the harder the alloy at room temperature, the softer it will be when heated. As indicated in Table 51 and Fig. 161, pure compounds in relation to neighbor compounds have minimum hardness coefficients in the temperature range 20 to 325°C, i.e., when heated, they soften less than their mixtures or alloys with considerable eutectic content.

Alloys near the MgZn₅ compound were found to be very sensitive to temperature. They have the highest temperature coefficient of hardness and are

TABLE 52

SPECIFIC ELECTRICAL CONDUCTIVITY AND THERMAL EMF OF MG-ZN ALLOYS

Temp. (°C)	MgZn		MgZn₅		MgZn₂		Remarks
	Conductivity (ohm·cm)⁻¹	Thermal emf (mcv/°C)	Conductivity (ohm·cm)⁻¹	Thermal emf (mcv/°C)	Conductivity (ohm·cm)⁻¹	Thermal emf (mcv/°C)	
−170	56,000	~5.0	95,000	~3.0	118,000	~4.0	
− 80	39,000		66,000		79,500		
+ 40	28,500		42,200		52,700		
70	26,700	Values range from 5 to 8	39,100	Values range from 3 to 6	47,200	Values range from 4 to 7	Thermal emf was evaluated in relation to copper electrodes. At 150°C, the thermal emf of MgZn₅ changes sign from plus to minus.
100	25,700		38,750		44,100		
150	24,500		32,700		41,800		
200	23,800		29,200		40,100		
250	22,800		...		37,200		
300	22,200		28,900		35,000		
350	21,800		27,900		33,000		
400	...		26,700		32,100		
450	...		25,100		30,100		

weaker than all other alloys at 325°C. From the viewpoint of ease of processing and the sharp increase in hardness observed after thermal processing,
alloys in the MgZn₅ region should be considered of practical importance.

Alloys of the Mg-Zn system, including those rich in metallic compounds, exhibit increased ductility when heated. This increase in ductility is so pronounced
that any of the Mg-Zn system alloys may be extruded through a cylindrical die
into good-quality rods at elevated temperature. Furthermore, cylinders made
of these alloys may be compressed into thin disks. The alloys are able to withstand a single stage deformation of 80 to 90 percent. It is only because of this
property to soften on heating that we have succeeded in obtaining deformed
samples from these compounds (see Chapter 5).

At our request, Obukhov and Boltaks of the LFTI, Akademia Nauk, U.S.S.R.,
have evaluated the electrical conductivity and the thermal emf of deformed
Mg-Zn compounds in the temperature range −170 to 450°C. Their results are
presented in Table 52. The absolute values of electrical conductivity of compounds as well as the strong dependence of electrical conductivity on temperature are noteworthy.

Mg-Al System

The phase diagram of the Mg-Al system is of special interest as it presents
basic information on the structural nature of a number of light and superlight
alloys.

The phase diagram for the Mg-Al system may be considered as well established except for the central part, i.e., in the range 35 to 60 percent Mg, where
a conflict of interpretation exists [439], [458]–[467].

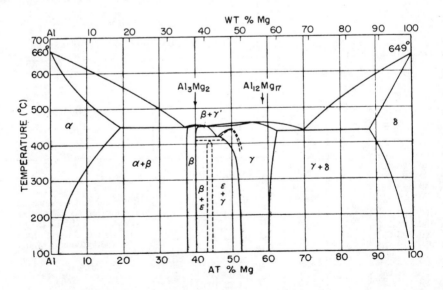

FIG. 162. Phase diagram for the Mg-Al system (according to summarized
published data).

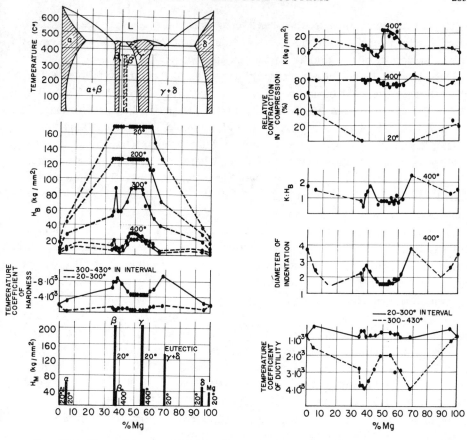

FIG. 163. Phase diagram of Mg-Al alloys (Kurnakov and Mikheyev) and composition–mechanical-properties diagrams for deformed alloys (Savitsky and Tylkina).

A detailed survey of the research efforts on the establishment of the Mg-Al phase diagram was published in 1953; its summarized version is submitted in Fig. 162 [467]. Our investigations of Mg-Al alloys, however, were based on the phase diagram developed by Kurnakov and Mikheyev; this diagram is presented in Fig. 163. The existence of the β and γ intermetallic phases is recognized by all of the authors and is not to be doubted; differences of opinion do exist, however, as to the limits of existence of these phases. The basic point of difference of opinion is related to the structure of the heterogeneous area between the β and γ phases, where several different phases were observed by a number of researchers. Also, it cannot be accepted as definitely proved in this diagram that chemical compounds are present in the disputed area of this or some other phase, since different authors point to different compositions of compounds. The basic cause of this discord may be best explained by variations in the degree of equilibrium of alloys studied; all investigations related to the middle part of the diagram were done with cast, undeformed samples when, in fact, the diffusion rate is very slow in these alloys.

It was decided to initiate an extensive program on studies of the microstructure of deformed alloys in view of the radical differences in the published data on the structure of the middle portion of the Mg-Al diagram.

The known data on the structure of β and γ phases is as follows. The β phase has a hexagonal structure with a lattice parameter of $a = 11.32A$, with a $c/a = 1.57$ and with 104 atoms in the unit cell. According to Kurnakov and Mikheyev, the β phase is a typical case of a double bertholide which does not possess characteristic points on the property lines [465]. The structure of the γ phase is cubic of the α-manganese type, where $a = 10.54A$. The unit cell of the α-manganese structure contains 58 atoms; consequently the compound best suited for the γ phase is $Mg_{17}Al_{12}$ (41.38 atomic percent of aluminum), the elementary nucleus of which contains 34 magnesium and 24 aluminum atoms.

The γ phase is formed by substitution of solid solutions [468]. For this reason, the substitution of large magnesium atoms in the γ phase by the smaller aluminum atoms results in a contraction of the lattice constant. As already mentioned in Chapter 1, the α phase of the Mg-Al system is a striking example of a crystalline material with a mixed type of cohesion [134].

We have published the only papers ([372]–[374]) dealing with systematic research on the mechanical properties of Mg-Al alloys in the entire range of composition. The brittleness of alloys at normal temperatures in the middle portion of the diagram has hampered such research. When we first began our work, the only known data were on the effect of composition on hardness at 300°C [465] and on changes in the elastic modulus in bend experiments at room temperature [455]. Both studies were conducted with cast samples which produced typically scattered results.

Our investigation of this system had two basic objectives—(1) to find out if wrought specimens made of alloys corresponding to the middle portion of the Mg-Al diagram could be obtained, and (2) to study certain mechanical properties of these alloys at various temperatures to obtain data for a composition-property diagram. As the work progressed, we found it necessary to make more detailed studies of the properties and structure of certain alloys in the area between the β and γ phases [378].

Experiments were conducted on 25 alloys at compositions related to the presence of intermetallic phases. Magnesium samples were made of the MG-1 grade and those of aluminum were of 99.7-percent purity. The alloys were cast in a preheated mold; on solidifiying, the hot ingots were placed in an electric furnace preheated to 200 or 300°C where they were left to cool slowly. These precautions were taken to prevent cracking of samples made of alloys near the γ-phase region. Ingots were cast in the form of cylinders 22 mm in diameter and 50 mm in height. The method of testing was the same as that previously described for the Mg-Zn system. The Mg-Al castings were extruded through a cylindrical steel die. Numerous preliminary tests proved that alloys which were extremely brittle at room temperature behaved like ductile materials under

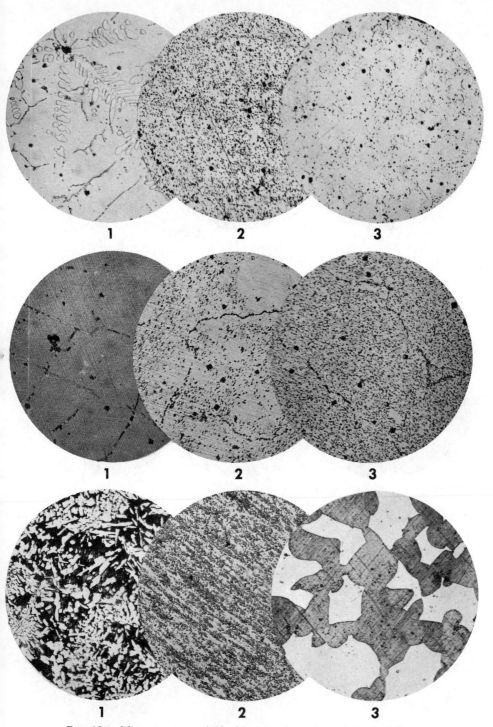

FIG. 164. Microstructure of Mg-Al alloys in various states (×250).

a. 35 weight percent of Mg: 1-cast ($\alpha + \beta$); 2-deformed (β); 3-annealed (β).

b. 36 weight percent of Mg: 1-cast (β); 2-deformed (β); 3-annealed (β).

c. 38.9 weight percent of Mg: 1-cast ($\beta + \gamma$) (×150); 2-deformed ($\beta + \gamma$) (×150); 3-annealed ($\beta + \gamma$).

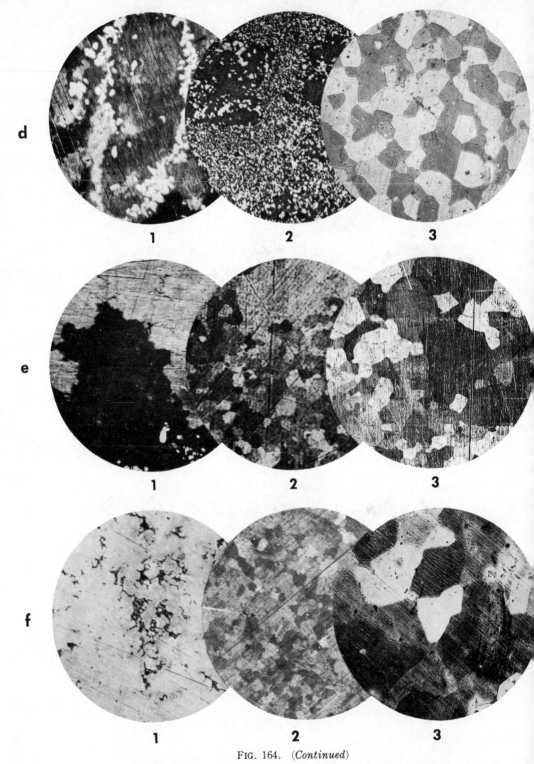

FIG. 164. (*Continued*)

d. 45 weight percent of Mg: *1*-cast ($\gamma + \beta$); *2*-deformed ($\gamma + \beta$); *3*-annealed ($\gamma + \beta$).

e. 5.5 weight percent of Mg: *1*-cast (γ + traces of β); *2*-deformed (γ); *3*-annealed (γ).

f. 57.5 weight percent of Mg: *1*-cast ($\gamma + \delta$); *2*-deformed (γ); *3*-annealed (γ).

certain temperature–exposure-time conditions. We have obtained samples made of deformed (up to 99 percent) alloys which showed no traces of cracking [376]. The samples, in the form of rods, were from 1 to 15 mm in diameter. Another important advantage of using deformed samples in this instance is their ability to achieve equilibrium in a considerably shorter time (a three-day annealing period in contrast to 20 and more for cast samples). The samples were annealed for three days at 400°C in sealed Pyrex ampules. Some of the alloys were furnace cooled while others were air quenched. The reason for quenching was to retain the microstructure at 400°C in order to compare the data on microstructure at 400°C with changes in mechanical properties. All the cast and wrought alloys were examined metallographically. Polished sections were etched in a 4-percent-alcohol solution of nitric acid, which provided a sufficiently clear observation of the γ phase structure. A 0.5-percent solution of HF was used to observe the grains in the β phase region.

Studies on the microstructure of alloys (Fig. 164) produced the following results.

1. In the cast state, Mg-Al alloys invariably reveal nonequilibrium structures. Out of 11 alloys which were prepared to correspond to the β and γ phases, only one alloy had a single-phase structure in the β region and two alloys in the γ region. Inclusions of metastable phases were observed on polished sections of the remaining alloys.

2. Hot plastic deformation tends to bring the alloys into equilibium. Distortion of grains and formation of new grains by recrystallization takes place in the process of deformation. These two factors contribute to the process of diffusion and to the stabilization of the alloy. The homogeneous γ-phase region of deformed alloys lies between 50 and 57.5 weight percent of magnesium.

3. The subsequent thermal processing of hot-deformed samples produces a state of equilibrium in a considerably shorter time.

The border line between the β phase and the heterogeneous $\beta + \alpha$ region should be further investigated to determine the possibility that it may be located at higher-Mg contents.

The mechanical properties studied were: hardness, microhardness, flow stress, and the resistance to slow deformation in compression. Tests were conducted at 20, 200, 300, 350, 400, and 430°C. The hardness of magnesium, aluminum and their α and δ solid solutions was evaluated at 70°C below the melting point. Indentation hardness was tested with a 5-mm ball under a 50-kg load. Microhardness was evaluated under a 50-g load. The flow stress was determined on cast, deformed, and annealed samples at 400 and 420°C; at lower temperatures the samples crumbled in the extrusion process. The maximum amount of deformation during extrusion was: 80 percent in a single pass and 99 percent after two passes. The relative contraction of samples was recorded after applying a static load of 5 t to predeformed samples 16 mm high and 15 mm in diameter. Experimental data are given in Tables 53–55 and in Fig. 163.

TABLE 53

Microhardness of Various Phases in the Mg-Al System

Mg Content (wt. %)	Microstructure	Phase Microhardness (kg/mm²)						
		Al	α	β	γ	Eutectic (δ + γ)	δ	Mg
0	Al	26						
5.0	α		60					
35.0	β + α		153	246				
36.0	(Al₈Mg₅)β			220				
37.5	(Al₃Mg₂)β			240				
38.9	γ + β			224	230			
41.3	γ + β			230	228			
45.0	γ + β			220				
46.0	γ + β			226	226			
47.5	(AlMg)α + β			245				
48.0	γ + β (in insignificant amounts)			215	232			
49.0	γ				228			
50.0	γ				226			
52.0	γ				230			
54.5	(Al₃Mg₄)γ				226			
55.0	γ				230			
56.0	γ(Al₂Mg₃)				226			
57.5	γ				226			
58.0	γ + eutectic (γ + δ)				230	109		
60.0	γ + eutectic (γ + δ)				220			
62.5	γ + eutectic (γ + δ)				220			
68.0	eutectic (γ + δ)					153		
95.0	δ + traces of γ						51	
100.0	Mg							35

Alloys between 35 and 58 weight percent of magnesium are noted for their extremely high hardness at room temperature; their ability to deform plastically under stress, however, is quite low because of their susceptibility to brittle fracture.

Above 200°C, the hardness of alloys decreases and the ductility increases. At temperatures above 300°C, a development of the individual characteristics of each metallic phase is observed. At 400 and 430°C, alloys in the γ-phase region stand out as to their high degree of hardness and flow resistance in contrast to neighbor alloys. No internal transformations appear to take place as a function of temperature in the γ-phase region, at least as observed by the mechanical test method. The hardness and flow stress increase slightly with increased aluminum content in the γ-phase region. These results seem to confirm Ageyev's prediction that at elevated temperature the maximum arrangement making up the γ phase strives to approach 50 atomic percent [29]. The

β-phase alloys reveal higher hardnesses and flow stresses at 300°C and higher than do neighboring alloys and, furthermore, internal transformations are absent. Thus we see that experimental data related to the mechanical properties of Mg-Al alloys at various temperatures indisputably establish the bertholide nature of the β and γ phases.

The behavior of alloys in the heterogeneous area between the β and γ phases is of special interest. Alloys in the 35.5- to 59-percent-Mg range are either β or γ phases or a mixture of both according to the phase diagram based on cast and annealed samples.

For this reason it should have been expected that, in conformity with the

TABLE 54

HARDNESS OF DEFORMED ALLOYS OF THE MG-AL SYSTEM

Mg Content (wt. %)	Hardness H_B (kg/mm²) at Temperature (°C)							
	20	200	300	350	400	400 After Annealing	430	$t = t_{melt} - 70°C$
0(100% Al)	16.7	10.4	6.9	....	4.0	3.5	2.6	0.9(590°)
5.0	47.2	42.9	26.0	....	10.4	8.7	7.8	5.3(500°)
35.0	169.0	127.4	51.8	42.9	13.5	15.3	7.1	...
36.0	169.0	....	....	....	20.0	19.0	8.7	...
37.5	169.0	127.4	87.2	....	10.3	12.4	8.4	...
38.9	169.0	127.4	57.9	27.7	8.0	13.5	4.3	...
41.3	147.0	127.4	57.9	36.7	10.4	27.7	6.4	...
45.0	169.0	127.4	70.8	51.8	16.7	22.0	13.5	...
46.0	169.0	....	....	....	25.0	26.0	....	...
47.5	169.0	....	....	....	....	25.1	....	...
48.0	169.0	127.4	87.2	51.8	27.7	25.1	23.0	...
49.0	169.0	127.4	98.1	70.8	27.7	27.7	25.0	...
50.0	169.0	127.4	87.2	57.9	27.7	29.6	23.0	...
52.0	169.0	127.4	98.1	57.9	27.7	31.3	23.0	...
53.5	169.0	127.4	....	....	26.0	26.0	15.3	...
54.5	169.0	127.4	....	....	....	17.0	....	...
55.0	169.0	127.4	87.2	57.9	25.1	27.7	19.0	...
56.0	169.0	127.4	79.6	51.8	25.1	27.7	19.0	...
57.5	169.0	....	....	....	19.0	19.0	....	...
58.0	169.0	127.4	63.7	42.9	19.0	17.0	15.3	...
60.0	169.0	111.8	63.7	27.7	19.0	16.0	11.4	...
62.5	147.0	111.8	47.2	23.0	13.5	11.4	8.04	...
68.0	127.4	70.8	36.7	....	4.0	6.0	....	...
95.0	36.7	27.7	16.7	....	8.7	8.4	6.6	6.4(460°)
100.0	26.0	16.0	9.2	....	4.9	3.9	4.0	1.1(590°)
Average for γ phase	169.0	127.4	93.0	57.9	27.7	....	2.30	...
Average for β phase	169.0	127.4	87.2	....	15.0	....	8.5	...

ALLOYS

TABLE 55

FLOW STRESS OF ALLOYS OF THE MG-AL SYSTEM AT $t = 400°C$, K (KG/MM²)

Mg Content (wt. %)	Reduction, 80% Cast	Reduction, 50 %		K : H_B	
		Deformed	Thermally Processed	Deformed	Thermally Processed
0 (Al)	15.0	6.8	4.6	1.7	1.3
5.0	41.1	15.7	17.1	1.5	2.0
35.0	37.6	12.9	16.0	0.9	1.0
36.0	26.8	9.7	15.3	0.5	0.8
37.5	17.6	12.9	9.4	1.2	0.7
38.9	80.0	11.1	16.7	1.4	1.2
41.3	21.3	8.5	13.4	1.8	0.5
45.0	26.8	6.4	16.3	...	0.8
46.0	27.6	5.2	15.3	...	0.6
47.5	30.7	9.7	10.5	0.6	0.4
48.0	51.0	11.5	19.1	0.4	0.8
49.0	66.3	22.8	18.9	0.8	...
50.0	49.0	22.5	19.2	0.8	0.6
52.5	48.6	22.8	22.4	0.8	0.7
53.5	48.4	18.7	16.2	0.7	0.6
54.5	38.6	21.4	20.0	1.0	1.2
55.0	55.2	20.5	22.3	0.8	0.8
56.0	49.0	17.5	16.2	0.7	0.6
57.5	23.4	17.8	19.1	0.9	1.0
58.0	42.6	21.4	19.5	1.1	1.1
60.0	29.2	13.5	15.9	0.7	1.0
62.5	26.4	12.2	9.5	0.9	0.8
68.0	8.4	9.8	5.0	2.4	0.8
95.0	26.6	10.5	12.0	1.2	1.4
100.0	15.0	7.3	7.0	1.5	1.8

linearity rule governing the properties of a mixture, isotherms of properties in this range would behave in a linear manner. This behavior, however, is observed only at lower temperatures. From 300°C and up, alloys containing mixtures of β and γ phases do not follow the linearity rule (see Fig. 163). At 300, 400, and 430°C, these alloys become considerably more ductile just as the β and γ phases become ductile and sharp minima are observed on the hardness isotherms. Thus, the hardness of a 38.9-weight-percent-Mg alloy at 430° is one fifth that of the γ phase and one half the hardness of the β phase. This anomaly may be explained either by a specific process of deformation of mixtures at high temperatures [187] or by the formation of some new ductile phase induced by temperature. The first hypothesis is supported by the presence of a maximum temperature coefficient of hardness which approaches the value of the temperature coefficient of hardness of the eutectic alloy. However, special studies have

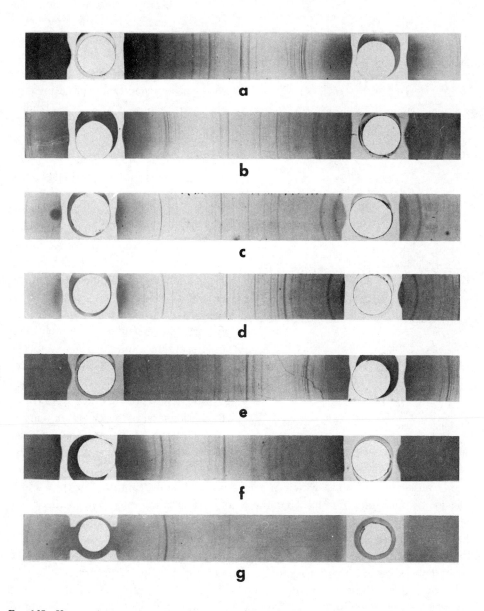

FIG 165 X-ray photographs of various phases in Mg-Al alloys, taken between 20 and 400°C.

a. β at 400°C.
b. β at 20°C.
c. γ at 400°C.
d. γ at 20°C.
e. $\beta + \gamma$ at 20°C.
f. $\beta + \gamma$ at 400°C.
g. $\beta + \gamma$ after annealing.

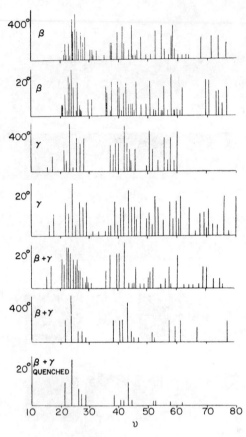

FIG. 166. Results of angle dispersion rating
ν and of the relative line intensity on X-ray
photographs of Mg-Al alloys.

led us to favor the second assumption.

The observed anomaly and the changes occurring in the heterogeneous alloys have prompted us to undertake a detailed study of their structure [376]. The basic problem, to evaluate the phase conditions of alloys at elevated temperatures, was studied by X-ray and microstructural analyses.

Three groups of alloys were investigated by the X-ray method—β phase alloys, γ phase alloys, and alloys containing a mixture of the two phases. X-ray photograms were taken at 20 and 400°C. The temperature was maintained constant during exposure. Wire samples 1 mm in diameter and 1 cm long were obtained by hot extrusion at 400°C. The Debye method was used with Fe-radiation (Fig. 165). Figure 166 presents the computation of dispersion angles ν related to the X-ray photograms. The relative intensities of the X-rays are defined by the heights of the lines. No transformations were observed in single-phase alloys of either β or γ phases alone when the temperature was increased to 400°C. Transformations were observed in alloys which in the annealed state contained both β and γ phases. Thus, lines representing the β and γ phases are observed in the X-ray photogram of an alloy with 38.9 weight percent Mg at 20°C (Fig. 165e). At 400°C, however, the X-ray photogram shows lines of one phase only, and these lines differ from the β and γ phase lines (Fig. 165f). These lines appear to be related to those of the γ phase with a somewhat simpler structure.

By quenching the predeformed samples from 400°C into ice-water we were able to obtain the single-phase structure of alloys in the 38.9 to 41.3-weight-percent-Mg range. These alloys, in conformity with the phase diagram shown in Fig. 163, in both the cast and wrought forms, become two-phase $\beta + \gamma$ alloys upon annealing (Fig. 167).

A check X-ray powder photogram of the quenched alloy of 38.9-weight-percent-Mg was found to be identical with that of the same alloy when X-rayed at 400°C (see Figs. 165 and 166).

Thus, X-ray and microstructural analyses demonstrated that deformed alloys with 38.9 to 41.3 weight percent of magnesium are single phased at 400°C. The anomalous property-composition curves above 300°C may apparently be explained by the transformation of the phases into a new phase. A final determination of the nature of the observed single-phase region may well be worth a special study.

We did not detect the β' phase, shown on the phase diagram of Fig. 163, through microstructural analyses; furthermore, the phase diagram indicates that the maximum temperature of its existence is 370°C, whereas the alloys behave abnormally above this temperature.

The higher values of flow stress quoted in Table 55 for cast materials in

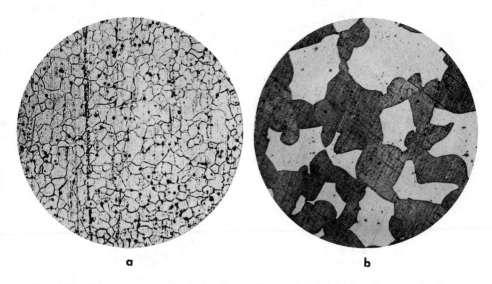

a   b

FIG. 167. Microstructure of an aluminum alloy containing 38.9 percent magnesium.
a. Quenched ($\times 150$).   b. Annealed ($\times 250$).

contrast to worked ones are due to a higher degree of deformation during extrusion (80 percent compression instead of 50 percent) and from the presence of a skin in the cast ingots. Alloys in the γ-phase region have the greatest resistance to deformation. Their flow stress at 400°C is 48 to 55 kg/mm^2 in the cast state and 17 to 23 kg/mm^2 when deformed. The lowest value of flow stress at 400°C was observed in the eutectic alloy (8.4 kg/mm^2 in the cast state and 5 kg/mm^2 when thermally worked). The flow stress was found to change substantially in those alloys where the phase state was changed by thermal processing. The ratio of flow stress to the hardness of alloys at 400°C varies from 0.4 to 2.4 in deformed as well as in annealed alloys (Table 55). Alloys located in the intermetallic phase region have the lowest ratio of flow stress to hardness, similar to the case previously observed in the Mg-Zn system. Thus,

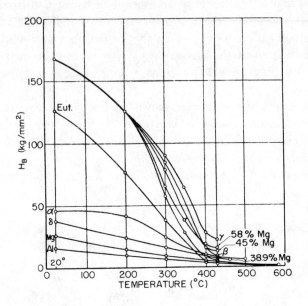

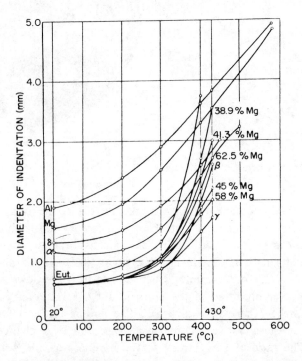

Fig. 168. The effect of temperature on the hardness
and indentation diameter of Mg-Al alloys.

for pure magnesium and aluminum the ratio is above 1.5, whereas alloys containing metallic compounds revealed ratios of only 0.4 to 0.8. The highest ratio, 2.4, was found in a deformed eutectic alloy; however after annealing, this ratio dropped to 0.8. The magnitude of the flow-stress-to-hardness ratio is apparently an index of the tendency of alloys to deform plastically under the given conditions.

It is worth noting that the reverse ratio—i.e., the ratio of hardness to flow stress—varies with composition in a way similar to that of the change in hardness and flow stress with composition.

All the alloys in the Mg-Al system soften rapidly as the temperature is increased. Pure aluminum and magnesium as well as their solid solutions exhibit a uniform decrease in hardness as the temperature is increased. The hardness of aluminum, which is 16.7 kg/mm^2 at 20°C, drops to 0.9 kg/mm^2 at 590°C; over the same temperature range magnesium decreases from 26 to 1.1 kg/mm^2. The hardness of the α solid solution is 47 kg/mm^2 at 20°C and 5 kg/mm^2 at 500°C; in the δ solid solution the hardness decreases from 37 kg/mm^2 at 20°C to 6 kg/mm^2 at 460°C.

The hardness of the eutectic composition alloy exhibits a decrease from 127.4 kg/mm^2 at 20°C to 4 kg/mm^2 at 400°C, proving that this alloy exhibits the highest temperature coefficient of hardness. Alloys of the central portion of the phase diagram exhibit a uniform and small decrease in hardness up to 200°C but above

TABLE 56

TEMPERATURE COEFFICIENT OF HARDNESS FOR MG-AL ALLOYS

Mg Content (wt. %)	Temperature Coefficient α			
	Lower Temperature Range		Upper Temperature Range	
	°C	α	°C	α
0 (Al)	20—590	$-2.0 \cdot 10^{-3}$	...	...
5.0	20—200	$-0.2 \cdot 10^{-3}$	200—500	$-3.0 \cdot 10^{-3}$
35.0	20—300	$-1.7 \cdot 10^{-3}$	300—430	$-6.6 \cdot 10^{-3}$
(36–37.5) (β)	20—300	$-1.1 \cdot 10^{-3}$	300—430	$-8.0 \cdot 10^{-3}$
38.9	20—300	$-1.3 \cdot 10^{-3}$	300—430	$-9.0 \cdot 10^{-3}$
41.3	20—300	$-1.3 \cdot 10^{-3}$	300—430	$-7.4 \cdot 10^{-3}$
45.0	20—300	$-1.2 \cdot 10^{-3}$	300—430	$-5.5 \cdot 10^{-3}$
(48–56) (γ)	20—300	$-0.9 \cdot 10^{-3}$	300—430	$-4.8 \cdot 10^{-3}$
58.0	20—300	$-1.4 \cdot 10^{-3}$	300—430	$-4.7 \cdot 10^{-3}$
60.0	20—300	$-1.4 \cdot 10^{-3}$	300—430	$-5.7 \cdot 10^{-3}$
62.5	20—300	$-1.8 \cdot 10^{-3}$	300—430	$-5.9 \cdot 10^{-3}$
68.0	20—300	$-2.0 \cdot 10^{-3}$	300—400	$-9.6 \cdot 10^{-3}$
95.0	20—200	$-0.7 \cdot 10^{-3}$	200—460	$-2.4 \cdot 10^{-3}$
100.0	20—590	$-2.0 \cdot 10^{-3}$	...	...

300°C their hardness decreases abruptly. The data presented in Fig. 168 and 104 clearly verify the above statements. It should be mentioned that, in determining the hardness under constant load, the diameter of the hardness indentation gives a measure of ductility although it is seldom used as such. Figure 104 shows average values of hardness and of microhardness of the β and γ phases based on all the alloys. Up to 430°C, alloys in the γ-phase region exhibit a considerably smaller degree of softening when compared to other alloys of this system.

The ultimate tensile strength of the γ phase at 400°C is about 2 kg/mm^2 based on a conversion of the hardness values to ultimate-tensile-strength values.

The temperature coefficients of hardness are recorded in Fig. 165 and in Table 56. The eutectic alloys have a maximum coefficient of hardness. Because of abrupt softening processes exhibited at 300°C by alloys associated with the middle part of the diagram, their temperature coefficients of hardness were tabulated into two separate ranges—from 20 to 300°C and from 300 to 430°C.

A study of ductility properties in extrusion and in compression proved that at 400°C and above all aluminum and magnesium alloys are highly ductile. Even alloys which are associated with the middle part of the diagram will withstand a deformation in excess of 80 percent in one stage, whereas they fracture in a brittle fashion at room temperature (see Fig. 163, relative contraction).

Thus we see that the presence of intermetallic phases in aluminum and magnesium alloys, although a cause of brittleness at room temperature, does not reduce ductility at elevated temperatures. Bertholide phases in this system were found to be more ductile than the daltonide compounds in the Mg-Zn system.

The trends obtained with light alloys on the increased ductility of intermetallic phases and compounds at high temperatures must certainly also apply to intermetallic phases of nonferrous, rare, and ferrous metals. The results obtained with Mg-Al alloys are of great scientific interest, and may also be of great practical value.

Mg-Cd System

Kurnakov, Zhemchuzhny, and Zasedatelev in 1914 discovered a new type of transformation in the Au-Cu system [367]. They discovered that chemical compounds form from solid solutions with a decrease in temperature. As a result of work done by Kurnakov and his associates as well as by other researchers, Kurnakov compounds were found in a number of other systems: Fe-Al, Cu-Pd, Cu-Pt, Fe-Pt, Au-Mn, Pt-Mo, Fe-Ir, Fe-Cr, Fe-Co, Fe-V [12], [18], [29], [156], [297], [366]. Metallic compounds formed from solid solutions are daltonides and, depending on the state, are characterized by minima on the hardness and electrical-resistance curves. Kurnakov compounds have properties which are invariably superior to those of the corresponding solid solutions. As is generally known, metallic compounds formed by crystallization from the melt have high values of hardness and electrical resistivity.

It should be noted that Kurnakov's detailed investigation of transformations of the solid solution in the gold-copper system was conducted to discover why the mechanical properties of such alloys were abnormal: wires made of 40 to 60 atomic percent gold were highly brittle after annealing [12].

In spite of the great scientific and practical importance of ordered solid solutions, their mechanical properties (besides hardness) have not been studied systematically as a function of concentration and temperature. The Mg-Cd system is typical of those systems that develop several metallic compounds by decomposition of a solid solution during cooling [469]. It is for this reason that we chose this system for our studies.

The phase-diagram of the Mg-Cd system has been studied by a number of Soviet scientists; among them are Urazov [470], Stepanov and Bulakh [471], [472], Kornilov [473]–[475], Ageyev and Ageyeva [476], Rovinsky and Kozhina [477], Khomyakov, Kholler, and Troshkina [478], and Grum-Grzhimaylo [387]. This system has also been investigated by a number of foreign researchers [479]–[484].

The results obtained proved the existence of three compounds—Mg_3Cd, $MgCd$, and $MgCd_3$. The structure of one of them is given in Fig. 169 [38]. The structure of the $MgCd_3$ compound is similar to it. The hexagonal structure of the $MgCd$ compound may be considered to consist of alternating layers of magnesium and cadmium atoms [44].

The structure of the Mg-Cd phase diagram is still rather vague in many respects. Some of the authors suggest that the $MgCd$ compound is formed from the melt in the process of solidification, while the two other compounds, Mg_3Cd and $MgCd_3$, are formed in the solid state as a result of ordering in the crystal lattice caused by a decrease in temperature. The same authors maintain

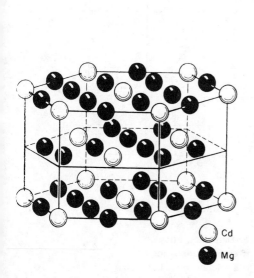

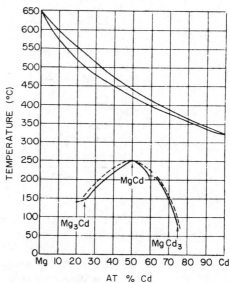

FIG. 169. Structure of Mg_3Cd.   FIG. 170. Phase diagram of the Mg-Cd system.

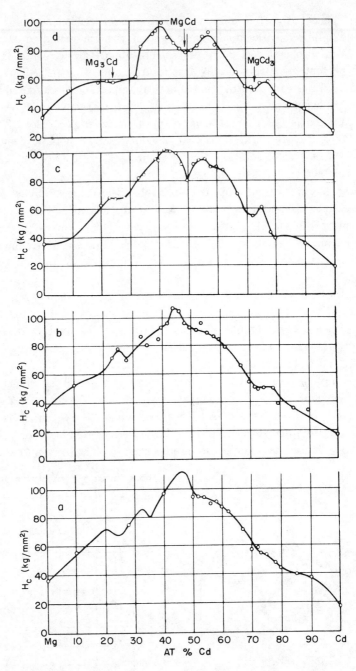

FIG. 171. Effect of prolonged annealing on the hardness of Mg-Cd alloys (Savitsky and Baron).

a. Cast alloys.   b. Deformed alloys.

c. Deformed alloys after 6-hr annealing.

d. Deformed alloys after 6-day annealing.

that the MgCd compound goes through an allotropic transformation at about 250°C.

Other authors state that solidification in this system always leads to formation of solid solution, which in turn becomes ordered as the temperature is decreased. One version of the phase diagram for the Mg-Cd system is presented in Fig. 170.

Based on the results of these investigations, the temperature ranges of the formation of the Mg_3Cd, MgCd, and $MgCd_3$ compounds are, respectively, 150, 250, and 89°C.

A study of the mechanical properties of alloys would contribute to the solution of a number of obscure points. Yet, as far as we know, the mechanical properties of Mg-Cd alloys have never been systematically investigated except for hardness measurements at room temperature. Hardness tests have been conducted on cast samples only, whereas it is a well known fact that equilibrium in alloys is achieved much more readily and to a greater degree in worked samples. Kornilov, Priakhina, and Chuyko, using the centrifugal method of testing the heat resistance of cast alloys of the Mg-Cd system (45 to 60 atomic percent Mg), found that the compound MgCd is characterized by a minimum in the bend angle at 200 and 300°C [485].

We determined the ultimate fracture strength, the ductility in dynamic and static tests, and the flow stress for cast and deformed alloys (31 alloys) in quenched and annealed states at various temperatures. Pure magnesium (Mg-1, 99.9 percent) and pure cadmium (Cd-2, 99.8 percent) were used for alloying. Melting was done under carnallite flux and, to prevent the magnesium from burning, the latter was introduced under a layer of molten cadmium. The hardness at room temperature was evaluated on cast cylindrical samples 23 mm in diameter and 50 mm high. The hardness of alloys was tested by means of a pobedit cone under a 60 kg-load.

After their hardness was measured, the cast samples were extruded 80 percent into rods 11 mm in diameter; the average length of the rods was 160 mm. These rods had a high-quality surface. Extrusion was done in a 35-t hydraulic press at 250°C. The degree of equilibrium in alloys was studied as a function of annealing time (2 hr to 6 days);* their hardness was recorded at regular annealing intervals and the results are recorded in Table 57 and in Fig. 171.

Hardness curves for cast and deformed alloys did not show any characteristic points. After annealing, and especially after prolonged annealing, minima were observed on the composition–hardness curve. In a wrought alloy corresponding to MgCd, the hardness reaches 75 to 80 kg/mm^2 after annealing for 6 hr but does not change with further annealing. On the other hand, the hardness of alloys corresponding to Mg_3Cd and $MgCd_3$ changed with annealing but finally levelled off after 4 days; this difference is apparently explained by the ability

---

* *Editor's Note*: Unfortunately, the author did not give the actual annealing temperature used.

TABLE 57

Hardness of Mg-Cd Alloys under Various Conditions

Cd Content		Hardness H_C (kg/mm²)							
			Deformed Alloys					Quenched Alloys	
					Annealed				
(at. %)	(wt. %)	Cast Alloys	Without Annealing	4 days H_C at 20°C	6 days H_C at 20°C	H_C at 280°C	H_C at 250°C	from 280°C	from 200°C
0 (Mg)	0 (Mg)	36.0	36.0	34.2	32.0	7.8	...	33.0	37.4
10.0	33.9	56.0	53.0	50.7	52.0	11.7	...	51.0	51.2
20.0	53.6	73.0	60.0	64.0	56.6	11.2	...	62.5	65.5
23.0	58.0	70.0	71.4	70.0	57.5	10.2	...	65.2	68.2
25.0	60.6	65.0	78.3	66.6	56.6	8.9	...	76.6	73.2
28.0	64.2	75.0	69.3	68.2	57.5	8.7	...	74.9	74.5
33.0	69.5	87.0	86.7	80.4	60.0	7.9	...	84.4	70.0
35.0	71.3	79.0	80.4	78.5	80.5	7.8	...	82.2	86.7
39.0	74.4	91.0	84.5	98.8	89.0	8.8	...	91.2	....
40.0	75.5	96.0	93.5	101.5	91.0	8.7	...	....	102.0
42.0	76.9	104.0	96.0	93.6	96.6	9.0	...	93.8	80.5
44.0	78.4	104.0	107.0	91.2	86.2	9.6	...	101.0	89.0
46.0	79.9	113.0	105.0	89.0	82.5	13.8	9.2	107.0	78.5
48.0	81.0	112.0	96.0	78.5	78.4	8.0	9.4	101.0	75.9
50.0	82.2	93.5	93.5	75.0	75.0	8.1	8.6	101.0	70.0
52.0	83.3	93.5	91.2	86.6	77.0	8.4	8.5	104.0	78.5
54.0	84.4	93.5	96.0	80.4	80.5	7.0	6.4	101.0	78.5
56.0	85.5	88.8	89.0	86.6	86.2	6.9	...	91.2	73.2
58.0	86.5	91.0	86.7	88.8	89.0	4.9	...	91.2	89.0
60.0	87.3	86.6	84.5	86.6	80.5	4.4	...	80.6	....
62.0	88.3	84.5	78.5	84.5	54.2	3.8	...	82.2	73.2
67.0	90.2	71.0	65.2	68.2	61.0	3.7	...	53.0	....
70.0	91.5	57.5	54.0	51.9	51.0	3.6	...	54.1	66.7
72.0	92.2	58.6	50.7	50.0	50.0	3.2	...	....	58.7
73.0	92.3	55.2	49.0	51.9	48.0	3.0	...	52.1	55.0
75.0	93.3	54.0	50.0	62.5	53.0	2.4	...	45.5	50.8
78.0	94.2	48.0	50.0	50.0	54.2	...	...	44.6	47.2
80.0	94.7	45.4	39.2	37.5	39.4	...	...	42.0	43.0
85.0	96.3	40.0	35.4	42.3	37.5	2.3	...	41.6	44.0
90.0	97.6	38.2	34.2	38.0	34.6	...	...	41.0	43.0
100.0	100.0	18.0	17.5	20.0	18.3	...	...	21.4	22.7

to achieve equilibrium more rapidly in alloys typified by MgCd than in alloys corresponding to Mg₃Cd and MgCd₃. An increase in hardness of alloys during the early stages of annealing was explained by a preprecipitation phenomenon (see Fig. 171c).

On the basis of previously described data and on published data related to the rate of transformation in solid-solution alloys in the Mg-Cd system [473] –[476], all the alloys were annealed for a period of six days: three days at 280°C for homogenization and then at a temperature approximately 10 to 15°C below the transformation temperature. The homogenization temperature (280°C) was selected with the assumption that it was sufficiently high to facilitate the transformation of all the alloys into a random solid solution, but low enough to avoid volatilization of components contained in the lower-melting alloys of this system. All the annealed alloys were sealed in evacuated glass ampules. Annealing was done in a muffle furnace. In addition to measuring the hardness we also evaluated their ultimate fracture strength and ductility in static and dynamic compression.

The samples (11 mm in diameter and 10 mm high) were not fractured in compression tests; in static compression the load was 7 t and the work capacity in dynamic compression was 8 kg·m. The data submitted show that the three annealed chemical compounds have lower values of hardness and strength than alloys that border them in composition (Fig. 172). It is worth noting that alloys in the compounds region stand out with respect to their ductility properties in compression tests. The maxima in hardness and strength and the minima in ductility are apparently related to the limits of solid solubility for the compounds.

The results of our mechanical tests did not reveal the presence of heterogeneous regions as the composition was changed from one solid solution to another. Neither is it always possible to determine the presence of such regions in other similar systems by alternate experimental methods (e.g., microstructure analysis).

The mechanical properties of alloys

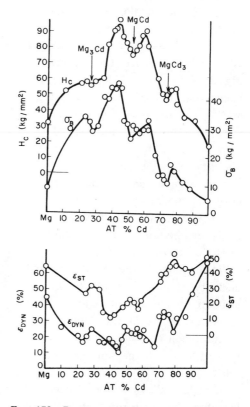

FIG. 172. Room-temperature mechanical properties of Mg-Cd alloys annealed 6 days.

in the solid-solution region were determined by quenching samples from 280°C. As in the case of the annealing temperature, the quenching temperature was made sufficiently high to assure that the alloys were in the solid-solution region yet was not high enough to cause volatilization. The alloys were sealed in evacuated glass tubes, soaked for 24 hr at temperature, and then quenched in water. To prevent the decomposition of the solid solution at room temperature, all experiments were conducted as soon as possible after quenching. For this reason just a few alloys were quenched at a time; in tensile-strength tests each specimen was quenched individually.

In addition to measuring the hardness of samples quenched from 280°C, we also studied samples quenched from 200°C. The transformation temperature for the Mg-Cd compound is still subject to question, but transformation at 200°C is admitted by every investigator of this system. Experimental data for room-temperature tests of alloys quenched from 280 and 200°C are presented in Fig. 173.

The fact that no maxima or minima are observed on the curves for mechanical properties of alloys quenched from 280°C proves that no chemical compounds are present at this temperature. The flow curve is typical for solid solutions. Quenched alloys corresponding to the compound composition are stronger but less ductile than annealed alloys. For instance, the hardness of MgCd alloy is 100 kg/mm² after quenching, and only 75 kg/mm² in the annealed state (see Table 57). Its strength, after annealing, was reduced from 39 to 26 kg/mm², while the impact ductility (ε_{dyn}) increased by 60 to 70 percent (Table 58). The hardness curve of alloys annealed for 3 days at 200°C and then quenched in water exhibited one minimum corresponding to the compound MgCd.

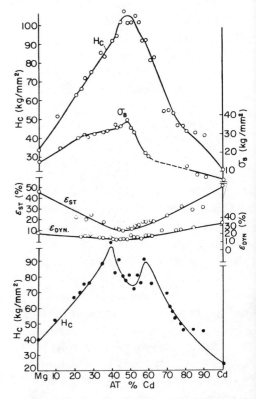

We evaluated the hardness and ductility of all alloys at 280°C, the ultimate tensile strength and the flow stress of alloys in the MgCd compound region at 280°C, and the hardness of alloys in the same region at 350°C.

Annealed alloys were studied at elevated temperature (Fig. 174) by heating the samples for one hour at

FIG. 173. Mechanical properties of Mg-Cd alloys after annealing at 280°C. The lower curve describes the hardness of alloys after annealing at 200°C.

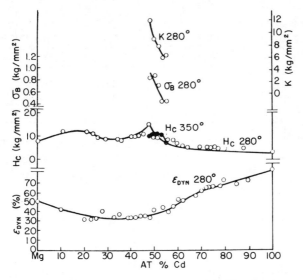

FIG. 174. Mechanical properties of Mg-Cd alloys at elevated temperatures (test temperatures are indicated above the curves).

Quenched from 280°C   Annealed

FIG. 175. Microstructure of Mg-Cd alloys (50 atomic percent) ($\times$150).

temperature before testing. Tests at 350°C were conducted in a protective atmosphere.

Summarized data on the mechanical properties of alloys—annealed, quenched, and tested at 280°C—are presented in Table 58. The shapes of the curves of hardness and ductility of alloys at 280°C are similar to those of alloys quenched

TABLE 58
MECHANICAL PROPERTIES OF MG-CD ALLOYS

Cd (at. %)	Ultimate Strength σ_B (kg/mm²) 20°C Annealed	20°C Quenched	280°C	Flow Stress at 280°C after Pre-annealing	Ductility in Compression ε (%) 20°C Annealed ε_{stat}	Annealed ε_{dyn}	Quenched ε_{stat}	Quenched ε_{dyn}	280°C ε_{dyn}	Temp. Coeff. of Hardness α 20-280°C	20-350°C	Flow Stress K of Cast Unannealed Alloys (kg/mm²)
0 (Mg)	22.0	20.3			45.2	45.0	....	19.6	50.0	$-2.4\cdot10^{-4}$		18.7
10.0	29.2	28.0			....	....	47.4	24.0	41.0	$-2.5\cdot10^{-4}$		42.0 ⎱ 400°
20.0	32.8	35.0			30.8	21.0	17.2	....	35.0	$-2.7\cdot10^{-4}$		26.3
23.0	32.2	38.0			....	16.9	....	14.6	34.0	$-2.9\cdot10^{-4}$		35.5
25.0	28.0	36.0			27.8	20.4	16.7	15.0	34.0	$-3.1\cdot10^{-4}$		11.0
28.0	30.0	38.2			32.2	25.0	19.5	16.6	38.0	$-3.5\cdot10^{-4}$		18.4 ⎱ 350°
33.0	40.0	40.0			29.8	17.6	11.1	12.8	35.0	$-3.4\cdot10^{-4}$		13.1
35.0	39.0	40.5			15.9	15.7	13.6	12.4	35.0	$-4.0\cdot10^{-4}$		17.1
39.0	42.8	44.5			....	18.0	....	11.1	32.0	$-3.8\cdot10^{-4}$		12.7
40.0	43.5	42.4			11.9	16.1	5.9	10.4	32.0	$-3.9\cdot10^{-4}$		8.0
42.0	44.7	42.0			13.7	15.3	4.1	8.8	32.0	$-4.0\cdot10^{-4}$		9.2
44.0	42.7	41.4			....	10.8	4.0	8.8	33.0	$-3.7\cdot10^{-4}$		9.2
46.0	31.6	47.5	0.82	12.0	24.4	18.5	7.0	9.5	33.0	$-3.0\cdot10^{-4}$	$-2.8\cdot10^{-4}$	8.7
48.0	31.2	41.8	0.87	8.7	18.6	25.4	4.6	10.1	33.0	$-3.8\cdot10^{-4}$	$-2.8\cdot10^{-4}$	6.3
50.0	26.1	39.0	0.72	7.7	20.9	24.0	7.6	14.6	38.0	$-3.7\cdot10^{-4}$	$-2.8\cdot10^{-4}$	8.4
52.0	29.6	24.0	0.40	6.0	....	21.5	8.0	12.0	40.5	$-3.7\cdot10^{-4}$	$-2.9\cdot10^{-4}$	8.4
54.0	28.6	....	0.42	6.0	18.2	22.0	12.0	12.5	41.0	$-4.1\cdot10^{-4}$	$-3.3\cdot10^{-4}$	9.2
56.0	27.5	25.0			....	24.6	12.3	10.4	....	$-4.2\cdot10^{-4}$		9.2 ⎱ 300°
58.0	29.7	23.0			....	21.0	13.2	14.2	42.0	$-4.8\cdot10^{-4}$		9.5
60.0	28.6	21.2			....	24.0	12.2	14.8	48.0	$-4.9\cdot10^{-4}$		7.6
62.0	29.0	....			....	18.5	....	13.8	47.5	$-4.7\cdot10^{-4}$		7.1
67.0	20.4	....			34.6	16.1	19.2	20.4	52.5	$-4.7\cdot10^{-4}$		8.7
70.0	12.7	....			39.8	33.4	....	33.0	57.0	$-4.4\cdot10^{-4}$		6.5 ⎱ 250°
72.0	12.6	....			40.0	33.0	....	30.2	60.5	$-4.7\cdot10^{-4}$		11.0
73.0	11.3	....			44.0	34.4	31.6	31.0	61.0	$-4.7\cdot10^{-4}$		3.7
75.0	10.7	....			51.6	32.5	....	32.0	61.0	$-5.2\cdot10^{-4}$		4.7
78.0	16.6	17.0			44.0	24.0	30.0	21.4	69.0	....		4.5
79.5	14.5	16.3			....	....	....	32.0	69.0	....		4.7
85.0	10.8	11.3			43.0	32.0	48.0	25.0	63.0	$-3.9\cdot10^{-4}$		3.9
90.0	9.2	9.6			40.0	47.0	43.2	24.0	68.0	....		4.5
100.0	5.6	7.5			51.0	68.5	62.0	30.0	78.0	....		3.1

from the same temperature. As expected, the hardness of alloys at 280°C is considerably less and ductility is considerably higher than in quenched alloys at room temperature. Similar shapes in the curves of alloys quenched from 280°C and tested at room temperature with those evaluated at 280°C indicates that the ordering process at low temperatures is slow; consequently, the high temperature phases can be studied by an evaluation of properties at ordinary temperature after quenching from the high temperature.

In measuring the hardness at 350°C and the strength and flow stress at 280°C of alloys in the region of the compound MgCd, we observed no minima. Studies of the microstructure of alloys have confirmed the data obtained from mechanical tests. Thus, the structure of an alloy (corresponding to the compound MgCd) quenched from 280°C has a homogeneous solid solution structure (Fig. 175a). On being annealed, this alloy exhibits twins in the solid-solution grains; these are caused by the conversion of the solid solution into a chemical compound (Fig. 175b), thus indicating that the MgCd compound was formed below 280°C.

7

Selecting Optimum Conditions for Hot Working Metal Alloys

It is common knowledge that the successful achievement of any technological process—be it related to the quantity or the quality of production—depends greatly on the ability to select the most favorable working conditions. To solve this problem by pure calculation alone is not possible. A complete empirical investigation of the various factors affecting the ductility of alloys should yield results on which to base the selection of the most favorable conditions for processing a given material or to produce the required changes in its internal structure.

Ductility is not an unalterable property of a material; it depends on the conditions of testing or processing. Just one heating or cooling cycle of a manufactured object may cause such profound changes in its internal structure as to render the object either brittle or ductile. The ductility of a metal or alloy is dependent on the following basic factors: 1) the nature of the metal (or alloy), its composition, and its structure; 2) the method of deformation, i.e., the type of stress state; and 3) the conditions of deformation (temperature, velocity, and degree of deformation).

The selection of hot-working process (rolling, forging, extrusion, and sheet punching) is governed by the same factors that control the mechanical properties of materials—namely, temperature, rate and degree of deformation, and the type of stress condition [57], [217]. These factors all act simultaneously and cooperatively during the working process. We shall now assume that this cooperation does not exist and shall, therefore, examine each factor separately, in an attempt to select the optimum conditions of hot working.

It should not be overlooked that the working of metals and alloys is governed by specific laws: of shear stress, of constancy of volume, of least resistance, of similarity, of auxiliary stresses, and of the heterogeneity of plastic deformation [57], [486], none of which will be discussed here in detail.

Temperature of Deformation

The highest temperature for working metals or alloys is always below the melting temperature. (We shall not examine the subject of ingotless working.)

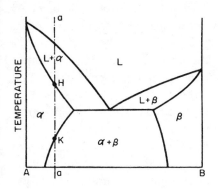

FIG. 176. Phase diagram of a limited solid-solution system.

In the working of alloys, the first consideration should be given to the phase diagrams of the base metal and the other metals forming the given alloy. The phase-diagram data furnish the initial orienting information of the possible temperature interval of deformation. Point H on the solidus curve indicates the highest temperature for working (Fig. 176). When the solid solubility (solvus line) is affected by temperature it becomes necessary to conduct the working in the single-phase, homogeneous, solid-solution region. Changes in the phase state during the process of deformation result in nonuniform deformation and in high internal stresses [57], [186]. Consequently, point K on the solubility line indicates the lowest hot-working temperature (see Fig. 176). When the phase diagram of a worked alloy is not available, its cooling curve may be determined on a Kurnakov pyrometer; other methods can also be used to determine the melting temperature and other solid-state-transformation points.

For a better evaluation of the temperature interval of working, it is imperative to know how ductility and strength change with temperature for a given alloy. The values of resistance to deformation and of specific pressure, in particular, are needed to estimate the required force of the equipment (power hammer, roller, press, or other device) for working ingots or the semifinished product. While it is necessary to know the temperature dependence of impact strength, this knowledge alone will not determine the temperature range for working of metals and alloys. In certain alloys, the temperature range over which a maximum impact strength is obtained coincides with the optimum temperature range of working; thus, according to Gubkin, Zakharov, and Baykov, the curve of the impact strength of brass accurately describes the range of hot rolling for this alloy [126]. Bobylev and Chipizhenko stated that for copper and brasses the value of the reduction in area may be viewed as a characteristic of ductility to be correlated with working [232]. However, the impact-strength–temperature curve for magnesium alloys is not always a reliable criterion. Thus, in alloys MA-3 (6 percent Al, 1 percent Zn, 0.3 percent Mn and balance Mg), the minimum temperature for impact strength is 350°C. It would then seem that, at this temperature, the alloy is brittle; yet MA-3 alloys at 350°C yield with great ease to working such as extrusion [217], [487].

In our studies on the ductility of magnesium and its alloys, special attention was directed to the role of temperature on the ductility of the material, especially in static and dynamic compression [147]. When the degree of deformation in compression tests was determined, it was found that the first crack is a reliable symptom for evaluating the ductility of metals or alloys. The first-crack method may be used in the laboratory as well as in the industry where rolling and forging are utilized. The obvious main advantages of this method are as follows:

1. It may be used for compression tests; compression is the main stress state in all basic methods of metal working: extrusion, rolling, and forging. This advantage is absent in other methods of testing.

2. The value of the maximum reduction in compression is clearly and significantly influenced by temperature and by the velocity of deformation.

3. No specially shaped samples (caps, attachments, or other) are necessary.

However, as stated earlier (Chapter 1), compression testing is a milder form of testing and is less sensitive than tension to the condition of grain boundaries.

The problem of which mechanical properties or technological tests should be used as criteria of ductility is a permanent subject in the professional literature [488]. The author believes that an absolute index of technological ductility does not exist, because ductility is not a property but a state of matter. It follows therefore that, in order to forecast the ductility of an alloy, the conditions under which the evaluation will be made must be stipulated. In the case of a test for technological ductility in rolling, one should choose only such criteria of ductility which, by condition of stress (especially with respect to the direction of deformation) and by the rate of deformation, are analogous to rolling conditions. Since none of the indices of ductility now available meet all of the requirements, one must use several indices and appraise technological ductility on the strength of the aggregate data.

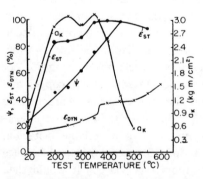

Fig. 177. Ductility diagram of a magnesium MA-2 alloy.

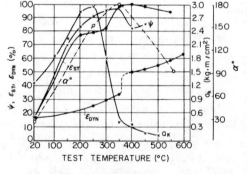

FIG. 178. Ductility diagram of a magnesium MA-3 alloy (α is angle of static bend prior to fracture of notched prismatic specimens).

We think that a satisfactory prediction of the temperature range for maximum ductility of an alloy worked under standard hot-working methods may be achieved only through an investigation of the following: 1) the effect of the temperature on the impact strength (or angle of bend); 2) reduction of area in both static and dynamic tension tests; and 3) deformations resulting in the appearance of the first crack in static and dynamic compression tests.

For the sake of practical convenience and graphic clarity, all numerical values of ductility properties related to a given alloy and obtained under various methods of mechanical testing should be shown as a function of temperature on the same graph. Gubkin applied the name "ductility diagram" to describe such data [216], [217].

The ductility diagram reflects the ability of a solid to undergo an irreversible change of form at various temperatures, strain rates, and types of deformation.

An illustration of such a diagram is shown in Fig. 177 and 178; it demonstrates the ductility of magnesium alloys MA-2 (3 to 4 percent Al; 0.5 percent Zn; 0.3 percent Mn, and balance Mg) and MA-3 (composition as previously stated) [217]. Ductility diagrams, by graphically describing the dependence of the optimum temperature of deformation on the strain and the type of stress state, may serve as a basic tool in determining the best temperature of working. These diagrams are being more and more extensively used in metal working and technological investigations. Some authors include the characteristics of resistance to deformation on the ductility diagram [345]. For a better picture of the influence of temperature on ductility and resistance of material to deformation, two separate diagrams should be plotted—one for ductility and another for resistance to deformation.

The theory of deformation of solids—especially that of technological deformation of metals and alloys—was thoroughly investigated by the late Gubkin and his associates [203], [489]-[491].

The results of the working of metallic alloys, and especially the quality of manufactured objects, depend largely upon the type of deformation mechanism occurring under the given conditions. In line with modern concepts and subject to the relationship between strain rate and the strengthening and weakening of materials, four mechanisms of deformation may be found: mechanism of cold deformation (cold deformation), mechanism similar to cold deformation (incomplete cold deformation), mechanism of hot deformation (hot deformation), and mechanism of deformation similar to hot deformation [57]. The last-mentioned mechanism is characterized by incomplete recrystallization and usually leads to poor mechanical properties and even to rejects [57], [492]. The cold-deformation mechanism requires a great deal of energy for working and hence is less efficient; furthermore, a number of alloys (for example, magnesium, titanium) do not yield to this process because of low ductility. Alloys are worked preferably under conditions of hot deformation (where recovery and recrystallization are achieved), or under conditions similar to cold deformation where only recovery is achieved.

Evaluation of the mechanism of deformation may best be accomplished by X-ray photograms of specimens tested under various conditions of deformation (to determine the degree of recovery or recrystallization). This method, however, is costly and time consuming. A different method was developed at the laboratory for mechanical testing of the Institute of General Inorganic Chemistry, Academy of Sciences, U.S.S.R.; this method was based on the correlation of stresses taking place in the neck region and at the moment of fracture in tension. The method is related to the plotting of the orienting true stress curves at different temperatures [216].

Rate of Deformation

According to the theory of metal working, the velocity of deformation does not refer to the rate of the testing machine but to the degree of deformation expressed by the maximum deformation and is related to the time during deformation [57]. As stated by Vitman, the mechanism correlating deformation with its velocity is

$$S = S_0(l/l_0)^n \, ,$$

where S is the stress at a strain rate equal to l, and S_0 is the stress at the starting strain rate l_0. According to data obtained by Vitman and Zlatin, n varies between 0.015 and 0.03 [493].[*] For example, when the strain rate is increased 100 times, n being equal to 0.03, the resistance to deformation increases by 15 percent. Thus,

$$S = S_0(100)^{0.03} = 1.15S_0 \, .$$

Resistance to deformation may increase more rapidly with strain rate than predicted by the above equation especially when the stress state is changed from unidirectional to volumetric.

For a majority of industrial metals, increased rates of deformation result in a rather pronounced increase in the yield strength in contrast to the effect of strain rate on the ultimate strength [103]. However, a number of published results show opposite trends.

The effect of strain rate on ductility and resistance to deformation is one of the inadequately studied areas in the theory of metal working. Views expressed by specialists on the subject are different [16], [21], [57], [103], [494]-[497]. Yet, according to recent studies, the following postulates may be considered as firmly established:

    1. The rate of deformation is often a decisive factor which may determine the best method of deforming the metal.

---

  * *Editor's Note*: This relationship is applicable only at low temperatures, below $0.5T_m$. At high temperatures n is found to be 0.2 for most materials.

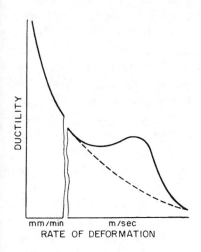

FIG. 179. Schematic drawing showing the effect of strain rate on the ductility of magnesium alloys (Savitsky).

2. The effect of strain rate on the properties of materials is related to the type of metal or alloy; it has more effect on materials of low ductility.

3. The influence of strain rate is extremely strong in the temperature ranges of transitions from one deformation mechanism to another.

4. In addition to the importance of establishing the proper rate of deformation in a steady-working process, it is also necessary to establish the rate of loading.

It should be noted that in most cases one deals with existing equipment made to run at predetermined velocities. In such cases a study of strain-rate effects will help determine the type of equipment best suited for working (for instance, presses or power hammers).

In planning a technological process for a new plant, such data may serve as a criterion for selecting, even developing, new machinery. A world-wide tendency for increased production prevails in contemporary technology. For working metals it is expressed by high velocities, high temperatures, super-compression, and so on.

The combined effect of both temperature and strain rate is of great importance. Furthermore, the role of strain rate on the ease of working should not be evaluated separately from the role of temperature [201]. The thermal strain-rate factor should be analyzed simultaneously. For a mechanism of deformation similar to cold deformation, the rate of deformation should not exceed the rate of recovery, in order to provide for relief of internal stresses arising from working. The rate of deformation may be considerably increased at temperatures where recrystallization can occur; it is known that an increase in temperature accelerates the rate of softening. Using a rough approximation of the chemical rule of kinetics, Sachs determined that the rate of recrystallization is doubled for a 10°C increase in temperature [497]. Our data reveal that magnesium and the alloy MA-3 recrystallize at 600°C, even under impact deformation [260]. The rate of deformation undoubtedly exerts a great and peculiar influence on the alloy's ductility. At a constant temperature an increase in the rate of deformation results in decreased ductility. As a result of heating effects from deformation, however, in a certain strain-rate interval, some increase in ductility is observed. A further increase in strain rate causes the ductility to decrease again. Figure 179 illustrates the effect of deformation rate on the ductility in the case of magnesium alloys; this effect has been confirmed by a number of other cases.

The data presented in Fig. 178 illustrate that, in elongation and reduction experiments with MA-3 alloys at low strain rates at 400°C, the ductility closely approaches 100 percent. With an increase in strain rate, the ductility begins to decrease and, under dynamic conditions (average rate of impact, 2.7 m/sec), the ductility decreases to about 50 percent. Upon a further increase in the strain rate, however, the ductility increases somewhat. Thus, at a given temperature, the first crack in the alloy appears only after a 60-percent deformation when the impact rate is 5 m/sec. The lowering of ductility as a function of strain rate may also be illustrated by the rolling of MA-3 alloy, whose stress state is primarily that of compression. At 400°C and at a rolling velocity of 0.6 m/sec the first crack is observed at a reduction approximately half as large as in slow deformation.

The effect of strain rate is similar for any condition of stress. For example, in a bend test on the Gagarin press (16-mm/min velocity) at 350°C, notched specimens of MA-3 alloy exhibited a tendency to limitless ductility (see Fig. 67). But in pendulum (ram-impact device) experiments (impact velocity, 2 to 4 m/sec)—i.e., when static velocity was changed to dynamic—the ductility was abruptly lowered and, under these conditions, the alloy exhibited a tendency toward brittleness.

Degree of Deformation

In selecting the optimum deformation for a worked metal, one should know:
1. the effect of that degree of deformation on the mechanical properties of the material at various temperatures;
2. the maximum permissible values of deformation compatible with the degree of alloy toughness, and its relation to temperature, strain rate, and condition of stress; and
3. the effect of deformation on the size of grain observed in the recrystallization diagrams.

There are two types of recrystallization diagram; both are dependent on the temperature of processing. Type one illustrates the relationship of grain size to the temperature of annealing and the degree of the initial cold-worked state [498]. Such a diagram serves as a base for proper annealing after cold working. Type-two diagrams illustrate the relation of grain size to the degree and temperature of hot deformation [499]. Both types trace the changes in the crystalline structure of an alloy under certain conditions and permit a selection of the temperature and the degree of deformation necessary to obtain the desired grain size. Type-two recrystallization diagrams may also furnish important data on the best temperature range for working. The best temperature corresponds to temperatures at which an intensive growth of grains takes place. These diagrams may also be used for evaluating the mechanism of deformation. Figure 180 shows a type-one recrystallization diagram of MA-3 alloy; figures 181 and 182 illustrate type-two diagrams for the same alloy [260], [500].

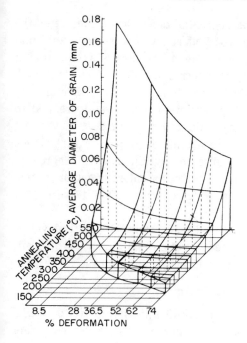

FIG. 180. Type-one recrystallization diagram of a magnesium MA-3 alloy. The samples were first cold-extruded and then annealed (Bochvar and Savitsky).

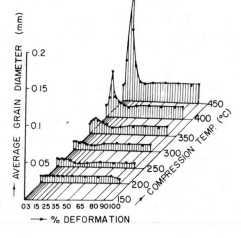

FIG. 181. Type-two recrystallization diagram of a magnesium MA-3 alloy under slow, hot deformation (Savitsky).

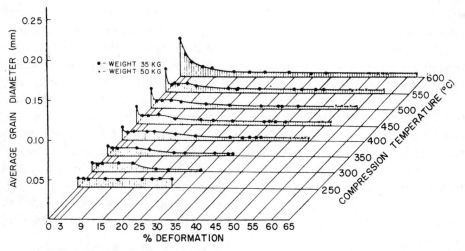

FIG. 182. Type-two recrystallization diagram of a magnesium MA-3 alloy under hot-impact deformation (Savitsky).

It should be noted that the greater the degree of deformation the better the quality of the worked alloys and the higher the efficiency of working. As found by Voronov, the hot-extruded MA-3 magnesium alloy possesses outstanding mechanical properties after a 90- to 98-percent deformation [487]. Low ("critical") stages of deformation should be avoided, since they result in a nonuniform coarse grain size. A "critical" degree of deformation is apparently related to the transition from intergranular to intercrystalline deformation.

Published data indicate that in certain pure metals, at extremely high stages of deformation (95 percent and over), the curve for "grain size vs. degree of deformation" exhibits a second maximum caused by an enlargement of grains, as a result of the development of a strong preferred orientation texture [89], [501]–[503].

This phenomenon, discovered by Soviet scientists, is of great practical value, especially for the technology of cold ductile deformation and annealing of semi-finished materials and products of highly ductile metals and alloys.

Type of Stress State

Working a material under pressure requires careful selection of the deformation method, particularly of the correct stress condition. As a rule, materials will withstand compression better than tension.

Hydrostatic compression (high lateral compression) leads to a condition favoring internal slip and contributes to a high resistance to grain-boundary shearing. As a result high-ductility properties can be obtained. Under such conditions, extrusion becomes feasible even for such brittle materials as marble, red sandstone, bismuth and, as discovered by Kurnakov, natural salts.

Hydrostatic tension, which leads to increased possibilities of grain-boundary shearing and low tangential stresses, is the least favorable for plastic deformation and contributes mostly to brittle fracture. Other states of stress are intermediate between the two conditions of stress mentioned. Nevertheless, metals should be worked under two conditions only: either a non-uniform triaxial compression or a compressed stressed state with a single-tension stress. When a metal is forged or stamped, it is affected not only by the deforming force, but also by friction arising between the working surface and that of the tool. One other factor is the reaction force caused by lateral pressure of the metal against the tool's edge. The deforming force and the forces of reaction produced by the container walls are the active forces in the process of extrusion. In the rolling process the acting forces are those of deformation and friction, which develop from widening and from acceleration. And, to conclude, the deforming force and the frictional forces occurring between the worked metal and the opening of the die constitute the working force in a drawing operation [494].

Other conditions being equal, the ductility of materials undergoing deformation is evaluated by the magnitude and the orientation of the stresses. When a solid has been stressed to a state where external forces prevent it from being fractured by tensile stresses, then a highly ductile state may be achieved even in a brittle metal. Hence, the ability of metals and alloys to deform plastically is sometimes considerably higher because of a hydrostatic nonuniform compression obtained under high major compressing stresses.

It follows, therefore, that metals and alloys which are low in ductility should be deformed under conditions of stress which exclude any tensile stresses contributing to brittle fracturing [494].

An increase in temperature is not always followed by an increase in ductility. Optimum ductility is found in a certain temperature range. It was found that the stress state (notably the presence or absence of tensile stresses) as well as the rate of deformation may cause the temperature of maximum ductility to be shifted toward higher or lower temperatures.

Temperatures corresponding to the maximum ductility of magnesium (see Fig. 33) and of its alloys MA-2 (see Fig. 177) and MA-3 (see Fig. 178) in slow tension and compression were found to lie between 350 and 450°C. In impact testing the maximum ductility shifts toward higher temperature ranges (500 to 600°C). In dynamic compression at impact velocities of about 6 m/sec, the maximum ductility for MA-3 alloy occurs at 500°C, whereas the maximum impact strength at the same velocity is in the 200 to 250°C range.

The data presented above lead to the conclusion that, in a uniaxial state of stress (uniaxial tension, compression), the ductility maximum occurs at successively higher temperatures with increasing rates of deformation. In a complex bend state such as in impact strength tests, however, the ductility maximum shifts towards lower temperatures; this is probably attributable to the hydrostatic tension stresses present in such tests.

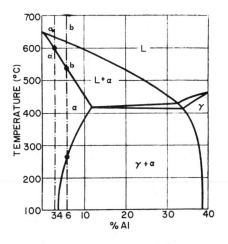

FIG. 183. Vertical cut of phase diagram of Mg-Al-Zn alloys (Mikheyev). a–b, composition of MA-2 alloy. b–b, composition of MA-3 alloy.

Property Diagrams

The above data clearly indicate the enormous importance of ductility properties in selecting the most favorable method of metal working. In planning an industrial engineering process, it is necessary to evaluate the effect of temperature, the rate and degree of deformation as well as the state of stress on the ductility properties of the worked alloy. The basic, orienting information may be furnished by three diagrams: the phase, ductility, and recrystallization diagrams. In estimating the effective capacity of the fabricating equipment it is necessary to know the diagram of deformation resistance. Diagrams reflecting the relation of mechanical properties to chemical composition, under various conditions of testing, may be very valuable for selecting new alloys and their optimum working conditions. A thorough investigation of the industrial properties of alloys in relation to chemical composition and to basic factors of deformation should be done next. Plotting and analyzing diagrams of composition–industrial properties, composition–industrial-properties–temperature (or rate) of deformation, and others will certainly help to select new alloys and the optimum conditions for working them. Examples of such diagrams could be composition vs. rollability (or forgeability or punchability), composition vs. rollability vs. rolling temperature, and composition vs. rollability vs. rate of rolling.

MA-2 and MA-3 Alloys

Figure 183 illustrates the vertical cut Al: Zn = 6: 1 traversing "the magnesium corner" of the Mg-Al-Zn phase diagram, in which alloy compositions MA-2 and MA-3 are indicated, according to data compiled by Mikheyeva [439].

The phase diagram shows that the melting point of MA-2 alloy is 607°C and that of MA-3, 530°C (in a homogenized state). The vertical line for MA-2 alloy does not cross the solvus line; in other words, the aluminum is always in complete solution in the Mg matrix at all temperatures. With a temperature decrease, precipitation of the second phase in the MA-3 alloy begins at 270°C. Thus the phase diagram indicates that the maximum temperature for working of MA-2 alloy is 607°C and for MA-3 alloy is 530°C; the lowest temperature of working for the latter alloy is 270°C.

Selection of the proper working temperature should be governed by data from ductility diagrams (see Fig. 177 and 178) on which the temperature ranges of maximum ductility under various methods of mechanical testing are clearly indicated. The precise choice of temperature for working should be coordinated with the temperature-ductility curve in the mechanical test which most closely approximates the selected methods of working. A correction for the rate-of-deformation effect should be made whenever necessary. Data on the ductility diagram (primarily based on the static-compression curves) suggest the following temperature ranges for hydraulic-press forging, extruding, and rolling: 350 to 450°C for MA-2 alloy and 350 to 400°C for MA-3 alloy.

The shapes of the temperature curves for impact strength and reduction in area are associated with a tension-stress state. These results suggest that sheet stamping be performed in a temperature range of 270 to 320°C for both MA-2 and MA-3 alloys. This conclusion is based on the fact that sheet stamping is also related to a tension-stress state, whereas its rate of deformation is intermediate between the rates used in impact-strength states and those used in ordinary tension tests. In accord with the trends observed in the impact-strength–temperature curve, it is permissible to increase the high-temperature limit of stamping for MA-2 alloy; such a procedure, however, is not expedient, since the ultimate tensile strength of this alloy is substantially decreased by an increase in temperature [217].

The ductility diagrams demonstrate that hammer-forging of these alloys should be done at temperatures above those for extruding and press forging. When selecting the lowest temperature for the last stages in hammer forging of MA-2 and MA-3 alloys, it should be remembered that a noticeable drop in ductility occurs in impact reduction at temperatures below 350°C.

Ductility diagrams, notably those exhibiting the first crack in static and dynamic compression, furnish immediate information as to whether hydraulic presses or impact forging should be used for forming magnesium alloys. Evidently, hydraulic forging in this instance has many advantages over impact forging, since, in slow-rate compression, ductility is twice that in impact forging. This deduction is confirmed by experience in industry [487]. Recrystallization diagrams should help to determine the conditions for proper grain-size control. It is obvious that diagrams should be obtained at rates of deformation related to the desired working method. It follows, therefore, that for extruding, hydraulic-press forging, and slow rolling of these alloys, diagrams plotted for hydraulic-press compression are quite appropriate (see Fig. 181 and 184). They serve to illustrate that the temperature intervals selected for compression working of these alloys (MA-2 from 350 to 450°C and MA-3 from 350 to 400°C), at low speeds of deformation, will secure the required grain size.

The existence of the so-called "critical" stages of deformation should be noted;

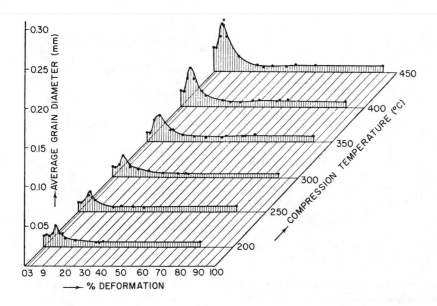

FIG. 184.   Recrystallization diagram of an MA-2 alloy under slow hot deformation (Savitsky.)

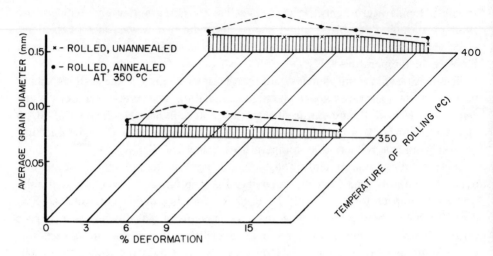

FIG. 185. Recrystallization diagram of an MA-3 alloy during hot rolling (Savitsky).

these stages contribute to the formation of very coarse, non-uniform grains. As indicated in the diagram (see Fig. 181 and 184), this may be avoided by deforming no less than 10 percent in a single pass. It is thus clearly evident that recrystallization diagrams contribute to a precise evaluation of the minimum permissible degree of deformation. Ideally, recrystallization diagrams should be plotted for every type of deformation of a given alloy, as was done in the rolling test for the MA-3 alloy (Fig. 185).

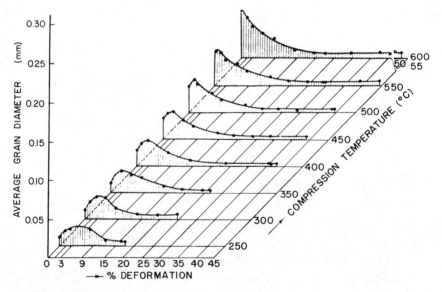

FIG. 186. Recrystallization diagram of an MA-2 alloy under impact deformation, after the samples were annealed at 300°C (Savitsky).

Pertinent information on the temperature of intermediate annealing after cold working of MA-3 alloy is available in the recrystallization diagram of Fig. 180. It is clear that the best conditions for hammer forging can be directly related to data from recrystallization diagrams associated with impact compression (see Fig. 182 and 186). As illustrated in Fig. 182, the processes of recrystallization in dynamic compression of magnesium alloys at temperatures prevailing in industrial production do not go to completion and the grains remain fine. It is nevertheless clearly indicated in Fig. 185 and 186 that recrystallization may occur in subsequent annealing or during the cooling process; it may also occur during subsequent processing of the still-hot material. Thus, forging of magnesium alloys should be done by infrequent powerful strokes rather than by frequent light strokes.

In conclusion, we wish to emphasize again the importance of concurrent study of the effects of both the temperature-deformation rate and the stress state on the ductility of the processed alloy. The optimum temperature for compression working of MA-3 alloy indicates that the high values of neck contraction and of the relative elongation of samples, the absence of fracture in notched samples, and unlimited ability to deform by compression in a press, as well as the related data on the recrystallization diagram, furnish convincing proof that, at 350°C, the MA-3 alloy is exceedingly ductile. To assert, however, that the optimum compression-processing temperature for this alloy is 350°C, making no reference to the rate of deformation, would not be correct. As we have stated above, switching to higher deformation rates, such as impact deformation, retards softening. Since from all viewpoints (quality of product, energy consumed in the process) the working of a material is best achieved through the mechanism of deformation (similar to cold deformation), it may be asserted that impact forging of this alloy (in a previously deformed state) should probably take place in the 400 to 500°C temperature interval. This processing will, naturally, require appropriate planning of heating materials and tools, as well as a determination of the required velocity and force of deformation. Data obtained from a related recrystallization diagram (see Fig. 182) proved that coarse-grain formation would not be expected at these temperature (that is, in impact forging). At high deformation rates, which cause considerable heating from the working process, the processing temperatures may have to be adjusted.

Thus, for MA-3 alloy, 350°C is the optimum temperature only for slow rates of working, such as extrusion.

In industrial production, the evaluation of the temperature-deformation rate on ductility should be coordinated with the influence of the stress state. This necessity becomes evident in rolling the very same MA-3 alloy. From the viewpoint of production velocities, rolling is placed between extrusion and hammer forging. Generally speaking, the optimum temperature for slow rolling should approximate that of extrusion, and the temperature for fast rolling should approximate forging temperatures. The character of the temperature curve plotted for impact strength of the MA-3 alloy (see Fig. 178) convincingly indicates the need of adjustments related to the evaluation of the effective forces. It is quite possible that rolling of this alloy (on a mill) under tensile stresses could be possibly done at 200 to 300°C.

The factors mentioned on the selection of the optimum working temperature under compression of magnesium MA-2 and MA-3 alloys are directly applicable to other alloys worked under similar conditions.

The selection of optimum temperatures for processing of allotropic metals should be in harmony with the rule of plasticity of the metals' high-temperature modifications.

The optimum conditions for working of metals and alloys, based on theoretical considerations, should first be verified and improved by larger-scale experiments.

8

Conclusions

Insufficient knowledge about the strength and ductility of materials is one of the basic problems of contemporary science because of the immense practical importance of these properties. Heating (or cooling) is one of the most potent means of obtaining the desired characteristics. The basic course to be followed for determining the relationship between property changes and changes of equilibrium factors (including temperature) should be a systematic experimental investigation coordinated with the latest theoretical discoveries.

In this work we have laid the foundation for systematic research on the influence of temperature on the mechanical properties of metals and alloys. The mechanical properties of more than 20 metals, 15 metallic compounds and phases, 16 binary and 2 ternary systems (of solid solutions) were evaluated at various temperatures.

A large majority of the data presented has never before been published. A number of experiments concerning properties were conducted in the temperature range between liquid nitrogen (−196°C) and the melting point of the metal under study.

The great variety of metals investigated has made it possible to formulate certain general rules with regard to the effect of temperature on the mechanical properties, as affected by the crystalline structure and the nature of the chemical interaction of components.

Mendeleyev's periodic law serves as a foundation for the determination of the physicochemical individuality of metals and alloys.

The structure of crystalline solids, in which category all metals and their alloys belong, is the result of chemical interatomic cohesion. The distinction between metals and alloys in this respect is that, in the latter, in addition to the interaction of like atoms, there is also the chemical interaction between the atoms of the components.

The basic factors which determine the changes of physicomechanical properties related to temperature are, for metals, the crystalline structure type and, for alloys, in addition to crystal structure, the type of phase diagram which reflects the nature of the chemical interaction between the atoms of components.

From this viewpoint the experimental investigations on ductility and strength of metals and alloys can be scientifically analyzed.

The crystalline structure of materials is of primary importance to their mechanical properties, since plastic deformation caused by slip, especially at low temperatures, is a specific feature inherent to crystalline solids alone and not to amorphous solids.

On the basis of material submitted in this book, the following conclusions may be derived for each group of metals studied.

Metals

In single-component systems, to which pure metals belong, the influence of temperature on mechanical properties depends upon the extent of changes in the crystalline lattice caused by heating. In this respect pure metals may be divided into three groups.

Cubic-Lattice Monomorphic Metals

Cubic monomorphic metals include those with type K-8 body-centered-cubic lattices: Li, K, Na, Rb, Cs, Ba, Eu, Nb, Ta, Cr, Mo, V, and W, as well as those with the K-12 face-centered-cubic lattice: Al, Th, Ni, Pt, Pd, Cu, Ag, Au, Pb, Yb, and Ir. Because of its closeness to the cubic structure, face-centered-tetragonal indium ($c/a = 1.08$) may be included in the same group of monomorphic metals (see Table 4). The high ductility of the majority of these metals is well known. The difference in the coordination number (12 and 8) of typical cubic lattices is unimportant because all have a large number of slip systems.

Heating of these metals does not produce any change in their crystalline structure. Heating or cooling results only in an expansion or contraction of the lattice. Changes in temperature will not cause discontinuous changes in mechanical properties.

As demonstrated, pure metals of this group are ductile at all temperatures and become more ductile with increasing temperature because of a lower cohesion of atoms. It is our opinion that the so-called brittle zones (blue and hot brittleness) observed in some of the potentially ductile metals of the cubic system, such as copper, are induced by impurities and by the atmospheric medium (formation of low-melting, brittle, intergranular layers). These physicochemical reactions are of vital importance to industrial metal processing because they create a detrimental effect on the processing and working characteristics of objects manufactured of industrial metals and alloys. As an example, it is worth mentioning here the blue- and hot-brittleness zones of iron. The nature of cold brittleness in chromium and other metals of the body-centered-cubic-lattice group is related to their degree of purity—with greater purity the critical temperature of brittleness veers toward lower temperatures; at elevated temperatures, even impure chromium is ductile.

Monomorphic Metals with Hexagonal and Rhombic Lattices

Some monomorphic metals of the hexagonal type (G-12 lattice) are Be, Mg, Zn, Cd, Y, Re, Ru, Os, Tc, Sc, and many rare-earth metals. The densely packed basal plane, which is active at ordinary temperatures, is common to all metals of the hexagonal type. Because of this, hexagonal-type metals, in spite of their ability to twin, do not yield readily to deformation at room temperature. These, then, are metals of low ductility under ordinary conditions. Formation of new slip planes caused by heating, however, causes an abrupt increase in ductility at certain temperature ranges. The high degree of ductility observed in low-temperature hexagonal forms of certain high-purity polymorphic metals (α-Ti, α-Zr, α-Tl) is apparently related to the activation of other slip planes (depending on the c/a ratio) and extensive twinning.

An abrupt rise in ductility caused by the heating of hexagonal metals is most convincingly demonstrated in the case of magnesium, which has elevated-temperature ductility properties in no way inferior to those of cubic metals. The behavior of beryllium, zinc, cadmium, and rhenium is similar to that of magnesium [419]. The temperature dependence of the mechanical properties of ruthenium, osmium, and rare-earth metals with a hexagonal lattice (gadolinium, terbium, dysprosium, and others) as well as yttrium and scandium, which have similar properties, has not yet been investigated. It is justifiable to assume, however, that their behavior will be analogous to that of the other hexagonal metals and softening will begin at the same ratio of the absolute melting temperature.

Diamond-type-structure metals (germanium and silicon) and rhombohedral and rhombic-lattice structure elements (semi-metals such as bismuth, antimony, arsenic, gallium, and quicksilver), show low-ductility properties at ordinary temperatures. It might be reasonable to expect that these materials will increase in ductility with an increase in temperature because new slip systems as well as twinning will come into play. In our experiments, we were able to deform plastically cylindrical samples of technical silicon at 1100°C and of germanium at 900°C in compression. Single crystals of certain semi-metals (bismuth), in exceptionally pure form, become ductile even at ordinary temperature. The plastic properties of semi-metals, however, have hardly been studied. Our experiments have proved that brittle materials (silicon, germanium, and others) exhibit a considerable increase in strength at elevated temperatures.

Polymorphic Metals

Polymorphic metals undergo changes in their crystalline structure at certain temperatures. Temperature allotropy is inherent in Ca, Sr, Sc, La, Ce, Pr, Nd, Sm, Ti, Hf, U, Np, Pu, Mn, Fe, Co, Rh, Tl, Sn, and probably certain others (see Table 11). Of the metals listed only three (tin, iron, and thallium) had previously been investigated as to the effect of temperature on their mechanical properties. We studied Ca, Sr, La, Ce, Pr, Ti, Zr, Mn, Fe, Co, Sn, and a few others, and we recorded, for the first time for a majority of these metals, the quantitative mechanical properties at various temperatures. Ductile and brittle zones were determined and the influence of impurities on the transformation temperature was evaluated. The magnitude of internal pressure in certain metals was determined as a function of temperature.

Polymorphic metals exhibit typically abrupt changes in mechanical properties when undergoing temperature transformations. These sudden changes are clearly manifested in transitions from structures which exhibit low ductility to structures which favor plastic flow (for example, in the transformation of gray tin to white, in the formation of γ-manganese).

Cubic-system structures are conducive to ductility since they have the greatest number of slip planes. The higher-temperature forms of allotropic metals are usually typified by such crystalline structures; this finding is true for 19 of the 20 allotropic metals investigated (the one exception is tin). Therefore, as demonstrated by experimental data, it became possible for the first time to formulate the rule according to which *the highest-temperature modification of an allotropic metal is the most ductile*. This rule apparently is also true for many other inorganic and organic polymorphic materials.

This rule makes it possible to (1) devise ways of creating ductile alloys of allotropic metals which are brittle under ordinary conditions by introducing additives to stabilize the high-temperature ductile phase (γ-manganese); (2) select the most favorable technological methods of hot-working allotropic metals; and (3) affirm that the highest-temperature modification should have a cubic lattice or similar structure conducive to ductility and, therefore, one can determine the previously unknown crystalline structure of metals. This last application has been confirmed by recently published data on the crystalline structure of high-temperature forms of samarium, neptunium, and plutonium, which could have been predicted by application of the above rule [193]. This rule will evidently make it possible to predict the crystalline structure of high-temperature modifications of new allotropic metals and alloys.

The relationship now known to exist between mechanical properties and changes in the crystalline structure caused by temperature make it possible to define and foretell the mechanical behavior of monomorphic and polymorphic metals as well as of solid solutions based on these metals, provided their crystalline structures are known.

Metallic Compounds

Metallic compounds also belong to single-component systems. Solid solutions based on compounds belong to single-phase systems. The effect of temperature on the mechanical properties of these solid solutions is similar to the effect of temperature on the mechanical properties of compounds. The crystalline structures of these compounds and phases have been little studied. In spite of the fact that the rules governing the behavior of pure metals should also apply to metallic compounds, the data on hand is insufficient for an analogous classification. Prior to this study, no investigations on the mechanical properties of metallic compounds have been conducted; it was only known that they were very brittle at room temperature.

We were first to study the effect of temperature on the mechanical properties of metallic compounds and of phases based thereon. The following types of compounds were studied: (1) daltonides: $MgZn$, $MgZn_2$, $MgZn_5$, Mg_2Si, Cu_2Mg, $CuAl_2$, $CoSi_2$, Ni_2Si, $CuSi_3$; (2) Kurnakov compounds: Mg_3Cd, $MgCd$, $MgCd_3$; (3) bertholides: β and γ phases in the Mg-Al system; and (4) beta brass type: β and β' phases in β brass. It was found that the existing concept of the brittleness of metallic compounds applies only for a certain temperature range. All the compounds and phases investigated are very hard but weaken rapidly as a function of temperature. Under proper conditions of temperature and strain rate these compounds behave as highly ductile materials and yield readily to considerable deformation without fracturing. *A considerable increase in ductility with increase in temperature is apparently a property inherent to all metallic compounds and phases based thereon.* This phenomenon may be attributed to several factors.

The effects of temperature on the ductility properties of allotropic metals and metallic compounds appear to be similar and lead one to suggest that the changes in the crystalline structure of both materials with temperature are somewhat analogous. It may be generally stated that an increase in temperature is conducive to the creation of structures favorable to ductility; these include simple cubic structures with a minimum number of atoms in a unit cell, with the greatest possible distance between atoms, and with pronounced metallic properties. To a certain degree, increased ductility is affected by increased atom mobility occurring in the dissociation of compounds as a result of heating as well as of a superposition of stresses observed in mechanical testing or working.

For the first time it was possible to obtain deformed samples of metallic compounds and their solid solutions by means of hot extrusion and hot compression. These methods may be utilized to shape objects made of brittle alloys.

It was found that *the effect of increasing temperature is first to increase the strength, which after reaching a maximum will begin to drop noticeably.* This phenomenon is related to the effect of temperature on the internal structure of compounds and depends on the interrelation of strength and ductility of materials.

The accumulated data on the deformation of intermetallic phases and on their properties at various temperatures have contributed to ways of developing new alloys based on chemical compounds of metals with special physical and mechanical properties.

Alloys

The effect of temperature on the mechanical properties of binary metallic systems in relation to the type of chemical interaction of components was investigated. Composition–mechanical-property diagrams were plotted at various temperatures.

Eutectic-Type Systems

To obtain samples for studies of eutectic-type alloys, we used casting, hot deformation, the powdered metal method, and also our own method of elimination of the low melting component. *It was shown that in metallic-mixture alloys, if the components differed radically in their hardness (for instance Al and Si), the mechanical properties were influenced considerably by the distribution of structural components arising from the difference in the melting temperature of the components. The presence of a soft component such as a eutectic along grain boundaries of the hard phase causes an abrupt decrease in the hardness of the alloy; in this case no additive change in properties is observed with a change in composition— that is, the relationship between mechanical properties and composition is not linear.*

Thus, in cast and annealed alloys of the Al-Si system, the hardness values only become additive when the Si content is in excess of 90 percent. The values of the mechanical properties of Cu-Al alloys become additive at elevated temperatures. This behavior is attributed to a weakening of the $CuAl_2$ compound under the raised-temperature conditions. To achieve linear changes in properties with composition in such systems as Al-Si it is necessary to distribute the soft component uniformly throughout the matrix of the material. Methods of thermal processing of alloys which would contribute to a better cohesion between the hard and soft components should be sought.

A selection of the procedure for achieving a desired distribution of components depends on the difference in the melting temperatures of the components. When the difference is small (as in the Cu-Al system), the required redistribution of components is achieved by hot deformation of cast alloys. When the melting temperatures are significantly different (as in Al-Si or Mg-Si), the most effective ways to achieve a proper distribution are the powder-metallurgy method and the pouring-off method. The hardness of powder-metallurgy alloys is high and approaches the additive value. The strong dependence of the properties of alloy mixtures on the distribution of structural components presents a definite possibility for obtaining alloys with predetermined mechanical properties.

Aluminum-silicon alloys with a 50-percent-Si content can adequately withstand hot and even cold working (extrusion and rolling).

Alloys based on Mg_2Si are noted for their high value of thermal emf when paired with copper (about 200 $\mu v/^\circ$). At elevated temperatures, alloys consisting of magnesium silicide crystals and eutectic Mg plus Mg_2Si exhibit a reduction of over 40 percent in height when compressed; samples with the eutectic present along grain boundaries are considerably less ductile. The latter, at 600°C, exhibit a severalfold increase in compression strength together with an increase in ductility.

The hardness of powder-metallurgy samples of Mg_2Si containing 5 percent Al or 30 percent Cu, is about 200 kg/mm² at 300°C. Cast and powder metallurgy alloys (with aluminum) based on $CuAl_2$ also retain high-hardness values up to 300°C (in excess of 200 kg/mm²).

The eutectic constituent of a 40 percent Cu–60 percent Al alloy was poured out and an Sn-Al aolloy was substituted for the eutectic; the resulting casting was hot extruded and was shown to have a higher hardness and ductility than the original Cu-Al casting.

Solid-Solution Systems

The effect of temperature on the mechanical properties of certain binary and ternary solid solutions was investigated in the systems Cu-Ni, Ni-Re, Re-Mo, Cu-Zn, Cu-Mn, Cu-Al-Zn, Mg-Al-Zn; mechanical-property–composition isotherms were plotted. Even though the metals differ in their crystalline structure, Ni-Re and Mo-Re belong to a type of system which is infrequently found—they form a large region of solid solution. Changes in the hardness of these alloys at ordinary and elevated temperatures are characterized by concave curves which are typical of solid solutions.

The hardness of α and β brass was investigated from 20 to 90°C. *The peculiar character of the hardness–composition curves at elevated temperatures and after aging confirms the suggestion that molecular formations exist in α brass.* It appears that there is a tendency to form the Kurnakov low-stability compound Cu_3Zn, which dissociates above 400°C.

The hardness of β brass decreases more than 100 times in the 20 to 500°C range. The order-disorder temperature for β brass diminishes from 450 to 300°C as a function of stress.

It was determined that zones of brittleness were observable by ductility measurements only under the presence of tensile stresses, which made it possible to correlate the existence of zones of brittleness to the strength of grain boundaries. This correlation is especially strong when the presence of a certain quantity of the second phase permits oxygen to diffuse to the boundaries of the crystals.

In the absence of factors detrimental to crystalline boundaries, no zones of brittleness are observed in copper and brass. The magnitude and position of the hardness maxima in α brass are dependent not only on the molecular interaction but also on the difference in the melting temperatures of the solvent and solutes in the solid-solution region in addition to the extent of the homogeneity region.

Taking the system of copper-manganese alloys as an example of a solid solution containing an allotropic metal, we conducted an investigation on its mechanical properties at various temperatures. It was found that, in the γ state, all alloys of the system were ductile at 20°C. Changes in hardness in the γ phase as affected by composition were typical for solid solutions. The ductility characteristics also revealed a maximum value in the 30- to 40-percent-Mn range; this maximum points to the existence of transformations in alloys at this level of concentration. The impact-toughness maximum coincides with the transition of the alloy from a single-phase structure to the two-phase structure. With an increase in temperature, the maximum shifts toward higher concentrations of manganese. The observable transition from a face-centered-cubic to a tetragonal lattice at 75- to 80-percent-Mn concentration is clearly detected by the hardness method. At these concentrations the thermal emf changes sign. It was found that in the 800 to 1000°C range, alloys of the Cu-Mn system are readily extruded into rods and yield to rolling.

The mechanical properties of 70 alloys in the region of ternary solid solutions of zinc and aluminum in copper were investigated; the effect of admixtures consisting of these metals on the properties of copper (to 50 percent Cu) were determined. It was proved that addition of aluminum to brasses is, in this respect, more effective than addition of zinc to aluminum bronzes. It was observed that the elongation and reduction in area of ternary solid solutions changed with concentration according to several different laws. Alloys in the range 18 to 30 percent of zinc and 3 to 5 percent of aluminum exhibit a considerable increase in strength from thermal processing—by quenching and aging. The hardness in some of these alloys increases by more than 100 percent and exceeds 250 kg/mm². Alloys in the two-phase region decrease in hardness much more rapidly than homogeneous solid-solution alloys above 400°C. Alloying of brass with aluminum does not contribute materially to its heat-resistance properties.

The mechanical properties of magnesium solid solutions in the Mg-Al-Zn system were evaluated. The geometrical method used for studying the resultant data showed that the properties (elongation and others) were found to be substantially different from the expected theoretical additive values. This difference is convincing proof of interaction between aluminum and zinc atoms in the solid solution as well as with the solvent magnesium atoms.

The daltonides formed in the Mg-Zn system from aging processes exert a greater influence on property changes in the ternary solid solutions than the bertholide β and γ phases in the Al-Mg system.

Experimental data on the mechanical properties of binary and ternary solid solutions generally confirm the opinion expressed by Mendeleyev, who viewed the solutions to be complex systems consisting of an aggregate of solvent compounds contained in the solution matrix, the compounds however existing in different stages of dissociation.

Systems Containing Metallic Compounds

The mechanical properties of alloys at various temperatures in the systems Mg-Zn, Mg-Al, and Mg-Cd were plotted for the first time. It was demonstrated that the shape of the mechanical-property–composition curve is determined by the chemical nature of the compounds in a given system (daltonides, bertholides, Kurnakov compounds). Test devices were built and conditions for plastically working these alloys were developed. Alloys rich in metallic compounds were extensively studied to determine the effect of pre-working the samples on their approach to equilibrium. It was found that the atomic mobility is increased and equilibrium is more rapidly achieved in pre-deformed specimens than in cast alloys.

Experiments with deformed samples led to a clearer presentation of the chemical interaction of components and to a method of changing alloy structures; these goals had not been reached by earlier researchers.

Mechanical tests and microstructural studies revealed that three metallic compounds (all daltonides) may be formed in the Mg-Zn system: $MgZn$, $MgZn_2$, and $MgZn_5$. It was shown that solid solutions of these compounds can exist. The boundaries of the three solid solutions are extended with an increase in temperature. It was observed that the hardness of alloys in the region of the $MgZn$ and $MgZn_2$ compounds increases considerably with annealing because of aging effects. Changes in hardness as a result of changes in composition of alloys containing mixtures of $MgZn$ and $MgZn_2$ follow the additivity rule at all temperatures. Alloys containing the compound $MgZn_5$ show a comparatively high ductility, and their ability to increase in strength from thermal processing may be of some practical interest.

The mechanical-test method conclusively proved the bertholide nature of the β and γ phases in the Al-Mg system. Above 300°C, all alloys corresponding to the middle part of the phase diagram soften rapidly, although the γ phase exhibits a somewhat higher degree of heat resistance. None of the phases investigated exhibited phase transformations as a function of temperature. Alloys in the intermetallic-phase region are characterized by a minimum ratio of flow stress to hardness (0.4 to 0.8 in contrast to 2 for pure metals).

A thorough study of the structure and properties of Al-Mg alloys revealed a new phase in the middle part of the diagram in the range of 38.9 to 41.3 weight percent of Mg.

Experiments with Mg-Zn-Al alloys demonstrated that bertholide-type phases soften more rapidly than daltonide type phases as a function of temperature.

The mechanical properties of Kurnakov compounds in the Mg-Cd system were investigated for the first time. The mechanical properties of these alloys in annealed and quenched states and at ordinary and elevated temperatures were evaluated. These tests clearly confirmed the existence of three compounds—

Mg_3Cd, $MgCd$, and $MgCd_3$—in the annealed alloys. It was found that all three compounds contribute to the formation of extensive regions of solid solutions. As alloys approach equilibrium after prolonged annealing, an increase in their hardness is observed in the region of the compounds Mg_3Cd and $MgCd$ because of aging. All three compounds of this system exhibit a higher ductility and a lower hardness than do the solid solutions from which they are created. It was proved by microstructural and mechanical test methods that the $MgCd$ compound is not formed from the melt but by solid transformation from the solid solution, i.e., a typical Kurnakov compound.

Selecting Optimum Conditions for Working Metals and Alloys

Until recently, hot working of metallic alloys was usually conducted by empirical methods. Attempts were made to evaluate the effect of certain basic factors (temperature, rate and degree of deformation, and the type of stress state) on the ductility of alloys and to use the data obtained for devising and regulating the most favorable methods of hot working.

It was shown that the basic information needed to predict the optimum conditions for hot working may be obtained from three sources: the phase diagram, the recrystallization diagram, and the ductility diagram. Possession of these data enables one to determine precisely the methods of hot working for known alloys and to devise sound procedures for processing new alloys. Selection of optimum conditions for hot working of MA-2 and MA-3 alloys was discussed as an example.

On Experimental Techniques

In the course of our work we developed new methods and new devices which, we hope, may be useful to scientific institutes and industrial laboratories.

A Universal Device for Micromechanical Testing. This device is for testing microsamples by all basic methods of axial loading at ordinary as well as at elevated and low temperatures, in air, in vacuum, or in protective atmospheres. A fact worth noting is that only two grams were needed to evaluate the basic mechanical properties of 11 Cu-Ni alloys.

This device will prepare microsamples for rupture tests with a minimum waste of material and perform a whole series of other technological experiments. Thin wire of any material may be processed with this equipment. A dense wire for evaluating resistance to electrical conductivity may be obtained with this device. It is now being successfully used in certain research institutes.

Production of Alloys by Substitution of the Low-Melting Component. Replacing the eutectic by a pure metal or by another alloy opens the way for new possibilities to structural changes at will and to a better control of the properties of alloys. This fact was demonstrated in experiments on silumins and alloys based on $CuAl_2$ and Mg_2Si.

The new possibilities presented by the method of substitution of alloy components merit an intensive investigation.

Determination of Beginning of Transformation of White Tin to Gray. A systematic evaluation of tin hardness is a better way to define the beginning of allotropic transformation in tin than the structural method. The hardness test may be used for detecting the start of tin plague during storage of commercial tin.

Evaluation of Internal Pressure of Materials as a Function of Temperature. An evaluation of the internal pressure in metals and in alloys as a function of temperature contributes to the detection of polymorphism and possibly of other phase transformations, as demonstrated in the case of allotropic transformations in iron and manganese.

Plotting of Experimental Data. Certain new methods of plotting experimental data to show the effect of temperature on the mechanical properties of metals and alloys have been suggested in this work (ductility diagrams for a number of metals and alloys, a "logarithmic analysis" of strength and of ductility characteristics, true-stress curves for tension and compression experiments with microsamples, and others). The methods suggested lead to a more precise evaluation of allotropic-transformation temperatures, recrystallization temperatures, and maximum ductility in metals and alloys.

References

Bibliographical Note. A substantial effort was given to verifying the references, particularly those of works translated from English, French, or German, for the Russian approach to bibliographies is different from that of American or British publishers. Some of the entries have not proved to be retrievable; they are therefore given substantially as they appeared in the Russian text.

A list is given below of abbreviated names of institutes, specialized journals, and places, and their complete transliterations and translations. Titles of books and monographs have been translated; titles of Journals have been transliterated only, except in the cases of Journals not easily recognized, where titles have been translated on first appearance.

Institutes

GONTI Gosudarstennoe obyedinennoe nauchno-technicheskoe izdatelstvo (State United Scientific and Technical Publishing House).

GOST Gosudarstvennyi Obshchesoyuznyi standardart (All-Union State Standard).

Gostekhizdat Gosudarstvennoe izdatelstvo tekhno-theoreticheskoi literatury (State Publishing House of Theoretical and Technical Literature).

Mashgiz Gosudarstvennoe nauchno-tekhnicheskoe izdatelstvo mashinostroitolnoy literatury (State Scientific and Technical Publishing House of Literature on Machinery).

Metallurgizdat Gosudarstvennoe nauchno-tekhnicheskoe izdatelstvo literatury po chernoy i tsvetnoy metallurgii (State Scientific and Technical Publishing House for Literature on Ferrous and Nonferrous Metallurgy).

MINTsVETMET Ministerstvo tsvetnoy metallurgii (Ministry for Nonferrous Metallurgy).

MVTU Moskovskoe vysshee Tekhnicheskoe uchilishe (Moscow Higher Technical School).

Oborongiz Gosudarstvennoe izdatelstvo oboronnoy promyshlennosty (State Publishing House for the Defense Industry).

ONTI Obyedinenie nauko-tekhnicheskikh Izdatelstv (United Scientific and Technical Publishing House).

Standartgiz Gosudarstvennoe izdatelstvo standartov (State Standards Publishing House).

Sudpromgiz Gosudarstvennoe Soyuznoe izdatelstvo sudostroitelnoye promyshlennosty (State All-Union Publishing House for the Shipbuilding Industry).

VNITOM Vsesoyeznoe nauchno-inzhenerno-tekhnicheskoe obshchestvo metallurgov (All-Union Scientific, Engineering, and Technical Society of Metallurgists).

Journals

Dokl. Akad. Nauk Papers of the Academy of Sciences.

Izv. Akad. Nauk SSSR, OKN Izvestia Akademii Nauk SSSR, Otdelenie Khimicheskikh Nauk (Journal of the Academy of Sciences, Division of Chemical Sciences).

Izv. Akad. Nauk SSSR, OTN Izvestia Akademii Nauk SSSR, Otdelenie Tekhnicheskikh Nauk (Journal of the Academy of Sciences, Division of Technical Sciences).

Izv. Sektora Platiny, Inst. Obshch. Neorg. Khim. Izvestia Sektora Platiny, Instituta Obshchey Neorganicheskoy Khimii (Journal of General Inorganic Chemistry, Platinum Section).

Izv. SFKhA Izvestia Sektora Fiziko-Kimicheskago Analiza (Journal of the Section on Physicochemical Analysis).

Izv. SPb. Politekhnich. Inst. Izvestia Sanct Peterburgskago Politekhnicheskago Instituta (Journal of Saint Petersburg Polytechnical Institute).

Usp. Fiz. Nauk Uspekhi Fizicheskikh Nauk (Progress in Physical Sciences).

Vest. Akad. Nauk Vestnik Academii Nauk (Herald of the Academy of Sciences).

Zhur. Exp. Teor. Fiz. Zhurnal Experimentalnoy i Teoreticheskoy Fiziki (The Journal of Experimental and Theoretical Physics).

Zhur. Priklad. Khim. Zhurnal Prikladnoy Khimii (Journal of Applied Chemistry).

Zhur. Tekh. Fiz. Zhurnal Tekhnicheskoy Fiziki (Journal of Technical Physics).

Places

M., Moscow; L., Leningrad; SPb., Saint Petersburg.

1. Davidenkov, N. N., in *Bolshaya Sovetskaya Entsiklopedia*, S. I. Vavilov, ed., 2d ed., Vol. 27, M.-L., 1954.
2. Russian Metallurgists, *Literature Index*, M., Lenin Library, 1950.
3. Prokoshkin, D. A., and Vishniakov, D. Y., *The Great Russian Metallurgist, P. P. Anosov*, M.-L., Metallurgizdat, 1950.
4. *D. K. Chernov and the Science of Metals*, M.-L., Metallurgizdat, 1950.
5. Shaposhnikov, N. A., *Mechanical Testing of Metals*, M.-L., Mashgiz, 1954.
6. Mendeleyev, D. I., *Studies on Metallurgy*, M., Standartgiz, 1936.
7. Gogoberidze, D. B., *Hardness and Its Evaluation*, M.-L., Mashgiz, 1952.
8. Kurnakov, N. S., *Introduction to Physicochemical Analysis*, M.-L., Akad. Nauk SSSR, 1940.
9. Kurnakov, N. S., *Collection of Selected Works*, Vol. I, M.-L., ONTI, 1938; Vol. II, M.-L., GONTI, 1939.
10. *Arkhiv Akad. Nauk SSSR*, op. 1, No. 63, 321.
11. Krestovnikov, A. N., and Shakhov, A. S., *Academician N. S. Kurnakov*, M.-L., Metallurgizdat, 1954.
12. Pogodin, S. A., and Anosov, V. Y., *Basic Principles of Physicochemical Analysis*, M.-L., Akad. Nauk SSSR, 1947.
13. Instructions of the 20th Conference of the CPSU on the Sixth Five-Year Development Plan of USSR, 1956–1960.
14. Shishokin, V. P., and associates, *Tsvetnye Metaly (Nonferrous Metals)*, Nos. 4, 5, and 11 (1930), No. 2 (1932); *Metallurg*, No. 11 (1935); *Izv. SFKhA*, No. 10 (1938).
15. Bochvar, A. A., *Izv. Akad. Nauk. SSSR, OTN*, No. 9 (1945), No. 5 (1946), No. 10 (1947), No. 5 (1948).
16. Gubkin, S. I., *Ductile Deformation of Metals*, M., Metallurgizdat, 1935; *Izv. Akad. Nauk SSSR, OTN*, No. 9 (1948), No. 8 (1949); *Dokl. Akad. Nauk SSSR*, **91**, No. 5 (1953).
17. Kornilov, I. I., *Dokl. Akad. Nauk SSSR*, **67**, No. 6 (1949), **77**, No. 6 (1950), **78**, No. 3 (1950); *Izv. SFKhA*, **18** (1949), **20** (1950).
18. Ageyev, N. V., *The Chemistry of Metallic Alloys*, M.-L., Akad. Nauk SSSR, 1941.
19. Yakovlev, K. P., *Practical Physics*, M., Gostekhizdat, 1943.
20. Konobeyevsky, S. T., *Vest. Akad. Nauk SSSR*, No. 7 (1955).
21. Kuznetsov, V. D., *The Physics of Solids*, Vol. II (1941) and Vol. V (1949), Tomsk, Krasnoye Znamia.
22. Schmid, E., and Boas, W., *Plasticity of Crystals*, London, Hughes, 1950 (translated from German).
23. Von Karman, T., *Mitteilungen ueber Forschungsarbeiten auf dem Gebeite des Ingenieurswesens*, No. 118, Berlin, 1912.
24. Frenkel, Ya. I., *Vest. Akad. Nauk SSSR*, No. 10 (1946); *Usp. Fiz. Nauk*, **30**, No. 1–2 (1946); *Introduction to the Theory of Metals*, M., Gostekhizdat, 1948.
25. Lomonosov, M. V., *Complete Works*, Vol. I, M.-L., Akad. Nauk SSSR, 1950.
26. Kornilov, I. I., *Priroda (Nature)*, No. 10 (1953).
27. Seitz, F., *Physics of Metals*, New York, McGraw-Hill, 1943.
28. Seitz, F., *The Modern Theory of Solids*, New York, McGraw-Hill, 1940.
29. Ageyev, N. V., *The Nature of Chemical Bonding in Metallic Alloys*, M., Akad. Nauk SSSR, 1947.
30. Ageyev, N. V., *Izv. Akad. Nauk SSSR, OKN*, No. 3 (1954).
31. Semenchenko, V. K., *The Chemical Bond and the Chemical Compound* (treatise on the concept of a chemical compound), M.-L., Akad. Nauk SSSR, 1953.
32. Akimov, G. V., *Dokl. Akad. Nauk SSSR*, **47**, No. 8 (1945).
33. Shreiner, L. A., *Physical Principles of Rock Mechanics*, M.-L., Gostoptekhizdat, 1950.
34. Bunin, K. P., *Iron Carbide Alloys*, M., Mashgiz, 1949.

35. *Encyclopedia of Metal Physics*, Vol. I, M.-L., ONTI, 1937.
36. *Bolshaya Sovetskaya Entsiklopedia*, S. I. Vavilov, ed, 2d ed., Vol. 27, p. 266, M.-L., 1954.
37. Kapustinsky, A. F., *Izv. Akad. Nauk SSSR, OKN*, No. 1 (1953).
38. Boky, G. B., *Introduction to the Chemistry of the Crystalline State*, M., MGU, 1954.
39. Guliayev, B. B., *Dokl. Akad. Nauk SSSR*, **70**, No. 5 (1950).
40. O'Neill, H., *Hardness of Metals and Its Measurement*, London, Chapman and Hall, 1934.
41. O'Neill, H., *Metallurgia*, **29**, No. 173 (1944).
42. Koester, W., *Zeit. Electrochem.*, **40**, No. 4-5 (1943).
43. Fersman, A. E., *Geochemistry*, Vol. III, M.-L., ONTI (1937).
44. Umansky, Ya. S., Finkelshteyn, B. N., and Blanter, M. E., *Physical Principles of Metallography*, M.-L., Metallurgizdat, 1949.
45. Shreiner, L. A., *Hardness of Brittle Solids*, M., Akad. Nauk SSSR, 1949.
46. Yakutovich, M. V., Yakovleva, E. S., Lerinman, R. M., and Buynov, N. P., *Izv. Akad. Nauk SSSR* (physics series), **15**, No. 3 (1951).
47. Kuznetsov, V. D., *Crystals and Crystallization*, M.-L., Gosteoretizdat, 1953.
48. Stepanov, A. V., *Zhur. Tech. Fiz.*, **23**, No. 7 (1953).
49. Klassen-Nekliudova, M. V., and Kontorova, T. A., *Usp. Fiz. Nauk*, **52**, No. 1 (1954).
50. Oding, I. A., Ivanova, V. S., Birdiuksky, V. V., and Geminov, V. M., *Theory of Creep and Long Term Strength of Metals*, M., Metallurgizdat, 1959.
51. Gurevich, L. E., and Zhurkov, S. N., "Seminar on the Theory of Dislocations," *Prog. in Phys. USSR.*, **64**, No. 4, 788 (Apr. 1958).
52. *Symposium Dedicated to the 70th Year Jubilee of the Academician A. F. Yoffe*, M., Akad. Nauk SSSR, 1950.
53. Bunin, K. P., and Malinochka, I. N., *Introduction to Metallography*, M.-L., Metallurgizdat, 1954.
54. Gubkin, S. I., *Izv. Akad. Nauk, OTN*, No. 5 (1950).
55. Oding, I. A., *Relaxation and Creep in Metals*, M.-L., Mashgiz, 1952.
56. Rebinder, P. A., and associates, *Dokl. Akad. Nauk SSSR*, **32**, No. 2 (1941); **56**, Nos. 7 and 8 (1947); **62**, No. 4 (1948); **69**, No. 2 (1949).
57. Gubkin, S. I., *The Theory of Working of Metals*, M.-L., Metallurgizdat, 1947.
58. Rovinsky, B. M., and Rybakova, L. M., *Izv. Akad. Nauk SSSR, OTN*, No. 10 (1952).
59. Mirkin, I. L., *Metallography and Working of Metals*, No. 1 (1955).
60. Kuznetsov, V. D., *Izv. Akad. Nauk SSSR, OTN*, No. 5 (1950).
61. Davidenkov, N. N., *Zhur. Exp. Teor. Fiz.*, **14**, No. 9 (1944).
62. Frenkel, Ya. I., *Usp. Fiz. Nauk*, **33**, No. 3 (1947).
63. Kobeko, P. P., *Amorphous Materials*, M., Akad. Nauk SSSR, 1952.
64. Alexandrov, A. P., *Vest. Akad. Nauk SSSR*, Nos. 7 and 8 (1944).
65. Kontorova, T. A., *Dokl. Akad. Nauk SSSR*, **54**, No. 1 (1946).
66. Pines, B. Ya., *Zhur. Exp. Teor. Fiz.*, **16**, No. 8 (1946).
67. Hollomon, H., and Zener, C., *Usp. Fiz. Nauk*, **31**, No. 1 (1947).
68. Jeffries, Z., and Archer, R. S., *Chem. Met. Eng.*, **25**, 697-704 (1921).
69. Ludwik, P., *Zeit. ver. Deutsch. Ing.*, **63**, 142-4 (1919).
70. Polanyi, M., *Zeit. Kristallogr.*, **61**, 49-57 (1925).
71. Dehlinger, U., *Zeit. Metallkunde*, **22**, 222 (1930).
72. Bielby, G. T., *J. Inst. Metals*, **6**, 5 (1911).
73. Rosenhain, W., *Internat. Zeit. Metallogr.*, **5**, 65 (1914).
74. Tammann, G., *Zeit. Metallkunde*, **28**, 16 (1936).
75. Seitz, F., and Read, T. A., *J. Appl. Phys.*, **12**, No. 2, 100 (1941).
76. Bragg, L., *Nature*, **149**, 511 (1942).

77. Hume-Rothery, W., *Electrons, Atoms, Metals, and Alloys*, London, Publ. for *Metal Industry* by Cassier Co., distr. by Iliffe, 1948.

78. Read, W. T., *Dislocations in Crystals*, New York, McGraw-Hill, 1953.

79. Kishkin, S. T., and Petrusevich, R., *Izv. Akad. Nauk SSSR, OTN*, No. 1 (1948); *Tekhnika Vozdushnago Flota*, No. 11 (1943).

80. Mirkin, I. L., Sergievskaya, T. V., and Novak, S. I., *Structure and Properties of Thermally Worked Steel* (*Trudy Kafedry Metallovedenia MMI*), M.-L., Mashgiz, 1951.

81. Davidendov, N. N., and Beliayev, S. E., *Zhur. Exp. Teor. Fiz.*, **22**, No. 1 (1952).

82. Friedman, Ya. B., *Deformation and Fracture of Metals Under Static and Impact Loadings*, M., Oborongiz, 1946.

83. Davidenkov, N. N., *Certain Problem of Material Mechanics*, L., Lenizdat, 1943.

84. Lashko, N. F., *Strengthening and Fracture of Metals*, M., Oborongiz, 1951.

85. Fridman, Y. B., *Mechanical Properties of Metals*, M., Oborongiz, 1951.

86. Guliayev, A. P., *Metallography*, M., Oborongiz, 1948.

87. Shchapov, N. P., *Zavodskaya Laboratoria*, **17**, No. 2 (1951).

88. *Achievements in the Physics of Metals* (a symposium), M.-L., Metallurgizdat, 1956.

89. Pavlov, I. M., *The Theory of Rolling*, M.-L., Metallurgizdat, 1950.

90. Pashkov, P. O., *Ductility and Fracture of Metals*, M., Sudpromgiz, 1950.

91. Flow Stresses, in *Bolshaya Sovetskaya Entsiklopedia*, S. I. Vavilov, ed., Vol. 13, M.-L., 1952.

92. Grozin, B. D., *Mechanical Properties of Quenched Steel*, M., Mashgiz, 1951.

93. Potak, Ya. M., *Zavodskaya Laboratoria*, **17**, No. 2 (1951).

94. *Izv. Akad. Nauk SSSR, OTN*, No. 1 (1950); *Zavodskaya Laboratoria*, Nos. 2, 7, and 17 (1951).

95. Uzhik, G. V., *Resistance to Tear and Strength of Metals*, M.-L., Akad. Nauk SSSR, 1950.

96. Pavlov, V. A., and Yakutovich, M. V., *Dokl. Akad. Nauk SSSR*, **77**, No. 1 (1951).

97. Slavin, D. O., and Shapiro, D. M., *Mechanical Testing of Metals*, M.-L., Metallurgizdat, 1950.

98. *Supervision of Machinery and Devices for Testing Metals*, M.-L., Metallurgizdat, 1936.

99. Davidenkov, N. N., *Dynamic Testing of Metals*, M.-L., Metallurgizdat, 1936.

100. *Nomenclature of the Theory of Elasticity, Testing, and Mechanical Properties of Materials and Structural Mechanics*, M.-L., Akad. Nauk SSSR, 1952.

101. *Methods of Mechanical Testing*, M., Standartgiz, 1952.

102. *Microhardness* (a symposium), Akad. Nauk SSSR, 1951.

103. Pashkov, P. O., *Tension and Fracture of Metals*, M., Sudpromgiz, 1952.

104. Avdeyev, B. A., *Technique for Evaluating Mechanical Properties of Metals*, M., Metallurgizdat, 1949.

105. Ginsburg, Ya. S., *Testing of Metals at Elevated Temperatures*, M.-L., Mashgiz, 1954.

106. Nadai, A., *Theory of Flow and Fracture of Solids*, N.Y., McGraw-Hill, 1950.

107. Minkevich, N. A., *Zhur. Russ. Metall. Obsch.*, Part I, 453 (1912).

108. Brinell, J. A., *Cong. int. methodes d'essai*, Paris, 1900. [For the first English account, see A. Wahlberg, *J. Iron and Steel Inst.*, **59**, 243 (1901).]

109. Davidenkov, N. N., *Mechanical Properties of Metals*, L., 1933.

110. Gudtsov, N. T., *The Science of Strength and Plastic Deformation*, M., Zhukovsky Academy, 1948.

111. Rosenberg, E. M., *Zhur. Tech. Fiz.*, **25**, No. 3 (1945).

112. Shevandin, E. M., *Zavodskaya Laboratoria*, **12**, Nos. 7-8 and 9-10 (1946).

113. Savitsky, E. M., and Slavina, N. P., *Izv. Akad. Nauk SSSR, OKN*, No. 2 (1943).

114. Golovin, S. M., *Studies of Working Nonferrous Metals, No. 2*, M., Metallurgizdat, 1941.

115. Chipizhenko, A. I., *Symposium of Scientific Papers Sponsored by the Government Institute for Treatment of Nonferrous Metals, No. 14*, M., Metallurgizdat, 1952.

116. Davidenkov, N. N., Zlatin, N. A., and Shevandin, E. M., *Zhur. Tech. Fiz.*, **9**, No. 12 (1939).

117. Vitman, F. F., *Zavodskaya Loboratoria*, **13**, Nos. 2 and 8 (1947).

118. Tammann, G., and Muller, W., *Zeit. Metallkunde*, **28**, No. 3, 49–54 (1936).

119. Vitman, F. F., Zlatin, N. A., Yoffe, B. S., and Shestopalov, L. M., *Zhur. Tech. Fiz.*, **24**, No. 3 (1954).

120. Vekshinsky, S. A., *New Metallographic Method of Testing Alloys*, M., Gostekhizdat, 1944.

121. Savitsky, E. M., and Ivanov, O. S., *Production of Metallic Alloys of Variable Composition by Means of Electrochemistry*, Patent No. 69308 (1944).

122. Petrov, D. A., and Bukhanov, A. A., *Zhur. Fiz. Khim.*, No. 1 (1954).

123. Davidenkov, N. N., *Zhur. Tech. Fiz.*, **13**, No. 7–8 (1943).

124. Davidenkov, N. N., Beliayev, S. E., and Markovets, M. P., *Zavodskaya Laboratoria*, **11**, No. 10 (1945).

125. Sichikov, M. F., Zakharov, B. P., and Kozlova, Y. V., *Zavodskaya Laboratoria*, **13**, No. 12 (1947).

126. Gubkin, S. I., and others, *Experimental Problems of Ductile Deformation of Metals*, No. I, 1934; No. II, 1936, M.-L., ONTI.

127. Ludwik, P., *Zeit. ver. Deutsch. Ing.*, **71** (part 2), 1532–38, (1927).

128. Friedman, Ya. B., and Volodina, T., *Zavodskaya Laboratoria*, **12**, No. 9–10 (1946).

129. Shchapov, N. P., and Kochetov, A., Appendix to N. N. Davidenkov's *Problems of Impact Effect in Metallography*, M.-L., Akad. Nauk SSSR, 1938.

130. Davidenkov, N. N., *Zavodskaya Laboratoria*, **13**, No. 11 (1947).

131. Gubkin, S. I., *The Flow Theory of Metallic Matter*, M.-L., ONTI, 1935.

132. Bobkov, O. S., and Samarin, A. M., *Izv. Akad. Nauk SSSR, OTN*, No. 2 (1954).

133. Roytman, I. M., and Friedman, Ya. B., *Zavodskaya Laboratoria*, **16**, No. 5 (1950).

134. Pevzner, L. M., and Yakimova, A. M., *Zavodskaya Laboratoria*, **19**, No. 5 (1953).

135. Morozov, B. N., *The History of the Development of Test Equipment*, M., MVTU, 1944.

136. Shchapov, N. N., *Zhur. Tech. Fiz.*, **1**, No. 4 (1931).

137. Roytman, I. M., and Friedman, Ya. B., *The Micromechanical Method of Testing Metals*, M., Oborongiz, 1950.

138. Chevenard, P., *Bull. soc. d'encour.*, No. 1 (1935).

139. Averkiev, V. S., Kolesnikov, G. I., Pavlov, V. A., and Yakutovich, M. V., *Zhur. Tech. Fiz.*, No. 11 (1946).

140. Yuriev, S. F., Rechitskaya, S. E., and Mishurinsky, A. N., *Zavodskaya Laboratoria*, **16**, No. 1 (1950).

141. Savitsky, E. M., and Lebedev, V. P., *Zavodskaya Laboratoria*, **15**, No. 5 (1949).

142. Savitsky, E. M., Patent No. 78001 (1949); *Biulleten Izobreteniy (Bulletin of Inventions)*, **11**, 54 (1949).

143. Savitsky, E. M., *Zavodskaya Laboratoria*, **16**, No. 11 (1950).

144. Kornilov, I. I., *Dokl. Akad. Nauk SSSR*, **86**, No. 4 (1952); *Zavodskaya Laboratoria*, **15**, No. 1 (1949).

145. Kornilov, I. I., *Creep and Fracture of Metals at High Temperatures*, London, Her Majesty's Stationery Office, 1956, 215–19.

146. Gubkin, S. I., and Savitsky, E. M., *Dokl. Akad. Nauk SSSR*, **28**, No. 2 (1940).

147. Savitsky, E. M., *Zavodskaya Laboratoria*, **11**, No. 10 (1945).

148. Smiriagin, A. P., *Symposium Sponsored by TSNIOTSVETMET on Substitute Alloys*, No. 1, M., Metallurgizdat, 1941.

149. Tammann, G., *Zeit. Metallkunde*, **27**, No. 10 (1935).

150. Nipper, H., and Lips, E., *Zeit. Metallkunde*, **27**, No. 10 (1935).

151. Bochvar, A. A., and Novikov, I. I., *Izv. Akad. Nauk SSSR, OTN*, No. 2 (1952).

152. Kurnakov, N. S., and Klochko, M. A., *Introduction to Physicochemical Analysis*, M.-L., Akad. Nauk SSSR, 1940.

153. Urazov, G. G., *Uspekhi Khimii (Progress in Chemistry)*, **21**, No. 9 (1952).

154. Urazov, G. G., *Institute of General and Inorganic Chemistry* (a symposium), Akad. Nauk SSSR. M.-L., Nauchtekhizdat, 1936.

155. Urazov, G. G., and Shushpanova, Y. I., *Izv. Akad. Nauk SSSR* (chemistry series), No. 2 (1936).

156. Nemilov, V. A., *General Metallography*, M.-L., Akad. Nauk SSSR, 1947.

157. Nemilov, V. A., Rudnitsky, A. A., and Vidusova, T. A., *Izv. Sektora Platiny, Inst. Obsch. Neorg. Khim. Akad. Nauk USSR*, No. 20 (1946).

158. Nemilov, V. A., *Izv. SZhKhA*, **19** (1949).

159. Nemilov, V. A., and Vidusova, T. A., *Izv. Sectora Platiny, Inst. Obsch. Neorg. Khim., Akad. Nauk SSSR*, No. 17 (1940).

160. Nemilov, V. A., and Strunina, T. A., *Vest. Moskovskago Universiteta (Moscow University Herald)*, No. 4 (1943).

161. Kuznetsov, V. G., *Izv. SFKhA*, **16** (1949).

162. Pogodin, S. A., and others, *Izv. SFKhA*, **4**, No. 1 (1929), **13** (1940), **14** (1941), **17** and **18** (1949).

163. Progodin, S. A., *Conductor and Rheostat Alloys*, M.-L., ONTI, 1936.

164. Petrov, D. A., *Theory Problems of Aluminum Alloys*, M.-L., Metallurgizdat, 1951.

165. Petrov, D. A., *Ternary Systems*, M.-L., Akad. Nauk SSSR, 1953.

166. Grigoriev, A. T., and Kudryavtsev, L., *Izv. Akad. Nauk SSSR, OKN*, No. 8 (1948).

167. Shamray, F. I., *Lithium and Its Alloys*, M.-L., Akad. Nauk SSSR (1952).

168. Pevzner, L. M., *Izv. Akad. Nauk SSSR, OTN*, No. 3 (1945).

169. German, V. L., *Dokl. Akad. Nauk SSSR*, **51**, No. 9 (1946).

170. Bridgman, P. W., *Physics of High Pressure*, London, Bell, 1949; *Studies in Large Plastic Flow and Fracture*, New York, McGraw-Hill, 1952.

171. Lepeshkov, I. N., Savitsky, E. M., Bodaleva, N. E., and Kotova, L. T., *Izv. SFKhA*, **19** (1949).

172. *Machine Construction*, vol. III, M., Mashgiz, 1948.

173. Tsiklis, D. S., *The Technique of Physicochemical Testing at High Pressures*, M., Goskhimizdat, 1951.

174. Vereshchagin, L. F., and Likhter, A. I., *Dokl. Akad. Nauk SSSR*, **86**, No. 4 (1952).

175. Zakharova, M. I., *A Jubilee Symposium of Scientific Papers of Mintsvetzoloto*, M., Metallurgizdat, 1950; *Dokl. Akad. Nauk SSSR*, **68**, No. 1 (1949).

176. Zakharova, M. I., *Dokl. Akad. Nauk SSSR*, **91**, No. 2 (1953).

177. Butuzov, V. P., Gonikberg, M. I., and Smirnov, S. P., *Dokl. Akad. Nauk SSSR*, **89**, No. 4 (1953).

178. Prosvirin, V. I., *The Effect of External Pressure on Phase Transformations in Steel and Cast Iron*, M.-L., Mashgiz, 1948.

179. Bochvar, A. A., *Izv. Akad. Nauk SSSR, OTN*, No. 7 (1940).

180. Konobeyevsky, S. T., Zakharova, M. I., and Tarasova, V. P., *Zhur. Tech. Fiz.*, **5**, No. 7 (1933).

181. Konobeyevsky, S. T., and Tarasova, V. P., *Zhur. Fiz. Khim.*, No. 9 (1937).

182. Berg, L. G., Yanatyeva, O. K., and Savitsky, E. M., *Dokl. Akad. Nauk SSSR*, **67**, No. 3 (1950).

183. Savitsky, E. M., *Dokl. Akad. Nauk SSSR*, **62**, No. 3 (1948).

184. Savitsky, E. M., Baron, V. V., and Tylkina, M. A., *Zavodskaya Laboratoria*, **15**, No. 6 (1949).

185. Beliaev, S. E., *Mechanical Properties of Aircraft Materials at Low Temperatures*, M., Oborongiz, 1940.

186. Bochvar, A. A., *Metallography*, M.-L., Metallurgizdat, 1945.
187. Bochvar, A. A., *Technology of Nonferrous Metals and Alloys* (a symposium), M.-L., Metallurgizdat, 1947.
188. Kornilov, I. I., *Dokl. Akad. Nauk SSSR*, **72**, No. 6 (1950).
189. Kostenets, V. I., *Zhur. Tech. Fiz.*, **16**, No. 5 (1946).
190. Kolesnikov, G. N., Pavlov, V. A., Yakovlev, E. S., and Yakutovich, M. V., *Zhur. Tech. Fiz.*, **19**, No. 1 (1949).
191. Kornilov, I. I., and Mikheyev, V. S., *Stal*, No. 2 (1946).
192. Osipov, K. A., *Dokl. Akad. Nauk SSSR*, **60**, No. 4; **61**, No. 1 (1948).
193. Savitsky, E. M., *Dokl. Akad. Nauk SSSR*, **73**, No. 5 (1950); **89**, No. 1 (1953).
194. Lebedev, V. P., Patent No. 79240, 1949.
195. Oding, I. A., Lozinsky, M. G., and Fedotov, S. G., *Dokl. Akad. Nauk SSSR*, **91**, No. 1 (1953).
196. Ito, S., *Science Reports of the Tohoku University*, **12** (1923).
197. Pogodin, S. A., *Mineral Raw Material and Nonferrous Metals*, Nos. 4 and 9 (1929).
198. Shishokin, V. P., *Zhur. Priklad. Khim.*, **2**, No. 6 (1929).
199. Gubkin, S. I., and Zakharov, P. A., *Izv. Akad. Nauk SSSR, OMN*, **41** (1937).
200. Kutaytsev, V. I., *Tsvetnaya Metallurgia* (Nonferrous Metallurgy), No. 20 (1941).
201. Gubkin, S. I., and Savitsky, E. M., *Izv. SFKhA*, **14** (1941).
202. Iveronova, V. I., *X-ray Investigation of Materials* (a symposium), M.-L., Mashgiz, 1949.
203. *Ability of Metals to Deform* (collected articles), M.-L., Metallurgizdat, 1953.
204. Trusova, E. M., *Zhur. Tech. Fiz.*, **20**, No. 1 (1950).
205. Fedotov, S. G., *Avtoreferat Dissertatsii*, Mintsvetmetzoloto, 1956.
206. GOST 1479-42, *Methods for Tension Testing of Metals*.
207. Bordzyka, A. M., *Mechanical Testing of Metals at High Temperatures*, M., Metallurgizdat, 1955.
208. GOST 2055-43, *Compression Testing*.
209. GOST 1524-42, *Methods for Evaluating Impact Strength*.
210. Savitsky, E. M., and Kurova, O. I., *Zavodskaya Laboratoria*, **7**, No. 5 (1941).
211. OST 10241-40, *Brinell Hardness Testing*.
212. OST 10242-40, *Rockwell Hardness Testing*.
213. Khrushchev, M. M., and Berkovich, E. S., *PMT-2 and PMT-3 Devices for Testing Microhardness*, M.-L., Akad. Nauk SSSR, 1950.
214. Khrushchev, M. M., and Berkovich, E. S., *The Indentation Method for Evaluating Microhardness*, M.-L., Akad. Nauk SSSR, 1943.
215. Davidenkov, N. N., and Spiridonova, N., *Zavodskaya Laboratoria*, **11**, No. 6 (1945).
216. Gubkin, S. I., and Savitsky, E. M., *Ability of Nonferrous Alloys to Deform* (a symposium), Akad. Nauk SSSR, 1947.
217. Savitsky, E. M., *Ductile Properties of Magnesium and Some of Its Alloys*, M.-L., Akad. Nauk SSSR, 1941.
218. Savitsky, E. M., *Zavodskaya Laboratoria*, **13**, No. 3 (1947).
219. Gavra, D. L., *Fundamentals of Nomography*, L., Mashgiz, 1949.
220. Blanter, M. E., *Methods of Metal Research and Treatment of Experimental Data*, M.-L., Metallurgizdat, 1952.
221. Worthing, A., and Geffner, J., *Treatment of Experimental Data*, New York, Wiley, 1943.
222. Novokreshchenov, P. D., and Markova, I. E., *Zavodskaya Laboratoria*, **14**, No. 7 (1948).
223. Savitsky, E. M., and Terekhova, V. F., *Dokl. Akad. Nauk SSSR*, **87**, No. 5 (1952).
224. Spedding, F. H., and Daane, A. H., *J. of Metals*, **6**, 5 (1954).
225. Bechtold, J. H., *J. Electrochem. Soc.*, **98**, No. 12 (1951).

226. Alexander, B. H., Dawson, M. H., and Kling, H. P., *J. Appl. Physics*, **22**, No. 4 (1951).

227. Nemilov, V. A., and Rudnitsky, A. A., *Izv. Sectora Platiny, Inst. Obsch. Neorg. Khim., Akad. Nauk SSSR*, No. 27 (1952).

228. Rudnitsky, A. A., *Izv. Sectora Platiny, Inst. Obsch. Neorg. Khim., Akad. Nauk SSSR*, No. 27 (1952).

229. Golovin, V. A., and Persiyantsev, V. A., *Ability of Metals to Deform* (a symposium), M.-L., Metallurgizdat, 1953.

230. Slavinsky, M. P., *Physicochemical Properties of Elements*, M.-L., Metallurgizdat, 1952.

231. Filiand, M. A., and Semenova, E. I., *Properties of Rare Elements* (reference book), M.-L., Metallurgizdat, 1953.

232. Bobylev, A. V., and Chipizhenko, A. I., *Zavodskaya Laboratoria*, **13**, No. 3 (1947); *Tsvetnye Metaly*, No. 3 (1945).

233. Bobylev, A. V., *Conference on Working of Nonferrous Metals*, M.-L., Metallurgizdat, 1946.

234. Smiriagin, A. P., *Industrial Nonferrous Metals and Alloys*, M.-L., Metallurgizdat, 1949.

235. *Properties of Metals and Alloys* (reference book), M.-L., Metallurgizdat, 1949.

236. Ormont, B. R., *Structure of Inorganic Materials*, M., Gosteoretizdat, 1950.

237. Wain, J., *J. of Metals*, **6**, 12 (1954).

238. Kornilov, I. I., and Mikheyev, V. S., *Usp. Khimii*, **22**, No. 1 (1951).

239. Kroll, W. J., Hergart, W. F., and Yerkes, L. A., *J. Electrochem. Soc.*, **97**, 258 (1950).

240. Gilbert, H. L., Juhansen, H. A., and Nelson, R. J., *Prob. Contemp. Metallurgy*, **13**, No. 1 (1954).

241. Sully, A. H., *Chromium*, New York, Academic Press, 1954.

242. Sergeyev, S. V., *Physicochemical Properties of Pure Metals*, M., Oborongiz, 1952.

243. Sully, A. H., Brandes, E. A., and Mitchell, K. U., *Prob. Contemp. Metallurgy*, No. 3 (1954).

244. Savitsky, E. M., and Terekhova, V. F., *The Chemistry of Rare Metals* (a symposium), No. II, M., Akad. Nauk SSSR, 1955.

245. Baron, V. V., and Savitsky, E. M., *Dokl. Akad. Nauk SSSR*, **94**, No. 2 (1954).

246. Savitsky, E. M., Terekhova, V. F., and Kholopov, A. V., *Dokl. Akad. Nauk SSSR*, **109**, No. 4 (1956).

247. Savitsky, E. M., and Terekhova, V. F., *Institute of Metallurgy, Akad. Nauk SSSR*, No. 1 (1957).

248. Goodwin, G. V., Gilbert, P. A., Schwartz, K. M., and Greenidge, K. T., *Prob. of Contemp. Metallurgy*, **13**, No. 5 (1954).

249. Ageyev, N. V., and Trapeznikov, V. A., *A Study on Heat-resistant Alloys* (a symposium), Akad. Nauk SSSR, 1956.

250. Barrett, C., *Structure of Metals: Crystallographic Methods, Principles, and Data*, New York, McGraw-Hill, 1943.

251. Spkowsen, *Chemisch. Weekblad*, **47**, No. 4 (1951).

252. *Bolshaya Sovetskaya Entsiklopedia*, S. I. Vavilov, ed., 2d ed., Vol. 5, M.-L., 1950.

253. Seybolt, A. U., Lukesh, J. S., and White, D. W., *J. Appl. Physics*, **22**, No. 7, 986 (1951).

254. *Beryllium* (a symposium), Part II, M., Lenin Inst., 1953.

255. Martin, A. J., and Moore, A., *J. of Less Common Metals*, **1**, 85 (1959).

256. Garber, R. I., Gindin, I. A., Kogan, V. S., and Lazarev, B. G., *Physics of Metals and Metallography*, **1**, No. 3 (1955).

257. Umansky, Ya. S., *The Role of Physics in the Science of Metals*, M., Pravda, 1948.

258. Kuznetsov, V. D., *Zavodskaya Laboratoria*, **17**, No. 2 (1951).

259. Portnoy, K. I., and Lebedev, A. A., *Magnesium Alloys* (reference book), M.-L., Metallurgizdat, 1952.

298   REFERENCES

260. Savitsky, E. M., *Aviapromyshlennost*. (*Aviation Industry*), No. 8 (1940).
261. Gubkin, S. I., and Savitsky, E. M., *Izv. Akad. Nauk SSSR, OKN*, No. 6 (1941).
262. Savitsky, E. M., *Zavodskaya Laboratoria*, **11**, No. 2-3 (1945).
263. Gubkin, S. I., and Savitsky, E. M., *Technology of Nonferrous Metals and Alloys* (a symposium), M.-L., Metallurgizdat, 1946.
264. Gubkin, S. I., and Savitsky, E. M., *B'ul. Aviapromyshlennosti* (*Bulletin of the Aviation Industry*), Nos. 11-12 (1946) and No. 5 (1947).
265. Savitsky, E. M., *Dokl. Akad. Nauk SSSR*, **89**, No. 1 (1953).
266. Burghardt, A., *Mechanical and Technological Properties of Pure Metals*, M.-L., Metallurgizdat, 1941.
267. Bochvar, A. A., and Sviderskaya, Z. A., *Izv. Akad. Nauk SSSR, OTN*, No. 7 (1946).
268. Tolansky, S., and Omar, M., *Phil. Mag.*, **44**, No. 352, 514 (1953).
269. Savitsky, E. M., and Baron, V. V., *Tr. Inst. Metallurgii* (*Papers of the Institute of Metallurgy*), *Akad. Nauk SSSR*, No. 3 (1957).
270. Boltaks, B. I., *Zhur. Tech. Fiz.*, **20**, No. 1 (1950).
271. *The Chemistry of Rare Metals* (a symposium), No. 1, M., Akad. Nauk SSSR, 1955.
272. Graf, L., Lakur, G., and Veyler, K., *Prob. Contemp. Metallurgy*, **13**, No. 3 (1954).
273. Carreker, R., *Prob. Contemp. Metallurgy*, **15**, No. 5, 141 (1956).
274. Zavyalov, A. S., *Phase Transformations in Iron Carbide Alloys*, L., 1948.
275. Lebedev, T. A., *The Basic Principles of the New Theory on Iron Carbide Alloys*, Leningr. Inst. usovershenstvovania inzhenerov, L., 1939.
276. Lebedev, T. A., *Certain Problems of the General Theory of Alloys*, L., Lenizdat, 1951.
277. Urazovsky, S. S., *On Molecular Polymorphism*, Kiev, 1950.
278. Khotkevich, V. I., *Zhur. Tech. Fiz.*, **22**, No. 3 (1952).
279. *Reference Book for an Experimental Physicist*, M., Lenin Inst., 1949.
280. Sheldon, E. A., and King, A. J., *Acta Crystall.*, **6**, 100 (1953).
281. Zachariasen, W. H., *Acta Crystall.*, **5** (1952) (five articles).
282. Fast, J. D., *J. Appl. Physics*, **23**, No. 3, 350 (1952).
283. Kats, D., and Rabinovich, E., *The Chemistry of Uranium*, M., Lenin Inst., 1954.
284. Jeager, Zanstra, *Proc. Akad. Amsterdam*, **34**, 151 (1931).
285. Bochvar, A. A., *Metallography*, M.-L., Metallurgizdat (1956), p. 27.
286. Konobeyevsky, S. T., in *Akad. Nauk SSSR Conference on the Peaceful Use of Atomic Energy* (a symposium), *OKN*, M.-L., Akad. Nauk SSSR (1955), p. 362.
287. Zholobov, V. V., and Zedin, N. I., *A Metallographic Atlas of Copper and Copper Alloys*, M., Metallurgizdat, 1949.
288. Chiotti, P., *J. Electrochem. Soc.*, **101**, 567 (1954).
289. Edwards, O. S., and Lipson, H., *J. Inst. Metals*, **69**, 177 (1943).
290. Soge, *Comp. rend.*, **230**, 14 (1950).
291. Barrett, C. S., and Trautz, O. R., *Metals Technol.*, **15** (1948).
292. Barrett, C. S., *Phys. Rev.*, **72**, 3 (1947).
293. Semenchenko, V. K., Pokrovsky, N. L., and Lazarev, V. V., *Dokl. Akad. Nauk SSSR*, **89**, No. 6 (1953).
294. Medvedev, A. S., *Tevetnye Metally*, No. 2 (1954).
295. Goriunova, N. A., *Dokl. Akad. Nauk SSSR*, **65**, No. 1 (1950).
296. Gurovich, N. A., Savitsky, E. M., and Terekhova, V. F., *Tsvetnye Metally*, No. 3 (1953).
297. Kornilov, I. I., *Iron Alloys*, Vol. II, M. L., Akad. Nauk SSSR, 1951.
298. Kantor, M. M., *Methods of Research on Transformations in Steel*, M.-L., Mashgiz, 1950.
299. Gallay, Ya. S., and Zlotnikov, M. I., *Metallurg*, No. 5 (1938).
300. Davidenkov, N. N., *Impact Problems in Metallography*, M.-L., Akad. Nauk SSSR, 1938.
301. Allen, N. P., Hopkins, B. E., and McLennan, J. E., *Proc. Roy. Soc.*, A, **234**, 221 (1956).

302. Rosenhain, W., *Zeit. Metallkunde*, **22**, 74 (1930).
303. Dobrovidov, A. N., *Izv. Tomskago Politekhnich. Inst. (Journal of the Tomsk Polytechnical Institnte)*, **58**, No. 1 (1937).
304. Pogodin-Alekseyev, G. I., *Tr. VNITOM*, Vol. 1, M., Metallurgizdat, 1954.
305. Lashko, N. F., Petrenko, B. G., and Slobodyaniuk, G. Ya., *Metallurg*, No. 5 (1938).
306. Rudbakh, I. V., *Plasticity of Steel in Deformation at Critical Temperature*, Moskovsky Institut Stali, Symposium 17 (1940).
307. Vratsky, M. V., and Frantsevich, I. N., *Stal*, No. 4-5 (1933).
308. Vratsky, M. V., and Frantsevich, I. N., *Stal*, No. 7-8 (1932).
309. Tammann, G., *Metallography*, M.-L., ONTI, 1935.
310. Zhemchuzhny, S. F., and Petrashevich, V. K., *Izv. Ross. Akad. Nauk*, 153 (1917).
311. Pogodin, S. A., *Izv. SZhKhA*, **13** (1941).
312. Grube, G., *Zeit. Electrochem.*, **42**, No. 11 (1936); **45**, No. 10 (1939).
313. Dean, R. S., *Trans. Am. Soc. Met.*, No. 29 (1941).
314. Tavadze, F. N., *Tr. Gruz. Inst. Metalov i Gornogo Dela*, No. 1 (1947).
315. Potter, E. V., and Lukens, H. C., *Met. Techn.*, **13**, Tech. Pub. No. 2032 (1946).
316. Zuicker, U., *Zeit. Metallkunde*, **42**, Nos. 8 and 11 (1951).
317. Sully, A. H., *Manganese*, New York, Academic Press, 1955, p. 141.
318. Kroll, W. J., *Zeit. Metallkunde*, **31**, 20 (1939).
319. Savitsky, E. M., and Terekhova, V. F., *Dokl. Akad. Nauk SSSR*, **68**, No. 1 (1949).
320. Sheldon, E. A., and King, A. J., *Acta Crystall.*, **6**. 100 (1953).
321. Perelman, F. M., Zvorykin, A. Ya., and Gudima, I. V., *Cobalt*, M.-L., Akad. Nauk SSSR, 1949.
322. Kehrer, V. J., and Leidheiser, H., *J. Chem. Phys.*, **21**, No. 3, 570 (1953).
323. Bernshtein, M. L., *Steel and Its Alloys for Use at High Temperatures*, M.-L., Metallurgizdat, 1956.
324. Savitsky, E. M., *Priroda*, No. 4 (1956).
325. Songina, O. A., *Rare Metals*, M.-L., Metallurgizdat, 1951.
326. Gudtsov, N. T., and Dubinin, G. N., *Izv. Akad. Nauk SSSR, OTN*, No. 4 (1951).
327. Loriers, J., *Comp. rend.*, **226**, 1018 (1948).
328. Bridgman, P. W., *Proc. Am. Acad. Sci.*, **76**, 55 (1948).
329. Lawson, A. W., and Ting-Yuen Tang, *Phys. Rev.*, **76**, No. 2 (1949).
330. Shure and Struliment, *Phys. Rev.*, **77**, No. 3 (1950).
331. Trombe, F., and Foex, M., *Ann. chim.*, **19**, 417 (1944).
332. Savitsky, E. M., and Terekhova, V. F., *The Chemistry of Rare Solids (Lanthanum and Cerium)* (a symposium), M., Akad. Nauk SSSR, 1955.
333. Schofield, T. H., and Bacon, A. E., *J. Inst. Met.*, **82**, 167 (1953).
334. *Titanium and Its Alloys* (a symposium), Part 2, M., Lenin, Inst. 1954.
335. Kornilov, I. I., *Izv. Akad. Nauk SSSR, OTN*, No. 3 (1954).
336. Kornilov, I. I., *Dokl. Akad. Nauk SSSR*, **91**, No. 3 (1953).
337. Kornilov, I. I., *Uspekhi Khimii*, **22**, No. 5 (1954).
338. Zelikman, A. N., Samsonov, G. V., and Kreyn, O. E., *Metallurgy of Rare Metals*, M.-L., Metallurgizdat, 1954.
339. Rose, F. D., Dube, C. A., and Alexander, B. H., *J. of Metals*, **5**, No. 2, 257 (1953).
340. McHargue, C. J., and Hammond, J. P., *Acta Metallurgica*, **1**, 700 (1953).
341. Churchman, A. T., *Proc. Roy. Soc.*, **226**, No. 1165, 216 (1954).
342. Ageyev, N. V., and Babareko, A. A., *Izv. Akad. Nauk SSSR, OTN*, No. 8 (1955).
343. Kroll, W. J., *Metaux-corrosion.*, **26**, No. 31 (1951).
344. Margolin, I. *Prob. Contemp. Metallurgy*, No. 3, 76 (1956).
345. Sokolov, L. N., Eliutin, V. P., and Zalessky, V. I., *Izv. Akad. Nauk SSSR, OTN*, No. 3 (1954).
346. Savitsky, E. M., and Tylkina, M. A., *Izv. Akad. Nauk SSSR, OTN*, No. 4 (1955).

347. Savitsky, E. M., Tylkina, M. A., and Turanskaya, A. N., *Dokl. Akad. Nauk SSSR,* **101**, No. 5 (1955).

348. Savitsky, E. M., Tylkina, M. A., and Turanskaya, A. N., *Izv. Akad. Nauk SSSR, OTN*, No. 7 (1956).

349. Zotyev, Yu. A., Savitsky, E. M., Tylkina, M. A., and Turanskaya, A. N., *Izv. Akad. Nauk SSSR, OTN*, No. 8 (1956).

350. Savitsky, E. M., and Tylkina, M. A., *Izv. Akad. Nauk SSSR, OTN*, No. 10 (1956).

351. Savitsky, E. M., Tylkina, M. A., and Turanskaya, A. N., *Dokl. Akad. Nauk SSSR,* **105**, No. 2 (1956).

352. Miller, G. L., *Zirconium*, London, Butterworths, 1954.

353. Keeler, D. T., Hibbard, W. R., and Dekker, B. F., *Prob. Contemp. Metallurgy*, No. 4 (1954).

354. Parker, E. R., *Trans. Am. Soc. Met.*, **42**, 399 (1950).

355. Savitsky, E. M., and Terekhova, V. F., *Sbornik Trudov In-ta Metallurgii (Collected Papers of the Institute of Metallurgy)*, *Akad. Nauk SSSR*, No. 3 (1957).

356. Savitsky, E. M., and Terekhova, V. F., *Dokl. Akad. Nauk SSSR*, **112**, No. 2 (1957).

357. Schwope, A. D., and Chubb, W., *Prob. Contemp. Metallurgy*, No. 5 (1953).

358. Budnikov, P. P., and Berezhnoy, A. S., *Reactions in the Solid State*, M., Promstroyizdat, 1949.

359. Leskovich, I. A., *Dokl. Akad. Nauk SSSR*, **79**, No. 2 (1951).

360. Sokolov, V. A., *Izv. SFKhA*, **19** (1949).

361. Kripiakevich, P. I., and Cherkashin, E. E., *Usp. Khimii*, **19**, No. 3 (1950).

362. Wulf, B. K., *Phys. Metals and Metallography*, **3**, No. 1 (1956).

363. Kurnakov, N. S., *Zhur. Russ. Fiz. Khim. Obsch.*, **31**, 927 (1899).

364. Ageyev, N. V., *Izv. SFKhA*, **27** (1956).

365. Ageyev, N. V., *Mendeleyev Periodic System, the Foundation for the Science of Metallic Alloys. Conference Reports on the Theory of Metal Alloys*, M., Akad. Nauk SSSR, 1952.

366. Kornilov, I. I., *Chemistry of Metals and Some of Its Problems. Conference Reports on the Theory of Metal Alloys*, M., Akad. Nauk SSSR, 1952.

367. Kurnakov, N. S., Zhemchuzhny, S. F., and Zasedatelev, M. I., *Izv. SPb. Politekhnich. Inst.*, **22**, 487 (1914).

368. Kornilov, I. I., *Izv. Akad. Nauk SSSR, OKN*, No. 5 (1953).

369. Meyerson, G. A., and Umansky, Ya. S., *Izv. SFKhA*, **22** (1953).

370. Meyerson, G. A., and Samsonov, G. V., *Izv. SFKhA*, **22** (1953).

371. Tammann, G., and Dahl, *Zeit. anorg. allg. Chem.*, **126**, 104 (1933).

372. Savitsky, E. M., *A Symposium of Scientific Essays of Chemical Institutes Akad. Nauk SSSR for Year 1944*, M., Akad. Nauk SSSR.

373. Savitsky, E. M., *Izv. SFKhA*, **19** (1949).

374. Savitsky, E. M., and Tylkina, M. A., *Dokl. Akad. Nauk SSSR*, **3**, No. 1 (1949).

375. Savitsky, E. M., and Baron, V. V., *Dokl. Akad. Nauk SSSR*, **64**, No. 5 (1949).

376. Savitsky, E. M., and Tylkina, M. A., *Dokl. Akad. Nauk SSSR*, **67**, No. 1 (1949).

377. Zakharov, M. V., *Izv. Akad. Nauk SSSR, OTN*, No. 1 (1949).

378. Zakharov, M. V., *Jubilee Symposium of Scientific Papers of the Mintsvetmetalzoloto*, M., Metallurgizdat, 1950.

379. Lowry, R., *Prob. Contemp. Metallurgy*, No. 5 (1953).

380. Klassen-Nekliudova, M. V., in *Symposium Dedicated to the 70th Year Jubilee of the Academician A. F. Yoffe*, M., Akad. Nauk SSSR, 1950.

381. Morral, F. R., *J. of Metals*, **5**, No. 5 (1953).

382. Baron, V. V., and Savitsky, E. M., *Dokl. Akad. Nauk SSSR*, **94**, No. 2 (1954).

383. Kikoini, A. K., and Fedorov, T. D., *Dokl. Akad. Nauk SSSR*, **92**, No. 6 (1953).

384. Abrikosov, N. Kh., *Proceedings of the Conference on Metal Binding*, M., Zhukovsky Inst., 1956.

385. Savitsky, E. M., *A Method for Obtaining Alloys Based on Metallic Compounds*, Patent No. 78001 (1949).
386. Badayeva, T. A., *Dokl. Akad. Nauk SSSR*, **64**, No. 4 (1949).
387. Grum-Grzhimaylo, N. V., *Izv. SFKhA*, **19** (1949).
388. Saldau, P. Ya., *J. Inst. Metals*, **41**, 1 (1929).
389. Shishokin, V. P., and Telitsin, A. A., *Zhur. Tech. Fiz.*, **22**, No. 10 (1952).
390. Korolkov, A. M., *Izv. Akad. Nauk SSSR*, *OTN*, No. 1 (1949).
391. Pashkov, P. O., *Zhur. Tech. Fiz.* **24**, No. 3 (1954).
392. Bochvar, A. A., Drits, M. E., and Kadaner, E. S., *Izv. Akad. Nauk SSSR*, *OTN*, No. 2 (1954).
393. Savitsky, E. M., and Baron, V. V., *Izv. SFKhA*, **27** (1956).
394. Kashchenko, G. A., *Practical Studies of Metallography*, M.-L., ONTI, 1936.
395. Kozolupova, R. G., *Papers of Vecherniy Metallurgucheskiy Inst.*, No. 1, 129 (1955).
396. Ageyev, N. V., and Guseva, L. N., *Izv. Akad. Nauk SSSR*, *OKN*, No. 1 (1952).
397. Savitsky, E. M., and Baron, V. V., *Tr. Inst. Metallurgii Akad. Nauk SSSR*, **1**, 1957.
398. Hume-Rothery, W., *Structure of Metals and Alloys*, London, Inst. Metals, 1939.
399. Hume-Rothery, W., and Raynor, G. V., *The Structure of Metals and Alloys*, London, Inst. Metals, 1956.
400. Kuznetsov, V. G., *Izv. SFKhA*, **16**, No. 4 (1948).
401. Kornilov, I. I., *Izv. Akad. Nauk SSSR*, *OKN*, No. 5 (1950).
402. Carapella, L. A., *Metal Progress*, **48**, No. 2, 297 (1945).
403. Guliayev, A. P., and Trusova, E. F., *Zhur. Tech. Fiz.*, **20**, No. 1 (1950).
404. Shishokin, V. P., and Ageyeva, V. A., *Fiz. Metal. i Metalloved.*, **2**, No. 1 (1956).
405. Abrikosov, N. Kh., *Dokl. Akad. Nauk SSSR*, **67**, No. 3 (1949).
406. Kornilov, I. I., *Dokl. Akad. Nauk SSSR*, **81**, No. 4 (1951).
407. Kuznetsov, V. G., and Makarov, E. S., *Izv. SFKhA*, **13** (1940).
408. *Aluminum Alloys with Magnesium and Zinc*, M., Akad. Nauk SSSR, 1947.
409. Semenchenko, V. K., in *Bolshaya Sovetskaya Entsiklopedia*, S. I. Vavilov, ed., 2d ed., Vol. 27, M.-L., 1954.
410. Mendeleyev, D. I., *Selected Works*, Vol. III, L., 1937.
411. Shternina, E. B., *Izv. SFKhA*, **18** (1949).
412. Buynov, N. N., and Savinykh, V. P., *Dokl. Akad. Nauk SSSR*, **88**, No. 2 (1953).
413. Zakharova, M. I., and Lashko, N. F., *Izv. Akad. Nauk SSSR*, *OTN*, No. 7 (1946).
414. Iveronova, V. I., Kuzmin, S., and Miliukov, V., *Zhur. Exp. Teor. Fiz.*, **13**, No. 6 (1943).
415. Konobeyevsky, S. T., *Zhur. Exp. Teor. Fiz.*, **13**, No. 6 (1943).
416. Kornilov, I. I., and Priakhina, L. I., *Dokl. Akad. Nauk SSSR*, **87**, No. 5 (1952).
417. Osipov, K. A., and Stiukhov, B. P., *Dokl. Akad. Nauk SSSR*, **80**, No. 4 (1951); **83**, No. 3 (1952).
418. Osipov, K. A., *Dokl. Akad. Nauk SSSR*, **53**, No. 9 (1946).
419. Savitsky, E. M., and Tylkina, M. A., *Tr. Inst. Metallurgii Akad. Nauk SSSR*, **1**, 1956.
420. Pogodin, S. A., and Skriabina, M. A., *Izv. SFKhA*, **25**, 1954.
421. Savitsky, E. M., and Tylkina, M. A., *Study on Heat Resistant Alloys* (a symposium), M., Akad. Nauk SSSR, 1956.
422. Gagen-Torn, V. O., *Zavodskaya Laboratoria*, **14**, No. 2 (1948).
423. Garwood, R. D., *J. Inst., Met.* **83**, 64 (1954).
424. Kurdiumov, A. P., *A Monograph on Copper-Zinc Alloys*, SPb., 1904.
425. Iveronova, V. I., and Zhdanov, G. S., *A Collection of Reports. Use of X-ray Technique for Studies of Materials*, M.-L., ONTI, 1936.
426. Martin, J. A., Herman, M., and Brown, N., *Trans. A.I.M.E.*, **209**, 78–81 (1957).

427. Zakharov, M. V., *Dokl. Akad. Nauk SSR*, **65**, No. 3 (1949).
428. Zviagintsev, C. E., *Bull. Akad. Nauk, Gruz. SSR*, **4**, No. 3 (1943).
429. Bauer, O., and Hansen, M., *Der Aufbau der Kupfer-zinklegierungen*, Berlin, Springer, 1927.
430. Ozerov, R. P., *Usp. Fiz. Nauk*, **65**, No. 4 (1951).
431. Bochvar, A. M., Supplement to *Metallography of Industrial Copper Alloys* by A. Shiml, M., Metallurgizdat, 1953.
432. Chertovshikh, A. K., *Tsvetnye Metaly*, No. 2 (1949).
433. Bakuniayeva, K. I., Bochvar, A. A., and Shaposhnikov, N. A., *Tsvetnye Metaly*, No. 9 (1936).
434. Turkin, V. D., and Rumiantzev, M. V., *Structure and Properties of Nonferrous Metals*, M., Metallurgizdat, 1947.
435. Bochvar, A. M., and Kestner, N. M., *Vest. Metallopromyshlennosti*, No. 11, 5 (1928).
436. Urazov, G. G., Filin, I. A., and Shashin, A. V., *Metallurg*, No. 6 (1940).
437. Sergeyev, L. N., *Metallurg*, No. 3 (1937).
438. Saldau, P. Ya., *Izv. SFKhA*, **19** (1949).
439. Mikheyeva, V. I., *Alloying Magnesium with Aluminum and Zinc*, M., Akad. Nauk SSSR, 1946.
440. Badayeva, T. A., *Izv. SFKhA*, **19** (1949).
441. Mendeleyev, I. A., *Alloying Manganese with Copper, Nickel, and Zinc* (in symposium *The Working of Light Metals and Alloys*), M., Metallurgizdat, 1953.
442. Agladze, R. E., Mokhov, V. M., Topchiashvili, L. I., and Gvaramadze, N. E., *Alloys of Manganese with Copper, Nickel, and Zinc*, Akad. Nauk Gruz. SSR, 1954.
443. *Bolshaya Sovetskaya Entsiklopedia*, S. I. Vavilov, ed., 2d ed., Vol. 26, M.-L., 1954.
444. Zhemchuzhny, S. F., Urazov, G. G., and Rykovskov, A., *Zhur. Russ. Fiz. Khim. Obshch.*, **39**, 788 (1907).
445. Hansen, M., *Structure of Binary Alloys*, M., Metallurgizdat, 1941.
446. Grube, G., *Zeit. anorg. allg. Chem.*, **49**, 77 (1906).
447. Chadwick, R., *J. Inst. Metals*, **39**, 285 (1928).
448. Hume-Rothery, W., and Rounsefell, E. O., *J. Inst. Metals*, **41**, 119 (1929).
449. Takei, *Kinzoku no Kenkyu*, **6**, 177 (1929).
450. Bochvar, A. A., and Velichko, I. P., *Trudy MITsMZ*, No. 1 (rabota Laboratorii Metallografii 1931–32), M., 1933.
451. Zakharova, M. I., and Mlodzeyevsky, A. B., *Izv. SFKhA*, **9** (1936).
452. Laves, F., and Werner, St. ., *Zeit. Kristallogr.*, **95**, 114 (1936).
453. Koster, W., *Zeit. Metallkunde*, **41**, 78 (1950).
454. Grube, G., and Burkhardt, A., *Zeit. Electrochem.*, **35**, 315 (1929).
455. Koster, W., and Rosenthal, K., *Zeit. Metallkunde*, **32**, 163 (1940).
456. Tarschisch, L., *Zeit. Kristallogr.*, **86**, 423 (1933).
457. Mirgalovskaya, M. S., *Dokl. Akad. Nauk SSSR*, **78**, No. 5, 909 (1951).
458. Grube, G., *Zeit. anorg. allg. Chem.*, **45**, 225 (1905).
459. Broniewsky, W., *Ann. de chem. et de phys.*, **8**, 25 (1912).
460. Holsted and Smit, *Trans. Electrochem. Soc.*, **49**, 291 (1926).
461. Hansen, D. and Gayler, M., *J. Inst. Metals*, **24**, 201 (1920).
462. Kawakami, *Kinzoku no Kenkyu*, **10**, No. 12 (1933).
463. Laves, F., and Muller, K., *Zeit. Metallkunde*, **30**, 232 (1938).
464. Urazov, G. G., *Izv. Inst. Fiz. Khim. A.*, **2**, No. 2 (1924).
465. Kurnakov, N. S., and Mikheyeva, V. I., *Izv. Inst. Fiz. Khim. A.*, **10** (1938); **13** (1940).
466. Shamray, F. I., *Izv. Akad. Nauk SSSR, OKN*, No. 6 (1947).
467. Eickhoff, K., and Vasskuhler, H., *Zeit. Metallkunde*, **44**, No. 5, 223 (1953).
468. Makarov, E. S., *Dokl. Akad. Nauk SSSR*, **74**, No. 5 (1950).

469. Savitsky, E. M., and Baron, V. V., *Izv. Akad. Nauk SSSR, OKN*, No. 3 (1952).
470. Urazov, G. G., *Izv.* St. Petersburg *Polyt. Inst.*, **14** (1910).
471. Stepanov, N. I., *Dokl. Akad. Nauk SSSR*, **4** (9), No. 3/72 (1935).
472. Stepanov, N. I., and Bulakh, S. A., *Dokl. Akad. Nauk SSSR*, **4** (9), No. 31/72 (1935).
473. Kornilov, I. I., *The Rate of Transformation in Magnesium-Cadmium Alloys in Solid Solutions*, M.-L., Akad. Nauk SSSR, (1935).
474. Kornilov, I. I., *Izv. Akad. Nauk SSSR* (chemistry series), No. 2 (1937).
475. Stepanov, N. I., and Kornilov, I. I., *Izv. Inst. Fiz. Khim. A.*, **10** (1938).
476. Ageyev, N. V., and Ageyeva, D. L., *Izv. Akad. Nauk SSSR, OKN*, No. 2 (1946).
477. Rovinsky, B. M., and Kozhina, P. K., *X-ray Studies on Magnesium-Cadmium Alloys*, M.-L., ONTI, 1938.
478. Khomyakov, K. F., Kholler, V. A., and Troshkina, V. A., *Vest. MGU*, No. 6 (1950).
479. Grube, G., *Zeit. anorg. Chem.*, **49**, 72, 183 (1906).
480. Valentin, *Revue de metallurgie*, **23**, 209 (1926).
481. Hume-Rothery, W., and Rowell, S. W., *J. Inst. Metals*, **38**, 137 (1927).
482. Natta, *Ann. chim. appl.*, **18**, 135 (1926).
483. Grube, G., and Schield, E., *Zeit. anorg. allg. Chem.*, **194**, 190 (1930).
484. Hume-Rothery, W., and Raynor, G. V., *Proc. Roy. Soc. A.*, **174**, No. 959, 471 (1940).
485. Kornilov, I. I., Priakhina, L. I., and Chuyko, T. F., *Izv. SFKhA*, **19** (1949).
486. Gubkin, S. I., *Zhur. Neorg. Khim.*, **1**, No. 6 (1956).
487. Voronov, S. M., *Aviapromyshlennost*, No. 1 (1939).
488. Presniakov, A. A., *Tsvetnye Metaly*, No. 1 (1956).
489. Gubkin, S. I., *Izv. Akad. Nauk SSSR, OTN*, No. 9 (1948).
490. Gubkin, S. I., *Zavodskaya Laboratoria*, **14**, No. 4 (1948).
491. Gubkin, S. I., *Izv. Akad. Nauk SSSR*, No. 3 (1950).
492. Bochvar, A. A., *Principles of Thermal Working of Alloys*, M., Metallurgizdat, 1940.
493. Vitman, F. F., and Zlatin, N. A., *Zhur. Tekh. Fiz.*, No. 3 (1949).
494. Korneyev, N. I., *Deformation of Metals by Forging*, M., Oborongiz, 1947.
495. Unksov, E. P., *Ductile Deformation in Forging and Stamping*, M.-L., Mashgiz, 1939.
496. Kirillov, P. G., *Zavodskaya Laboratoria*, **15**, No. 4 (1949).
497. Sachs, G., *Practical Metallurgy*, Part II, M., 1938.
498. Zochralski, *Zeit. Metallographie*, **17**, 102 (1916); *Zeit. Metallkunde*, **18**, 17 (1927).
499. Hanemann, H., and Haentzschel, E., *Zeit. Metallkunde*, **17**, 57 (1925).
500. Bochvar, A. A., and Savitsky, E. M., *Tsvetnye Metaly*, No. 5-6 (1937).
501. Pavlov, I. M., Gelderman, L. S., and Zhukova, A. I., *Metallurg*, No. 12 (1936).
502. Kushakevich, L. A., *Metallurg*, No. 8 (1936).
503. Severdenko, V. P., and Sartan, Ya. Kh., *Stal*, No. 12 (1947).

K71